Innovation Pathways to Sustainability

The book offers insights into reconciling innovation with sustainability and identifying key stakeholders responsible for the reconciliation. Through conversations with experts in various fields, the intersection of innovation, sustainability, governance and complex systems in a rapidly changing climate-driven world is discussed.

Countries around the world face the urgent existential challenge to tackle climate change and CO_2 emissions. In its discussions of case studies of key economic sectors in Australia, this book focuses on the emerging experience with harnessing innovation to sustainability. The interdisciplinary approach to the complexity of climate change and policymaking provides readers an opportunity for thoughtful discussions and lessons to be learnt from multiple angles.

This is a vital resource for scholars in climate studies, innovation and sustainability that also confronts important challenges facing policymakers, government and society.

Michael Lester is an independent economist, writer and radio presenter. A former public-sector executive in Australia, he has worked and lived internationally. His experience spans science, technology, innovation, environment, resources, industry, trade and investment domains. He has undergraduate and postgraduate degrees in engineering, public administration and economics.

Marie dela Rama, PhD (UTS), is an independent researcher. She participated as an accredited civil society observer in these multilateral meetings: G20 ACWG, OECD GACIF, UNCAC IRG, UN COSP9, UNGASS, UNODC ISM COSP UNGASS and UN SPT OPCAT. Her publications include *The Changing Face of Corruption in the Asia Pacific (Elsevier)* and *Corporate Governance and Corruption (Journal of Business Ethics).*

Routledge Frontiers of Business Management

Statistical Modelling and Sports Business Analytics
Edited by Vanessa Ratten and Ted Hayduk

China's Drive for the Technology Frontier
Indigenous Innovation in the High-Tech Industry
Yin Li

Digital Transformation in Aviation, Tourism and Hospitality in Southeast Asia
Edited by Azizul Hassan and Nor Aida Abdul Rahman

Football Entrepreneurship
Edited by Vanessa Ratten

Digitalization and Development
Ecosystem for Promoting Industrial Revolution 4.0 Technologies in Malaysia
Edited by Rajah Rasiah, Wah Yun Low, and Nurliana Kamaruddin

Air Travel Industry
Theories, Methods and Recent Issues
Edited by Azizul Hassan, Nor Aida Abdul Rahman and Nurhayati Mohd Nur

Innovation Pathways to Sustainability
Conversations Towards Complex Systems of Governance
Edited by Michael Lester and Marie dela Rama

The Future of Work in the Asia Pacific
Addressing Critical Skills Shortages for Sustainable Development
Edited by Subas P. Dhakal, Alan Nankervis and John Burgess

For more information about this series, please visit www.routledge.com/Routledge-Frontiers-of-Business-Management/book-series/RFBM

Innovation Pathways to Sustainability

Conversations Towards Complex Systems of Governance

Edited by Michael Lester and Marie dela Rama

Foreword by Andrew Leigh

Routledge
Taylor & Francis Group
LONDON AND NEW YORK

First published 2025
by Routledge
4 Park Square, Milton Park, Abingdon, Oxon OX14 4RN

and by Routledge
605 Third Avenue, New York, NY 10158

Routledge is an imprint of the Taylor & Francis Group, an informa business

British Library Cataloguing-in-Publication Data
A catalogue record for this book is available from the British Library

Library of Congress Cataloging-in-Publication Data
Names: Lester, Michael (Economist), editor. | Rama, Marie dela, editor.
Title: Innovation pathways to sustainability : conversations towards complex systems of governance / edited by Michael Lester and Marie dela Rama.
Description: Abingdon, Oxon ; New York, NY : Routledge, 2025. | Series: Routledge frontiers of business management | Includes bibliographical references and index.
Identifiers: LCCN 2024025297 (print) | LCCN 2024025298 (ebook) | ISBN 9781032248295 (hardback) | ISBN 9781032248318 (paperback) | ISBN 9781003280316 (ebook)
Subjects: LCSH: Sustainable development—Technological innovations. | Technological innovations—Environmental aspects. | Environmental policy—Economic aspects.
Classification: LCC HC79.E5 I56 2025 (print) | LCC HC79.E5 (ebook) | DDC 338.9/27—dc23/eng/20240614
LC record available at https://lccn.loc.gov/2024025297
LC ebook record available at https://lccn.loc.gov/2024025298

ISBN: 978-1-032-24829-5 (hbk)
ISBN: 978-1-032-24831-8 (pbk)
ISBN: 978-1-003-28031-6 (ebk)

DOI: 10.4324/9781003280316

Typeset in Galliard
by Apex CoVantage, LLC

Access the Support Material: www.routledge/9781032248295

The electronic version of this book was funded to publish Open Access through Taylor & Francis' Pledge to Open, a collaborative funding open access books initiative. The full list of pledging institutions can be found on the Taylor & Francis Pledge to Open webpage.

Contents

The Interviewees

Robert Atkinson

Dr. Robert Atkinson is the founder and president of the Information Technology and Innovation Foundation (ITIF), in Washington, D.C. A prolific and widely published scholar and researcher with hundreds of articles and reports, he has been an advisor on innovation policy to the Clinton, Bush, Obama and Biden Administrations.

Richard Beasley

Richard Beasley SC is a leading Sydney barrister. His particular expertise in law is in government practice and planning and environmental law. His appointments include as Senior Counsel in the COVID-19 Ruby Princess inquiry and in the Murray–Darling Basin Commission about which he wrote the book *Dead in the Water.*

Pru Bennett

Pru Bennett is a Sydney-based partner practicing in environmental, social and governance (ESG) services with the global corporate strategic advisory firm Brunswick Group. She has over 30 years of experience of engaging with boards.

Bob Carr

The Hon. Bob Carr is Industry Professor at the University of Technology, Sydney (UTS) focusing on business and climate change. He is the longest continuously serving premier of New South Wales (NSW) (1995–2005) and was also Australia's Foreign Affairs Minister (2012–2013).

Mark Dodgson

Emeritus Professor Mark Dodgson AO is an academic and author at the Business School, University of Queensland, Visiting Professor at Imperial College London and University of Oxford. He produced the landmark *Oxford Handbook of Innovation Management.*

Chris Dunstan

Dr. Chris Dunstan is Research Director, Institute for Sustainable Futures (ISF), and Adjunct Professor at the University of Technology Sydney (UTS). He is a public commentator on issues of climate change, renewable energy and the electricity sector.

Allan Fels

Professor Allan Fels AO, an economist and lawyer of Melbourne, Monash and Oxford universities is Australia's leading consumer crusader. He was the first chairman of the Australian Competition and Consumer Commission (ACCC) (1995–2003). He was foundation Dean of the Australia and New Zealand School of Government (2003–2012). He has chaired many major federal and state government-appointed committees of inquiry and is currently Chair of the Public Interest Journalism Initiative (PIJI). His publications include *Tough Customer: Chasing a Better Deal for Battlers.*

Sean Foley

Professor Sean Foley is Professor of Applied Finance at Macquarie University. He is Head of Decentralised Assets within the Digital Finance Cooperative Research Centre. His research interests and publications include fintech, cryptocurrencies, trading, market design and regulation.

Kevin Fox

Professor Kevin Fox has been at the University of New South Wales (UNSW) Business School since 1994. He is Director of the Centre for Applied Economic Research, and his focus is on the measurement of productivity and prices.

Ross Garnaut

Professor Ross Garnaut AC is Vice Chancellor's Fellow and Professorial Fellow of Economics at the University of Melbourne. He wrote the landmark report at the request of Australian governments, *The Climate Change Review for Australia*. Previously, he was economic adviser to Prime Minister Bob Hawke (1983–1985) and Australia's ambassador to China (1985–1988). His books include *Superpower: Australia's Low-Carbon Opportunity* and *The Superpower Transformation: Making Australia's Zero-Carbon Future.*

Jim Green

Dr. Jim Green is National Nuclear Campaign Director with Friends of the Earth (FOE). He writes on nuclear power, including an extensive blog 'Nuclear Free Campaign'. His latest articles include *The Latest Nuclear Power 'Renaissance' Is Going In Reverse* and *Small Nuclear Reactors: A History of Failure.*

Roy Green

Emeritus Professor Roy Green AM is Special Innovation Adviser at the University of Technology Sydney (UTS) and former Dean of UTS Business School. He has held appointments to numerous federal and state government committees and inquiries into research, innovation and business management. He is Chair of the Advanced Robotics for Manufacturing Hub and the Port of Newcastle and board member of the CSIRO.

Nicholas Gruen

Dr. Nicholas Gruen is a policy economist, adviser, entrepreneur and a commentator with particular expertise in innovation in the digital technology era. He was formerly Chair of the Australian Centre for Social Innovation, Chair of Innovation Australia, a member of the major *Review of Australia's Innovation System* and sat on Australia's Productivity Commission. He is the founder and CEO of Melbourne-based Lateral Economics.

Richard Heath

Richard Heath is CEO, Zero Net Emissions from Agriculture, Cooperative Research Centre (CRC); and Director, Grain Research and Development Corporation (GRDC). He was formerly (2018–2024) Executive Director of the Australian Farm Institute (AFI). He was previously a farmer.

Lesley Hughes

Emeritus Professor Lesley Hughes, an ecologist, is Distinguished Professor of Biology, Interim Executive Dean, Faculty of Science and Engineering at Macquarie University, and formerly Deputy Vice Chancellor of Research. She is a member of the Climate Change Authority (CCA), Councillor and Director of the Climate Council of Australia (CCA), a former federal Climate Commissioner, and a lead author of the IPCC's 4th and 5th assessment reports.

Ray Ison

Ray Ison is Emeritus Professor, Applied Systems Thinking in Practice Group (ASTIP) at the Open University in the UK, where he was formerly Professor of Systems (1994–2023). He is an Australian-British cybernetician and systems scientist known for his work on systemic governance and the design and practice of learning systems. His books include *The Hidden Power of Systems Thinking* and *How to Act in a Climate Change World.*

Barry Jones

The Hon Dr. Barry Jones AC is an eminent Australian public intellectual, lawyer, writer and activist. He holds a number of honorary degrees and doctorates and is Fellow of the Australian Academies of Science, Humanities, Social Sciences, Technological Sciences and Engineering. He was

National President of the Australian Labor Party (ALP) (1991–2000) and the longest-serving Minister for Science (1983–1990). His books include *Sleepers, Wake! Technology and the Future of Work* and *What Is to Be done? Political Engagement and Saving the Planet.*

Sami Kara

Professor Sami Kara is from the University of New South Wales's (UNSW's) Sustainable Manufacturing and Life Cycle Engineering, School of Mechanical and Manufacturing Engineering. His books include *Efficiency of Manufacturing Processes: Energy and Ecological Perspectives.*

Peter Khoury

Peter Khoury is Spokesperson and Media Manager for the National Roads and Motorists Association (NRMA), part of a listed company, Insurance Australia Group (IAG). He advocates and provides advice on everything from petrol prices and transport costs to road safety.

Charles Massy

Dr. Charles Massy OAM is a NSW fifth-generation farmer, scientist and author. He is Honorary Visiting Lecturer, Fenner Institute for Climate, Energy & Disaster Solutions, at the Australian National University (ANU), Canberra. His highly awarded book about regenerative agriculture is *Call of the Reed Warbler.*

Warwick McKibbin

Warwick McKibbin AO is Distinguished Professor of Economics at the Crawford School of Public Policy and Director of the Centre for Applied Macroeconomic Analysis (CAMA) at the Australian National University (ANU). He served for a decade on the Board of the Reserve Bank of Australia (RBA) and as a member of the Australian Prime Minister's Science, Engineering and Innovation Council. His many books include *Climate Change Policy After Kyoto: A Blueprint for a Realistic Approach.*

Aaron Mertz

Dr. Aaron Mertz is Founder and Director of the Aspen Institute, Science and Society Program, Yale University. He is Rhodes Scholar with a doctorate in Physics. He is committed to advocacy for scientific communities and he coordinated the global report *In Favor of Pure Science.*

Abhilash Mishra

Dr. Abhilash Mishra is Founding Director, Initiative on Science, Technology and Global Development at the Harris School of Public Policy, University of Chicago. He is Rhodes Scholar, physicist, entrepreneur and educator.

Giles Parkinson

Giles Parkinson is the founder and editor of the authoritative and widely read online renewable energy newsletter 'reneweconomy'. He was former business and deputy editor of the Australian Financial Review (AFR).

Bruce Pascoe

Professor Bruce Pascoe is Professor of Indigenous Education & Research at the University of Technology Sydney (UTS) and Enterprise Professor, Indigenous Agriculture, University of Melbourne. He wrote an insightful book into First Nations agriculture, *Dark Emu: Black Seeds, Agriculture or Accident*.

Michael Piore

Michael Piore is an Emeritus Professor, eminent economist and political scientist. He is Emeritus Professor of Political Economy at Massachusetts Institute of Technology (MIT) and with the Department of Political Science, MIT. He is also Visiting Senior Fellow, International and Public Affairs, Brown University. His books include *Innovation: The Missing Dimension* and *The Second Industrial Divide*.

Tony Wood

Tony Wood AM has been Director of the Energy and Climate Change Program at the Grattan Institute, based at the University of Melbourne since 2011. He had a long industry career in energy, including 14 years with Origin Energy.

Foreword

Andrew Leigh

For years, Michael Lester has been interviewing interesting thinkers for his radio programme, *Innovation Talk*. Modest and curious, his conversations take the form of a modern-day coffee *salon*, a Writers' Festival, or your favourite dinner party. Having sat in the metaphorical interviewer's chair on a few occasions, I can say that being interviewed by Michael is always a pleasure, and never a chore. If you've written a book, you can be sure he's read it, thought about it, and prepared at least a few questions that no one else thought to ask.

In this book, Michael Lester draws together more than two dozen interviews conducted over recent years about his favourite topics: innovation and sustainability. The conversations are lightly edited and helpfully footnoted, topped and tailed with a profile of the expert and a summary of the interview. Edited collections sometimes have a jumpy feel about them but this one flows well. And the issues matter.

In an era defined by the rapid pace of technological advancement and the pressing need for sustainable solutions to environmental crises, *Innovation Pathways to Sustainability: Conversations Towards Complex Systems of Governance* emerges as a critical compendium of insights and analyses. This book, through its engaging dialogues with leading thinkers, explores the intricate dance between innovation and sustainability, shedding light on how we can harness the power of economic and technological advancements for the greater good.

To whet – but not spoil – your appetite, let me give you a taste of what is to come.

Summing up Australia's innovation performance, Roy Green says that

> *we have a very strong performance in our research output, the production of ideas through our universities through the CSIRO and other research institutions. . . but the efficiency or effectiveness with which we turn those ideas into commercial outcomes is lacking.*

One intriguing attempt to address the problem comes from Green's university, UTS, which has been attempting to build entrepreneurship skills across a broad swath of the student body.

In his interview, Mark Dodgson challenges us to see beyond the conventional view of innovation as merely technological breakthroughs, presenting it instead as a force for comprehensive change that addresses pressing global issues. Dodgson recounts his surprise when he told senior managers in the pharmaceutical and construction sector that they needed to 'play' more: 'they got it straight away'.

In a discussion of the economics of innovation, Kevin Fox points to the risk that new technologies lead to 'stranded capital assets', as firms are left holding too much capital given a technological change. He gives the example of innovation in the accommodation sector that leaves hotels feeling out-of-date, an example that will resonate with those of us who tend to stay in budget hotels.

In a conversation with polymath Nicholas Gruen, we learn about the approach of 'disagree and commit', and how rarely corporate leaders welcome robust disagreement from subordinates.

US technology policy writer Robert Atkinson headed up the advisory team on emerging technology policy for US President Biden's 2020 campaign. Atkinson emphasises his concern that share market investors might deter long-term investment, arguing that 'investment incentives in the US have shifted the innovation system towards too much conservatism and too much short-termism'. He also accuses former Hewlett-Packard CEO Mark Hurd of 'gutting' the company – pushing up the stock price by 'basically robbing the future of HP and putting it into the short term'.

Turning to climate change, interviews with Ross Garnaut and Warwick McKibbin discuss the economics and politics of reducing greenhouse gas emissions. Both cite the work of Nobel Prize-winning economist William Nordhaus and seek approaches that maximise economic and environmental outcomes, while minimising unnecessary political pain. Garnaut's conception of Australia as a 'renewables superpower' is crisp and powerful, while McKibbin notes the value of seeking to 'create "constituencies" within an economy that find it in their own financial interest to not block the policy'.

The conversation then shifts to the impact of technological disruption on societal norms and economic structures, with Michael Piore and Bob Carr offering contrasting perspectives on the role of innovation in shaping the future of work and corporate responsibility in the age of climate change. Piore's critique of the Silicon Valley model of innovation, juxtaposed with Carr's call for corporate engagement in sustainability efforts, highlights the complex interplay between technological advancement and social responsibility.

Sami Kara offers practical examples of how to build a 'circular economy'. Products, he says, should last longer and be easier to disassemble. He gives the example of the Fuji Xerox 'One-Shot' camera, which is posted back to Fuji, taken apart, and then reassembled for the next customer – an approach that certainly seems better than throwing it away (although still not quite as environmentally sound as taking electronic photos on your smartphone).

Just because a technology is new to Australia, it does not follow that it will improve well-being. In his interview, Jim Green debunks the hype about nuclear power, pointing out that the level of private funding for small modular reactors is 'laughably low and not nearly enough to get projects off the ground'. Nuclear power, Green notes, has relied on governments being willing to kick in billions of dollars – money that could be better spent on investment in renewables.

In the energy space, a more promising technology is hydrogen. As energy expert Tony Wood notes, the hydrogen cycle is nicely circular: 'If we start with renewable electricity from the sun to split water to make hydrogen, then, if we burn that hydrogen, for example in a power station, the product of that combustion is water'.

In agriculture, the discussion with Richard Heath delves into the potential uses of data to improve efficiency, such as by selective spraying of weeds. This is followed by an intriguing interview with Lesley Hughes, who points to the emergence of synthetic biology and food technologies as harbingers of a more sustainable and efficient future for food production. Impossible burgers, and non-dairy alternatives to milk, ice cream and yoghurt are just some of the sustainable innovations she foreshadows.

Drawing the book to a close, Michael Lester's concluding chapter synthesises the many insights offered by the interviewees, weaving them into a coherent narrative that highlights the book's central thesis: the inseparability of innovation and sustainability in the quest for a better future. Lester's analysis not only reiterates the importance of the discussions contained within the book but also invites readers to actively engage with the economic, technological and environmental challenges presented.

My hope is that this book will not only inform but also challenge and encourage all of us to take an active role in crafting innovative solutions that bridge the gap between technological advancement and sustainable development. Together – through thoughtful engagement and collaborative effort – we can navigate the complexities of the coming decades, forging a path towards a future where innovation and sustainability are inextricably linked.

***

Dr. Andrew Leigh MP is a member of the Australian Parliament and author of over ten books, including *Innovation + Equality: How to Create a Future That Is More Star Trek Than Terminator* (with Joshua Gans, MIT Press, 2020) and *The Shortest History of Economics* (Black Inc. Books, 2024).

Preface

This book has its proximate genesis in my ongoing series of 'Innovation Talk' radio interview programme at Sydney, Radio Northern Beaches (88.7 and 90.3FM *www.rnb.org.au*). I have had the privilege over the course of the years of programming since 2018 to discuss a wide range of issues with leading science, technology and society experts and commentators in their fields in Australia, the UK and the US. A small selection of these conversations forms the core of this book focused on the interrelationship between innovation and sustainability within the context of responses to climate change.

Without my interviewees' generous contributions and agreement to be included here, there would be no book. I am indebted not only to them as contributors to this book but also to the pursuit of my own curiosity and knowledge.

My interest in innovation goes back many years. I worked primarily from an economics perspective on policies for science, technology, trade and industry including at the Organisation for Economic Cooperation and Development (OECD) and with the Australian Science and Technology Council (ASTEC). With an early background in water engineering, natural resources and environmental policies, and latterly with Land and Water Australia (LWA), I have a continuing interest in environment and sustainability.

The book opens in its first of four sections by introducing two intertwined questions. What is innovation, how is it driven and how does it interact beyond economics with science, technology and society to shape our lives and hopefully well-being? What is sustainability and how is it impacted by technology and innovation, particularly in a time of global climate emergency?

The book's two central sections take as case studies the issues of climate change and energy; and agriculture, land and water. While these focus on an Australian perspective given its unique continental scale endowments of natural resources, these sections afford insights into our broader inquiry and into global climate change-driven challenges facing these two key sectors.

The fourth and final section asks who is responsible and how, for addressing the challenge of sustainability and innovation posed by climate change. The discussions turn on the forms of operation of governance institutions in confronting the interaction of the complex systems of innovation and sustainability.

The idea for the book came from my co-author, academic Marie dela Rama, my long-time friend and colleague in writing published papers with her interests in governance and political integrity. With her familiarity in academic publishing and her eye for topicality, she urged me to submit a book proposal. Without Marie's enthusiasm and initiative, organising skills, and subsequent deft collaboration in writing and editing, attention to detail and referencing, this book would not have been completed. Thank you Marie.

A link to all my interviews, including those covered in this book, can be accessed through the following page: www.mixcloud.com/michael-lester5/

Michael Lester, Sydney, 2024
melester@yahoo.com

***

This publication is the culmination of decades of policy experience and the network effect of bringing subject-matter experts – and their accumulated knowledge – together to come up with innovation pathways for solutions to the ongoing sustainability challenges we face today.

I have spent countless hours over many, many years with Michael arguing, debating and discussing in a *salon* or *tertulia* type of environment over the various topics covered in this book. Organising eclectic ideas in a coherent form has allowed us to explore these themes in greater detail, and Michael's high-calibre interviewees called for a compilation that allowed the power of their ideas to shape the structure of the book. Subjects discussed in his interviews needed to be shared with a wider audience, beyond its initial radio listeners, as a contribution to clearer understanding of the existential issues. Hence, this publication.

Equally as important, I'd like to thank the team at Routledge Singapore for their encouragement, understanding, patience and support in seeing this publication to completion, especially Yongling, Kendrick and Chelsea. Thank you for your perseverance.

Human sustainability requires innovation to confront the many existential challenges of the twenty-first century. Curiosity and enquiry are prime motivations to understand and to provide answers to current problems. While issues may be albeit resolved, inevitably, new ones arise.

My vision for this book is that it primarily contributes to the growing body of work that emphasises innovative and positive policy solutions to address complex problems; and as a testament to the influence and enduring power of ideas.

All links were accessed at the time of writing, but internet sources are always in a state of flux and we hope that some of these links are still working when you read this book. Furthermore, each chapter contains keywords reflecting at least one Sustainable Development Goal (SDG) number. The UN SDGs are 17 universal goals for humanity by the year 2030.

You are welcome to send us your thoughts, suggestions and comments on the topics covered in this book.

The art of civil conversation can be sometimes lost when covering complex, contentious and controversial topics. I hope you find this book encourages that art to continue and that you enjoy this book as much as we have had fun compiling, writing, editing and tweaking it.

Marie dela Rama, Sydney, 2024
delaramawork@gmail.com

Acronyms (Country or Organisation in Parentheses)

AATE	Australian Academy of Technology and Engineering
ABARES	Australian Bureau of Agriculture and Resources Economics and Sciences
ABS	Australian Bureau of Statistics
AC	Companion of the Order of Australia
ACCC	Australian Competition and Consumers Commission
ACCI	Australian Chamber of Commerce and Industry
ACCR	Australian Centre for Corporate Responsibility
ACCU	Australian Carbon Credits Units
ACOLA	Australian Council of Learned Academies
ACMA	Australian Communications and Media Authority
ACP	Abatement Certificate Providers
ACT	Australian Capital Territory
AEMC	Australian Energy Market Commission
AEMO	Australian Energy Market Operator
AFI	Australian Farm Institute
AFR	Australian Financial Review
AI	Artificial Intelligence
AICD	Australian Institute of Company Directors
ALP	Australian Labor Party
ANAO	Australian National Audit Office
ANSTO	Australian Nuclear Science and Technology Organisation
ANU	Australian National University
AM	Member of the Order of Australia
AO	Officer of the Order of Australia
APRA	Australian Prudential Regulatory Authority
ARENA	Australian Renewable Energy Agency
ASC	American Science Corps
ASIC	Australian Securities and Investments Commission
ASPI	Australian Strategic Policy Institute
ASTEC	Australian Science and Technology Council
ASTIP	(UK) Applied Systems Thinking in Practice Group
ASX	Australian Stock Exchange

AUKUS	Australia-UK-US trilateral security pact
AUM	Assets Under Management
AUSTRAC	Australian Transaction Reports and Analysis Centre
BAAD	Big, Anticompetitive, Addictive and Destructive to Democracy
BCA	Business Council of Australia
BHP	Broken Hill Proprietary Limited
BTC	Bitcoin
CAMA	(Australia) Centre for Applied Macroeconomic Analysis
CAS	Complex Adaptive Systems
CBA	Commonwealth Bank of Australia
CBDC	Central Bank Digital Currency
CCA	Climate Council of Australia
CCS	Carbon Capture and Sequestration
CMI	Carbon Market Institute
COAG	Council of Australian Governments
COP	UN Conference of the Parties of the UNFCCC
COVID-19	Coronavirus disease of 2019
CPM	Carbon Pricing Mechanism
CPRS	Carbon Pollution Reduction Scheme
CRC	Cooperative Research Centres
CSIRO	Commonwealth Scientific and Industrial Research Organisation
CSR	Corporate Social Responsibility
DAFF	(Australian) Department of Agriculture, Fisheries and Forestry
DCCEEW	(Australian) Department of Climate Change, Energy, the Environment and Water
DeFin	Decentralised Finance
DICE Model	Dynamic Integrated model of Climate and the Economy
DIISR	(Australian) Department of Innovation, Industry, Science and Research
DISR	(Australian) Department of Industry, Science and Resources
EPA	(US) Environmental Protection Agency
ERF	Emissions Reduction Fund
ESB	(Australian) Energy Security Board
ESG	Environmental, Social and Governance
ESS	Ecosystem Services
ETF/s	Exchange-Traded Fund/s
ETS	Emissions Trading Scheme
EU	European Union
EV/s	Electrical Vehicle/s
FAO	(UN) Food and Agricultural Organisation
FASB	(US) Financial Accounting Standards Board
FCA	(UK) Financial Conduct Authority
FOE	Friends of the Earth
GE	General Electric

GDP	Gross Domestic Product
GGAS	(NSW) Greenhouse Gas Reduction Scheme
GII	Global Innovation Index
GRDC	(Australia) GRDC Grain Research and Development Corporation
GUI	Graphical User Interface
HESC	Hydrogen Energy Supply Chain
IAEA	International Atomic Energy Agency
IBM	International Business Machines
ICAC	(NSW) Independent Commission Against Corruption
ICT	Information and Communication Technology/ies
IEA	International Energy Agency
IFRC	International Financial Reporting Council
IFSR	International Federation for Systems Research
IIRC	International Integrated Reporting Council
IMF	International Monetary Fund
IOT	Internet of Things
IP	Intellectual Property
IPART	(NSW) Independent Pricing and Regulatory Tribunal
IPCC	Intergovernmental Panel on Climate Change
IRECUSA	Interstate Renewable Energy Council of the USA
IRENA	International Renewable Energy Agency
IRF	Integrated Reporting Framework
ISA	Innovation and Science Australia
ISF	Institute for Sustainable Futures, UTS
ITIF	Information Technology and Innovation Foundation
LNG	Liquefied Natural Gas
LWA	Land and Water Australia
MCA	Minerals Council of Australia
MDB	(Australia) Murray–Darling Basin
MDBA	(Australia) Murray–Darling Basin Authority
MDBP	(Australia) Murray–Darling Basin Plan
MEAA	(Australia) Media, Entertainment and Arts Alliance
NAB	National Australia Bank
NACC	(Australia) National Anti-Corruption Commission
NASDAQ	National Association of Securities Dealers Automated Quotations
NBER	(US) National Bureau of Economic Research
NBN	(Australia) National Broadband Network
NCSES	(US) National Center for Science and Engineering Statistics
NDC	Nationally Determined Contribution/s
NEC	(US) National Economic Council
NEG	(Australia) National Energy Guarantee
NFF	(Australia) National Farmers' Federation
NFT	Non-fungible tokens
NGAC	NSW Greenhouse Gas Abatement Certificates
NIS	National Innovation Systems

NIST	(US) National Institute of Standards and Technology
NRAR	(Australia) National Resources Access Regulator
NRMA	(Australia) National Roads and Motorists Association
NSF	(US) National Science Foundation
NSW	New South Wales, state of Australia
NWI	(Australia) National Water Initiative
OAM	Medal of the Order of Australia
OECD	Organisation for Economic Cooperation and Development
OSTP	(US) Office of Science and Technology Policy
OUP	Oxford University Press
PACs	(US) Political Action Committees
PARC	Palo Alto Research Center
PC	(Australia) Productivity Commission
PIJI	Public Interest Journalism Initiative
PING	Public Interest News Gathering
PISA	(OECD) Programme for International Student Assessment
PMSEIC	(Australia) Prime Minister's Science Engineering & Innovation Council
PRI	(UN) Principles for Responsible Investment
PoW	Proof-of-Work mining
R&D	Research and Development
RBA	Reserve Bank of Australia
RET	(Australia) Renewable Energy Targets
RICE Model	Regional Integrated Climate-Economy (RICE) model
RRDCs	(Australia) Rural Research Development Corporations
SASB	Sustainable Accounting Standards Board
SBS	(Australia) Special Broadcasting Service
SC	(Australia) Senior Counsel
SDG	(UN) Sustainable Development Goal/s
SMH	Sydney Morning Herald
SMMT	(UK) Society of Motor Manufacturers and Traders
SMRs	Small Modular Nuclear Reactors
SRI	(Australia) Science, Research and Innovation
STEM	Science, Technology, Engineering and Maths
STI	(OECD) Science, Technology and Innovation
SWIFT	Society for Worldwide Interbank Financial Telecommunications
TFP	Total Factor Productivity
UNEP	United Nations Environment Programme
UNFCCC	United Nations Framework Convention on Climate Change
UNSW	University of New South Wales, Australia
UQ	University of Queensland
UTS	University of Technology Sydney, Australia
WIPO	World Intellectual Property Organisation
WRI	World Resources Institute
WTO	World Trade Organisation

1 Introduction

Exploring the Opportunities and Challenges of Innovation, Technology, Climate Change and Sustainability

The world faces the twin challenges and opportunities of climate change adaptation and digital technology disruption. Both also pose existential risks to sustainability on a human and global scale.

Key Questions

Historically, technology and innovation have fuelled global economic prosperity and population growth, while at the same time underpinning the unprecedented rate of energy use required that now confronts us with the global climate change crisis and a challenge to global sustainability.

- Can we trust in technology and the seemingly limitless options that it affords in the hope that it will provide a 'silver bullet' to climate change and a path to global and human sustainability?
- Will the complexity of technology itself dictate the pathways we will tread in a form of 'technological determinism' that overrides our human agency?
- Are our political systems and governance practices 'fit for purpose' and sufficiently innovative to guide us systemically to a sustainable future?

Each succeeding year of climate change brings new, all-time global temperature increases at a rate faster than predicted towards the agreed 1.5 degree target at the 2015 Paris Agreement, with and the accompanying natural disasters. 2023 was the hottest year since global records began in 1850. The threat posed is on the scale of the 6th global extinction of living species; only this time around, it is driven by our own human activities in the Anthropoecene Era.

The Industrial Revolution and its 'wave' of associated mechanical and electrical technologies – heavily reliant on fossil fuel energy – lifted economic and population growth to historically unprecedented levels through the nineteenth century. The 'long-wave' technological paradigm shift to our era of digital technologies beginning in the late nineteenth century has already disrupted long-established social and economic norms globally. Poised on the doorstep of Artificial Intelligence, its impacts promise to grow exponentially to challenge the very notion of what it is to be human.

DOI: 10.4324/9781003280316-1

Method

This book takes you on a journey of exploration that reflects our own attempts to better comprehend and fathom the nature of both innovation and sustainability in their interrelationship. In particular, this inquiry is about the ways in which technology might either confound our attempts to tackle the global climate emergency or offer a pathway to a future sustainable global environment.

Innovation is not a linear process driven at the front end by genius basic research and science, and transformed by entrepreneurs through development into a vast array of products and services then diffused and adopted widely for social impact. It rather operates as a complex ecosystem in a series of feedback loops at each stage and within a complex array of social, cultural, economic, political and institutional components of each individual national innovation system. A little like this book which unfolds in an inductive exploratory manner across the many dimensions of innovation ecosystems in search of the complexity of sustainability.

Our inquiry in this collection of chapters based on a selection of 27 interviews with a wide range of experts explores options for innovative pathways to sustainability. Those interviewed range across disciplines including agriculture, economics, engineering, governance, history, journalism, politics, public policy and science. They work as academics, authors, bureaucrats, consultants, farmers, journalists, politicians, journalists, researchers and scientists.

I believe that the conversational tone of the interviews drawn on in this book allows a degree of freedom of expression and spontaneity from our experts that is not normally found in their more formal writings and presentations. The informal, vernacular language rather than diminishing the substance and impact of their positions and arguments illuminates and adds emphases to their informed and important messages. I hope you will find that it gives added immediacy and accessibility to their expert and technical voices on our important topics.

In framing the conversations, I have attempted to explore the big-picture ideas and long-view perspective underlying the developments and news of the day. The many references to media reporting provide an anchor and context for the discussions which have taken place over a number of years. References to academic and institutional papers, reports and books point the reader to detailed and analytical materials that underpin and develop the points covered in the interviews. We believe that the structural and dynamic insights they afford maintain their value notwithstanding any subsequent developments in technology and policies. Footnoted references do provide relevant updates on both where deemed material.

In our selection of interviews from among the 150 or so broad-ranging conversations on innovation over the past few years of my programme, we have adopted a case study approach focused on sustainability and climate change in particular. The chosen focus in the book is on two key economic sectors based on use of natural resources: climate and energy; and agriculture, land and water resources. These sectors are examined in the Australian context, not least because it is an essentially natural resources-based economy. Their discussion is complemented and contextualised by broader international perspectives drawing on a wider range of international experts.

Layout and Logic

If you enjoy an unfolding sense of discovery, do please turn straight to the first of our interview chapters or you might prefer to dip into selected interviews that attract your particular attention. If, however, you are more comfortable having some idea of the lay of the land ahead, then this introduction provides a roadmap.

SECTION I: UNDERSTANDING INNOVATION AND SUSTAINABILITY

The book begins in the first of its four sections with an interview with Mark Dodgson by asking what we know of the ideas of innovation and sustainability, how they have developed over time and where they stand today. Adam Smith back in the eighteenth century identified technological change and innovation as drivers of economic growth and the 'wealth of nations'. It was not until late in the twentieth century that economists such as 1987 Nobel Prize winner Robert Solow took a closer look at the process of economic growth focusing on the drivers of labour and capital from a neoclassical perspective.

The role of technology remained a mysterious 'black box', a *deus ex machina* until the early part of this century when it was recognised by economist 2018 Nobel Prize winner Paul Romer as an 'endogenous' component of growth arising from within the economy. Nevertheless, as discussed with Kevin Fox, its impact and measurement have proved elusive and challenging particularly in the paradox of large investment and development of digital technology but with limited empirical evidence of improved economic performance through productivity.

The work of Joseph Schumpeter identified risk-taking entrepreneurs as the principal agents of technological change and at the centre of economic growth through a process of 'creative destruction'. We discuss with Nicholas Gruen the role, motives and values of digital age Silicon Valley, garage start-up entrepreneurs and the unprecedented rate of growth of their subsequent global 'big tech' corporations to capitalisations previously unheard of. We ask if we are in a new age and breed of young entrepreneurs who face much lower barriers to entry than ever before.

It is nations that face new 'existential' geopolitical challenges of national security and global climate change that require systematic government intervention to deliver innovation, competitiveness and sustainability putting them arguably at a 'tipping point', as discussed with Robert Atkinson. We explore the dimensions of these challenges and responses at the scale and cultural complexity and transformation of 'national innovation systems' with Roy Green.

Yet we see that the pathway through technology and innovation to sustainability, as dramatised in the case of global 'climate change', while reliant on government action is stymied and frustrated by 'partisanship' and 'politicisation'.

We discuss with Ross Garnaut how the advice of scientists and economists for efficient and effective solutions and transition pathways is thwarted. As the globe confronts the 'tragedy of the commons', the effective economic integration of a sustainable energy transition in response to climate change advocated by 2018 Nobel Prize winner William Nordhaus confronts the complexity of modelling and weighing of costs and benefits which is elusive in itself as William McKibbin elaborates.

In discussion with Sami Kara, he explains how ideas such as the 'circular economy' suggest broader innovative pathways to sustainability that have the potential to decouple growth from resource use and waste. These involve the systemic transformation of manufacturing business models and management practices, accompanied by significant changes in consumer expectations and behaviour.

SECTION II: CLIMATE CHANGE AND ENERGY RESOURCES

In the second section of the book, we consider the first of two case studies drawn from Australian experience, which open up the processes of innovation as they bear on the opportunities for sustainability in two key economic sectors. This section deals with the challenges of decarbonisation from fossil fuels in response to global climate change. We discuss how despite the availability of disruptive and transformative competitive renewable solar and wind energy technologies the political climate can impede a sustainable energy transition. As a significant global fossil fuel energy supplier, Australia is also richly endowed with globally competitive renewable energy resources so the challenges and opportunities are particularly acute.

Policy uncertainty and lack of stability can undermine the large and necessary investment in the transformation and decarbonisation of the electricity industry as discussed with Giles Parkinson. The exercise of vested and powerful interests in fossil-fuelled electricity has contributed to Stop-Start policies. Party politicisation has characterised the highly contested, partisan and divisive 'climate wars' and compromised the adoption and acceptance of practical solutions, as explored with Chris Dunstan.

We examine the factors determining the rate of diffusion and adoption of new renewable technologies. In the particular case of electric vehicles (EV), we discuss with Peter Khoury the importance of individual consumer motivations in the face of barriers to adoption that are influenced by government policies bearing on price, and infrastructure provision.

Much hyped, emerging new digital technologies that are potentially transformative in the global financial services industry are not necessarily environmentally benign or sustainable. We explore with Sean Foley the case of cryptocurrencies and their reliance on heavy electricity power and labour exploitation.

New unproven, presently uneconomic technologies are touted as sustainable technology 'fixes' in the energy sector. We illustrate by discussing with Jim Green how and why long-established mature and uneconomic technologies such as nuclear power are promoted as a solution on the basis of their contribution to sustainable net zero in the form of overhyped and politicised 'small modular reactors' with Jim Green.

The final chapter in the Energy case study section discusses the sustainable energy transition with Tony Wood. It concludes with the captivating promise of complex optional technology pathways to a 'hydrogen-based economy' potentially transforming Australia's energy and manufacturing sectors into a global renewable energy superpower, 'shipping sunshine to the world'.

SECTION III: AGRICULTURE, LAND AND WATER RESOURCES

Our second set of case study interviews feature the agriculture, land and water resources sector that face particularly acute climate change issues in Australia as a global food exporter and the driest continent. Long dependent on innovation to maintain sector global competitiveness, the innovation pathways for a transition to sustainability are complex and formidable.

We explore the key part played by innovation over decades in lifting agriculture sector productivity and consider the opportunities presented by digital technologies alongside the funding of research, development and extension with Richard Heath. As a major user of land and water resources, issues of sustainability in the face of climate change loom large along with the social and structural adjustment implications.

We ask if the biotechnology revolution of 'precision fermentation' heralds a new era of food production without animals with Lesley Hughes. While minimising the environmental impact of agriculture, this revolution affords the promise of feeding ever more people on a scale described as the 'second domestication' of animals.

Innovation over the decades for the sustainable use of water resources upon which agriculture is fundamentally dependent has proven catastrophically difficult in the case of the nation's most significant environmental asset, the Murray–Darling River Basin. We discuss with Richard Beasley how application of the best available scientific knowledge has been compromised politically, at great public expense of billions of dollars, in an example of gross public policy mismanagement with the Basin.

Lack of new knowledge and science is not always in itself necessarily the key to evidence-based policy and institutional innovation for sustainability. We discuss with Bruce Pascoe how Indigenous Australians and their culture have survived over 60,000 years in this driest of continents over vast cycles of environmental and climate change and why colonising and modern Australia has deliberately ignored and even denied that history of adaptive land management.

The knowledge and practices of decades of modern and widespread experience with a suite of innovative and sustainable regenerative practices of cultivation and agriculture prompt us to ask about the barriers to widespread, scaled-up adoption. We explore, with Charles Massy, a long history of individual attempts to break through the institutionalised practices of large-scale industrialised agriculture and the commercial and cultural impediments standing in the way of ecological literacy of landowners about the self-regenerating and sustainable nature of complex adaptive ecosystems of land, water and biodiversity.

SECTION IV: GOVERNANCE ROLES AND RESPONSIBILITIES

In the course of eight discussions that make up the fourth and final part of the book, we consider the roles and responsibilities of the various key actors and institutions involved in the governance of our quest down the innovative pathways to sustainability.

We are living in an era characterised by the Silicon Valley Consensus about the power and beneficence of disruptive innovation championed by the tech entrepreneurs. We consider, with Michael Piore, to what extent this form of technological determinism has been adopted by governments with the result that many feel 'left behind' and attracted to the appeal of populism.

Corporations and the private sector are key drivers of productivity and growth but what is their responsibility and capacity often in the face of their own vested interests in taking forward an innovation agenda towards a sustainable response to climate change? We discuss with Bob Carr the circumstances under which governments, often laggard in their own responses, might find ways to partner effectively with business.

With Pru Bennett, we discuss whether the finance industry plays a role by channelling capital investment to businesses promoting and pursuing sustainability goals and governance (ESG) or in the absence of enforceable standards does it all amount to a 'woke' form of 'greenwash'.

On the other hand, from a business point of view there are clearly significant opportunities in decarbonising and moving to renewable energy sources. There are many viable and innovative pathways to the sustainable transformation of the Australian economy into a global renewable energy 'superpower', 'exporting sunshine' to the world. We explore these opportunities and the leadership supportive government role in the transition with the second Ross Garnaut interview in this book.

Governments, and indeed business, rely on maintaining the trust and confidence of the people that in recent decades has fallen precipitously. In our democracy, journalists and the media play a key role in informing the public and contributing to transparency and accountability of government. We discuss, with Allan Fels, the ways in which that role has been substantially undermined by technology, media concentration, growing secrecy and disinformation, thereby prejudicing the role and future of public interest journalism.

Scientists themselves have a role in contributing to public confidence as we see with COVID-19 and Climate Change. We consider how public understanding of and confidence in science, its methods and uncertainties can be built both through education and by the actions of scientists themselves with the only joint interview in this book, Aaron Mertz and Abhilash Mishra.

This book concludes the final section with two chapters addressing the broader systemic questions of roles, responsibilities and governance. Can the collective failure of our institutions in their timely response to the climate emergency be explained by its traditional hierarchical, top-down, maximising, command-and-control governance models? Might a more systems-based, decentralised and adaptable approach to governance enable a more sustainable future, as discussed with Ray Ison.

Finally, we discuss with Barry Jones the need for political systemic reform to deliver effective public trust and engagement. Is anything short of a political and cultural transformation of the distribution of democratic power in our governance likely to confront the global existential challenge of climate change and deliver sustainability.

Happy Reading

We hope you will now join us with a focused sense of purpose on our journey of inquiry that we have been privileged to undertake in the company of our many eminent and distinguished interviewees.

Section I

Understanding Innovation and Sustainability

2 The Things That Matter

Understanding and Communicating the Process and Impact of Innovation

Interview With Mark Dodgson

Introduction

Adam Smith in *Wealth of Nations* (1776)[1] identified a concern with the economics of technological change and innovation as a driver of economic growth and wealth of nations. The idea of innovation has a long and complex history both in theory and in practice.[2] Just what is innovation? The term is widely applied to a broad range of concepts, ideas and practices. Why is it important to our societies, to our well-being and to our businesses?[3] How does innovation operate in businesses and in governments which both promote it and regulate it in the public interest? How has our understanding of innovation developed over the past century or two? And where is innovation taking our economies and societies in the future? These are important questions as we find ourselves caught up in the current wave of transformational digital technology innovation.[4]

Keywords: destructive innovation; disruptive innovation; economic growth models; entrepreneurship; government-led innovation; innovation; innovation ecosystems; playful entrepreneurs; productivity paradox; SDG8; SDG9; technology black box; total factor productivity.

Interviewee Profile

Mark Dodgson **(MD)** (AO)[5] is Professor Emeritus, Innovation Studies at the Business School, University of Queensland; and Visiting Professor of Innovation at Imperial College, Business School in London. His research and writing have spanned many decades, and his influence on innovation management and policy has been worldwide.[6] He has worked in over 60 countries and particularly focused on the importance of organisations and organisational learning and business strategies including issues of collaboration between firms, and between firms and research organisations. Mark produced a landmark handbook on industrial innovation[7] and participated in the review of Australia's National Innovation System.[8,9]

DOI: 10.4324/9781003280316-3

The Interview

ML: Mark, how and why did you come to devote a long career to the study of 'innovation'?

MD: I was very fortunate as a youngster choosing an area of study which has proven very fruitful and never anything less than interesting. I suppose it started with my choice of degree back in 1974. It was called Society and Technology, and it was about the impact of technology on society. There were a bunch of, let's put it impolitely, 'hippies' that wanted to change the world and were interested in alternative technologies and so forth. It was an ideological fascination and an almost utopian interest in technology in that era.[10]

There was also great concern about the depletion and exhaustion of resources and the environmental consequences of technologies,[11] that was also very resonant with today's discussions about how computerisation was going to affect employment levels and skills, and so forth. One of the things I have noticed over a long career is that many of the issues that we're facing and talking about today have been confronted in the past.

ML: You recently launched the second edition of your very successful book from Oxford University Press (OUP), *Innovation: A Very Short Introduction*.[12] How do you account for its popularity in many languages and around the world?

MD: Yes, it's done very well and it's part of a very good series of these OUP books that have sold six or seven million copies. They're very handy, fit in your purse or your jacket pockets and they're on a wide range of issues. Writing a short book is like writing a short article: it's much more difficult than writing a long book. One of the books that I edited on innovation is over 2,000 pages long, so there's an awful lot known about this subject and being able to condense it into a short book of 25,000 words to look at the main issues related to innovation – its causes, its effects and its future – is quite a challenge and was very enjoyable.

ML: A feature of your book is that you confront the challenge of communicating effectively about the complexity of innovation, with a wider, non-specialist audience. Our former Prime Minister, Malcolm Turnbull arrived with a great flurry promoting an innovation agenda but soon found himself having to back off politically because he didn't seem to be able to communicate to the electorate a positive and relevant vision behind his talk about entrepreneurship and innovation.[13] People were worried about job losses, which they could see at the front end of innovation and change. How do you tackle the communication challenge in your book?

MD: Well, I think you're right. I think that they got the message completely wrong because the association with innovation was people in laboratories, in white coats and it was about people with ponytails and funky haircuts and drinking lattes in coffee bars and talking about start-ups, and so on; it was very, very different from the everyday experience of the population and citizenry: the voter.

So, I try to bring innovation down to a personal level and think about how innovation has changed the quality of our lives and our families. For example, my grandfather, who I grew up with, when he was born and grew up there were no radios; there were no cars, no internal combustion engines, no planes or cinemas or cinematography or anything like that. His world was incredibly different from today. I was recently very happy that I became a grandfather for the first time and looking at my grandson I wonder what kind of life that he's had. Since my grandfather and probably his great-grandfather, life has progressed positively, the technologies that we have now that we didn't have 150 years ago. They've had a marvellous effect on our quality of life. It's given us better health, longer lives. It's given us the freedom to travel, better opportunities for education, the democracy of freedom, of automobiles and being able to travel and fly and so forth. So many improvements. But the question I have is whether my grandson will enjoy that wonderful trajectory we've been on in the last 150 or so years, where innovation has improved the quality of our lives and our standards of living.

So I think we've had to turn to the question of what effect is innovation having on us? In our everyday lives? And that means pushing some hot buttons of what things mean to people.

What does innovation mean to people driving to work? How we can make transport systems more efficient and less polluting so you don't have so much time spent in traffic; maybe that's something your listeners may struggle with, their driving home from work. That's an issue that really matters. But you know, smart cars and more efficient planning and our electric engines and so forth will help address some of those problems, as may fast transportation systems which are much more efficient. So that's an issue.

People have concerns about health care and worries about the expansion of the cost of health care. But digital technologies in the home are able to provide data remotely and some analytics that can provide preventative medicine based on your watch or some device you may wear produces much more effective information, more rapid decision or sometimes better decision-making rather than clogging up hospitals. What matters to people is when Auntie Nora goes in for a hip transplant, how quickly she is going to come out and will she be much much better? Well, innovation will get her out quicker. It'll give her a better hip, will get her a better quality of life. So we need to relate this issue and its innovation to everyday experience rather than talking in some vague terms about biotechnology start-ups, or AI start-ups, which doesn't mean a lot to people.

ML: That's a pretty strong point about communicating the meaning of innovation, and in your book,[14] you address that in terms of the impact on people's everyday lives. So usually, over the long haul, the impact is for the better, and you can do this well in stories such as you tell in the book. But innovation can also be very important for people in driving as it has over time, significant productivity growth, economic growth by which we all benefit and in which we all share;[15] and certainly here in Australia, one of the richest countries in the world, in prosperity, which is spread widely in our society and which is centrally driven by innovation and technology. Or is that not so?

MD: No, absolutely. Most economic growth since the Industrial Revolution has been driven by innovation, and I think the problem we face today is that around the developed world, productivity is actually declining.[16] In terms of what they called total factor productivity,[17] which is the amount of productivity that occurs after you allow for investments in capital and labour, which can be seen as innovation. So there's declining productivity, but when you actually go down and start looking at companies and different industries, you find tremendous variation. You find innovative companies in virtually every sector that do invest in technology, they do invest in skills and management training and so forth, and they use innovation very effectively. And they're the ones where productivity will increase, but unfortunately there's a large rump of companies that don't invest in innovation, they don't invest in new skills and they're the ones that drag the whole economy down.[18]

So I think the question is how to create more of that top tier of companies that are externally oriented, market-facing, technology-savvy, being interested in dealing with international markets and so on. We need more of those firms and we need to raise the game of other companies across the board to get them more involved in innovation, more innovative in order to raise their productivity because it's in those companies where productivity is lagging in the nation as a whole. And without productivity, we don't have the money to be able to pay for the things we want, like a health system, an education system and defence and so on.

ML: Economists have long and particularly in recent times with the digital age, technological change grappled with what is referred to as the 'productivity paradox', namely the observation, attributed to Nobel Economist Robert Solow in the 1970s and 1980s, that everywhere around us in society we see the new products of new digital technologies. We all know them and live with them, and overall we are pretty happy with them and there's been big investments obviously made towards all that. And yet, as you say, the productivity performance of the economy seems to be lagging.[19] Economists have changed their way of thinking, haven't they, over time about how innovation works in the economy? Haven't they traditionally thought of it as what might be called a bit of a 'black box' in driving economic growth? They've always focused on capital and labour: if you increase the amount of capital, if you increase the amount of labour, you get growth. But they tended to have ignored, as you say, the role and the understanding of how technology actually contributes to growth?

MD: Well, I think that's right. There is a new generation of economists that is thinking more clearly about the impact of innovation. That's not to say there haven't been people in the past, I mean Schumpeter with the classic analysis of the importance of technology and innovation, in the 1930s and 1940s.[20,21] He ended up as a Professor of Economics at Harvard University and he's the one who argued the classic analysis of innovation being a process of 'creative destruction', that innovation will create and destroy at the same time.[22] Then you have other economists such William Baumol at Princeton who showed that innovation is the cause of all economic growth.[23]

The problem, I fear, is that economists don't spend enough time actually understanding what goes on in companies, because companies are hugely important to the innovation process. Government is a very important player of course; but the companies are hugely important, if not the most important player in innovation.

One of the greatest economists, a British economist who understood the importance of innovation at a regional level, was Alfred Marshall. He spent one day a week going to a different company finding out how the company worked, how it made decisions, why it was doing things the way it did, and that influenced his understanding of his economic model.[24]

So, I think more appreciation of what actually happens in firms, the decisions that companies have to make that balance the choices they have to make, the risks they have to take, the organisational realities of innovation; these are things which don't tend to impinge on many economists and models which tend to be rather static and simplistic – with due apologies to my economist friends.

ML: Mark, we're discussing the view that economists have held of how innovation fits into things and more recently the 2018 Nobel Prize for Economics was awarded to Paul Romer, an American economist at New York University, for looking more closely than has been done before at the technical change factor as a driver of economic growth.[25] But as you say, it is the role of companies and their entrepreneurs first and foremost, and businesses in making the investments, taking the risks and developing the products that is the key to innovation. In your latest book, *The Playful Entrepreneur: How to Adapt and Thrive in an Uncertain World* (2018),[26] is the entrepreneur a Schumpeterian driver of creative destruction?

MD: I've been interested in the notion of play that is sometimes considered rather frivolous, but I think it's actually very serious. Play is something we do when we're experimenting, and when we're exploring new things, it's how we learn and how we learn to adapt. It's how sometimes we express our freedom in life and have fun.[27]

I wrote a book called *Think Play Do* (2005),[28] which argues that innovation is a process of thinking, coming up with an idea and doing it; you have to put it into practice for it to be an innovation, but play is in connecting, play is the tinkering, the testing, the prototyping and so on. I'm really interested in the notion of play. I was collecting lots of cases of great entrepreneurs and not just people who start companies, but entrepreneurs in large organisations or entrepreneurs in government; people who are taking risks, seizing opportunities and being entrepreneurial. In the interviews I was interested in, I asked what play meant to them and how they used this sort of playful behaviour as an attitude of constant exploration, adaptation and learning. Simply put, the world is very uncertain and changing, with opportunities emerging, left, right and centre, and the entrepreneur is the person who takes most advantage of that uncertainty and that change that's happening, and so the ability to be playful to learn and adapt, to experiment and explore is crucial.

ML: Your book has been described as a 'pathfinding'. How is the 'playful entrepreneur' different from the way that business schools and others portray entrepreneurs and their role in innovation, and might the difference lie in the nature of the current wave of digital technology?

MD: Well, yes, I think the technologies provide an opportunity to innovate at a smaller scale than in the past. But also, hopefully, this book provides an antidote to some of the awful prevailing characterisations of 'entrepreneurs'. We see in programmes like *Shark Tank*[29] or that dreadful programme *The Apprentice*,[30] that Donald Trump used to present where it's 'dog eat dog', 'nature is red in tooth and claw' and there's only one winner. Where to succeed you've got to put other people out of business and to get on in your career you've got to step on other people's heads. That's just appalling. It's not a reflection of the reality of many of the entrepreneurs that I've studied.

In my experience, they tend to be cooperative, collaborative and supportive of one another. They recognise their own personal shortcomings and supplement that by working with people who've got complementary skills, working together to a common shared end. I think if this book has a message and is to make an impact, it is the idea that you can be an entrepreneur, a successful entrepreneur, you can make a difference and you can make money, you can employ people and change their lives, and you can make a difference to your community and your society, while still being and remaining a decent human being. You don't have to kick, stand on anyone's heads and put them out of business. You know that you can be a successful entrepreneur and at the same time retain your basic decency and humanity.

ML: Historically in America at least, and probably currently too, most of the significant innovations and technology change come out of big corporations.[31] How relevant is a 'playful' innovation strategy for such corporations? Do their large, hierarchical, corporate structures allow them to work 'playfully', or is what you're describing only applicable in small, flexible innovation start-ups?

MD: I think there's a big appetite among larger companies to think of alternative ways of working and how they might emulate some of the conditions of working in small companies, bearing in mind that the majority of the workforce are now 'millennials' and millennials want to have work that's meaningful, and they want to do work that they enjoy.[32]

If you have got the digital skills particularly, they're in very high demand, so there's a high degree of mobility. In order to attract and retain talent, large companies have to think in new ways. For example, when we came up with the idea of innovation as 'play', we – with some trepidation – went to talk to the head of one of the world's largest pharmaceutical companies and one of the UK's and Australia's largest construction companies. These are two of the most hard-headed business people I've ever met in my life and we went in and told them that they needed to 'play' more; we expected to be thrown out on our ear. But they got it straight away. They understood that when they started their careers and the companies that they built were small, there was an atmosphere of adventure and exploration and excitement. But as the company grew, they lost that by putting in all sorts of processes and procedures, and rules and regulations which basically acted as innovation antibodies that kill any new idea.

So I think there is an appetite on the part of large organisations to think about ways to transform their workplaces, to make them more engaging, more collaborative, more exciting. 'Play' is not something that resonates with everyone, but certainly it does with some people in large organisations who are concerned about how to create a new kind of workplace for the future.

ML: We might take some encouragement from what you say Mark, but it is true, isn't it that the current wave of digital technology innovation has been basically driven not by large, incumbent corporations but by disruptive, small start-ups? The wave of young, Silicon Valley, entrepreneurial, garage start-up 'geeks' seem almost overnight to have built the dominant, biggest companies that the world has ever seen.[33,34,35] They started out with a pretty utopian image, a playful image, one might say, but they had clear visions and missions of wanting to 'make a difference'. Were they representative of your 'playful entrepreneurs'?

MD: We need to be clear that they did it not on the basis of their own investments, but on the basis of sustained long-term government investments in basic science and a government that was purchasing and prepared to be adventurous in their purchasing of equipment. Silicon Valley is often talked about as being created by these start-ups but actually, it was very much a government-driven phenomenon.[36] Government investment in R&D, government investment in property, government purchasing, educational institutions as well as legal and financial systems supported those start-ups.

So these small firms didn't come up with the science and technology themselves. They saw an opportunity that the basic public investments in research and science had created. They were quicker at doing that than some of the large firms, although some of the large ones had developed the technologies but didn't have the processes to be able to commercialise it because they were slow and bureaucratic. The smaller companies were more nimble and fast moving.

On the question about utopianism, I'm not sure. Some will claim some kind of utopianism, and certainly the early progenitors of the Internet were very utopian but I think that many of these companies wanted to make a lot of money. Has that ever been different? Bill Gates and Mark Zuckerberg wanted to create and build a business and they wanted to make a lot of money. And you know that's fine. But having made a lot of money, they then started to think about how they could give it away.[37]

ML: The idea of 'disruptive' innovation, technology and change, which is such a cliche these days. I think we owe it initially, to Christensen of the Harvard Business School with his 1997 book *Innovators' Dilemma: Why Do Incumbents Fail?*[38] What is your take on this concept as a valid way of thinking about the process of innovation from the point of view of companies, governments and society?

MD: It's a useful tool. There's a history of ideas in the domains of innovation and management that come out of practicing companies being written up by Business School professors and spawning a consulting industry. A broader population of companies enthusiastically embrace these ideas because they desperately need some help but then they become increasingly disillusioned because all their problems are not solved. These things fade away, leaving a little legacy of improvement and that's something we've seen in a whole range of things. I'd put this whole notion of 'disruption' in that bucket.

There is disruption, but some companies that have been around a long time have managed to get through these disruptions, companies like IBM. They're still going and they faced numerous disruptions with various degrees of difficulty. They haven't always done it very, very well but there are a number of companies, Dupont is another one, that have faced up to these challenges. But because they're properly managed, because they invest in research and development, because they have an external orientation and because they keep an eye on basic science. They're prepared slowly, steadily, but they are prepared to deal with these changes, and there is disruption. But the idea that disruption is fatal to every incumbent I think is incorrect. With the right management you can deal with these waves of technological change, but it involves a very high quality and perceptive management style.

ML: The disruptive innovation mantra 'disrupt or be disrupted'[39] is perhaps more of an ideology than a theory of how things happen in the world of innovation.

MD: It's a very good marketing term for a consultant trying to scare a company.

Conclusion

What matters about innovation is its impact on everyday people's lives, delivering a better quality of life and standard of living. Communicating this nexus is a public policy challenge and risks sounding esoteric, ivory tower and self-interested on the part of innovators.

The digital transformation era gave rise to a 'productivity paradox', whereby obviously large investments in new technology did not appear to drive significant productivity improvements or to be visible in an improved quality of daily life. To the contrary, the resulting process of 'creative destruction' engendered fears in the community about loss of jobs, industries and communities.

Economists have over time come to better understand how technological change contributes to productivity and economic growth. Malthusian concerns about the resources and demographic 'limits to growth' have been confounded.[40] They have looked inside the 'black box' in their models of the process of technological change and innovation. The central role of entrepreneurs and of the organisation of firms are better understood. 'Play'-based approaches to innovation and creativity emphasise the importance of flexible, smaller-scale organisational forms and are particularly attractive to the generation of 'millennials' now making their way in the workforce. Some adroitly managed, large, established corporations have been able successfully to ride out the wave of 'creative disruption' often oversold and overhyped by business schools and management consultants. Successful entrepreneurs – contrary to public images of cut-throat, dog-eat-dog mentalities – operate in largely cooperative and collaborative modes. Their success far from the image of lone, single-handed 'genius' is recognised as building upon important government-led innovation support programmes and wider economic ecosystems of law and finance.

Notes

1 Smith, A. (1776) *Wealth of Nations,* London: Strahan and Cadell
2 Ziemnowicz, C. (2013) Joseph A. Schumpeter and innovation, in Carayannis, E.G. (ed) *Encyclopedia of Creativity, Invention, Innovation and Entrepreneurship*, pp. 1171–1176, New York: Springer https://doi.org/10.1007/978-1-4614-3858-8_476
3 Schumpeter, J.A. (1934, 1984) *The Theory of Economic Development*, Piscataway, New Jersey: Transaction Books
4 Sibel, T.M. (2019) *Digital Transformation: Survive and Thrive in an Era of Mass Extinction*, New York: Rosetta Books
5 Dodgson was awarded the Order of Australia in 2019 www.markdodgson.org/awards
6 See Dodgson, M. and Besant, J. (1996) *Effective Innovation Policy: A New Approach*, London: International Thomson Business Press
7 Dodgson, M. and Rothwell, R. (eds) (1994) *Handbook of Industrial Innovation,* Cheltenham, UK: Edward Elgar
8 Australian Department of Innovation, Industry, Science and Research (2009) *Powering Ideas: An Innovation Agenda for the 21st Century,* Canberra: DIISR www.voced.edu.au/content/ngv%3A6954
9 Dodgson, M., Hughes, A., Foster, J. and Metcalfe, S. (2011) Systems thinking, market failure, and the development of innovation policy: The case of Australia, *Research Policy*, 40 (9): 1145–1156
10 Smith, A. (2005) The alternative technology movement: An analysis of its framing and negotiation of technology development, *Human Ecology Review,* 12 (2): 106–119
11 Meadows, D.H., Meadows, D.L., Randers, J. and Behrens III, W.W. (1972) *The Limits to Growth, Report to the Club of Rome*, New York: Potomac Associates Book www.clubofrome.org/publication/the-limits-to-growth/
12 Dodgson, M. and Gann, D. (2018) *Innovation: A Very Short Introductio*n, 2nd ed., Oxford: Oxford University Press
13 Patrick, A. and Redrup, Y. (2017) Turnbull 'innovation agenda' was a political failure, government concedes, *Australian Financial Review*, 20th September www.afr.com/policy/turnbull-innovation-agenda-was-a-political-failure-government-concedes-20170919-gyk617
14 Dodgson and Gann (2018), op cit
15 Aghion, P., Antonin, C. and Bunel, S. (2021) *The Power of Creative Destruction: Economic Upheaval and the Wealth of Nations*, Boston: Belknap, Harvard University Press
16 Dieppe, A. and Kose, M.A. (2020) *The Global Productivity Slump: What Policies to Rekindle?*, Essay, Brookings Institution, 17th November www.brookings.edu/articles/the-global-productivity-slump-what-policies-to-rekindle/
17 Kohli, U. (2015) *Explaining Total Factor Productivity*, EMG Workshop UNSW, November www.business.unsw.edu.au/About-Site/Schools-Site/Economics-Site/Documents/Explaining-Total-Factor-Productivity.pdf
18 Andrews, D., Hambur, J., Hansell, D. and Wheeler, A. (2022) *Reaching for the Stars: Australian Firms and the Global Productivity Frontier*, Australian Treasury Working Paper, 2022–01, January https://treasury.gov.au/sites/default/files/2022-02/p2022-243535.pdf
19 Krishnan, M., Mischke, J. and Remes, J. (2018) Is the Solow paradox back? Digitization isn't stimulating productivity growth – yet, *McKinsey Quarterly*, 4th

June www.mckinsey.com/capabilities/mckinsey-digital/our-insights/is-the-solow-paradox-back

20 Schumpeter, J.A. (1939) *Business Cycles: A Theoretical, Historical and Statistical Analysis of the Capitalist Process*, New York: McGraw Hill

21 Schumpeter, J.A. (1942) *Capitalism, Socialism and Democracy*, New York: Harper and Brothers

22 Schumpeter (1934), op cit

23 Baumol, W. (2010) *The Microtheory of Innovative Entrepreneurship*, Princeton, NJ: Princeton University Press

24 Marshall, A. (1890) *Principles of Economics*, London: MacMillan and Company

25 Romer, P. (1990) Endogenous technological change, *Journal of Political Economy*, 98 (5): S71–S102

26 Dodgson, M. (2018) *The Playful Entrepreneur: How to Adapt and Thrive in an Uncertain World*, New Haven, CT: Yale University Press

27 For a different take on the notion of play and new gadgets, see the movie Playtime (1967), directed and acted in by Jacques Tati www.imdb.com/title/tt0062136/

28 Dodgson, M., Gann, D. and Salter, A. (2005) *Think, Play, Do: Technology, Innovation, and Organization*, Oxford: Oxford University Press

29 Shark Tank (2009–) *IMDB* www.imdb.com/title/tt1442550/

30 The Apprentice (2004–2017) *IMDB* www.imdb.com/title/tt0364782/

31 Arora, A., Belenzon, S., Patacconi, A. and Suh, J. (2019) *The Changing Structure of American Innovation: Some Cautionary Remarks for Economic Growth,* Working Paper 25893, Cambridge, MA: National Bureau of Economic Research, May www.nber.org/system/files/working_papers/w25893/w25893.pdf

32 Shameem, S. (2019) Things that millennials expect from their jobs, *Entrepreneur India*, 25th March www.greatlakes.edu.in/chennai/uploads/nmedia/pdf/Things_that_Millennials_Expect_from_Their_Jobs_Dr_Shameem_Entrepreneur_Magazine_March_2019.pdf

33 Berlin, L. (2018) *Troublemakers: Silicon Valley's Coming of Age,* New York: Simon and Schuster

34 O'Mara, M. (2019) *The Code: Silicon Valley and the Remaking of America*, New York: Penguin Press

35 Harris, M. (2023) *Palo Alto: A History of California, Capitalism and the World*, New York: Riverrun Books

36 Hacker, J.S. and Pierson, P. (2016) Remembering Andy Grove and government's role in modern technology: Why technological innovation relies on government support, *The Atlantic,* 28th March www.theatlantic.com/politics/archive/2016/03/andy-grove-government-technology/475626/

37 Huddleston Jr., T. (2022) Bill Gates plans to give away 'virtually all' his $113 billion, *CNBC: Stock Market & Business*, 15th July www.cnbc.com/2022/07/15/bill-gates-plans-to-give-away-virtually-all-his-113-billion-fortune.html

38 Christensen, C.M. (1997) *Innovators' Dilemma: Why Do Incumbents Fail?* Boston, MA: Harvard Business School Press

39 Ruettgers, M. (2000) Opportunity and upheaval ahead: The information economy in overdrive, CEO of EMC Corporation Speech to The Economic Club of Detroit, *Vital Speeches of the Day*, 66 (17) 17th April: 531–533, Chicago City News Publishing

40 Neurath, P. (2015) *From Malthus to the Club of Rome and Back: Problems of Limits to Growth, Population Control and Migrations*, New York: Routledge

3 The Delayed Growth Impact of Disruptive Digital Technologies

Measuring and Accounting for the 'Productivity Paradox'

Interview With Kevin Fox

Introduction

Economists have traditionally studied and modelled economic growth by focusing on two main drivers – capital and labour – most notably in the work of Robert Solow,[1] for which he was awarded the Nobel Economics prize in 1987.[2] Neoclassical economics regarded knowledge and technology as a 'black box', 'residual' or unexplained driver of growth: something that came in from the outside, exogenously, that they didn't particularly focus on or understand.[3]

In 2018, the Nobel Prize committee awarded the prize for economics to Paul Romer, professor at New York University, jointly with William Nordhaus.[4] Romer's specific citation for the award was for 'integrating knowledge and technology into long run, global sustainable growth and welfare'.[5] Paul Romer's contribution, arguably, is that he's opened up the so-called 'black box' of technology within economic growth so that we can better understand just how technology and innovation drive economic growth and productivity.[6]

This is particularly timely because not only are we in the throes of great 'disruption' with the 'digital technology age' but from an economic point of view, there seems to be a repeat of the earlier 'productivity paradox' noted in the late 1980s by Nobel Economist Solow that we see the computer age everywhere around us but we don't see it in the productivity and growth statistics.[7] While productivity subsequently improved, we have more recently seen in response to a similar paradox the observation most prominently made by economist Robert Gordon that perhaps the economic impact of these new generation technologies is of less significance than previous technologies.[8]

Keywords: creative destruction; delayed diffusion; diffusion lags; economic growth, endogenous growth; externalities; human capital; imputed prices; increasing returns; innovation, market failure; measurement data; monopoly rents; non-rival consumption; positive spillovers; productivity, productivity paradox, productivity slowdown; rival goods; SDG 8; SDG 9; spillovers; stranded assets; technology; total factor productivity (TFP); workforce reorganisation

DOI: 10.4324/9781003280316-4

Interviewee Profile

Professor Kevin Fox (**KF**) has been at the University of New South Wales (UNSW) Business School since 1994 and headed it up between 2008 and 2012. Kevin is Director of the Centre for Applied Economic Research, and his focus is on productivity and prices, and especially how these things are measured in economic terms.[9] He's an advisor to the Australian Treasury, has worked with the Australian Bureau of Statistics (ABS) as an advisor and is co-editor of the *Journal of Productivity Analysis.* Kevin has worked with the learned academies on a major report on productivity[10] and also reported to the Prime Minister's Science, Engineering and Innovation Council (PMSEIC).[11]

The Interview

ML: Kevin, how do you see the contribution of Romer and his work on technology to the theory and the modelling of economic growth?

KF: It was very large, was widely acknowledged by the award of the Nobel Prize in economics and I don't think it came as a surprise to anyone. Before Romer, the basic growth model was the Robert Solow model (1956), and in that model you got diminishing returns to capital investment. Technology was basically a constant, and there are limits to growth by just adding more capital. That model predicted that countries' growth performance eventually converges, but Romer observed that wasn't happening in practice. Over a 25-year period that he looked at, there were some countries which had high average growth rates and some that persistently had very low growth rates. He asked, why is that, what could be the cause of that? Maybe some countries are doing things differently that are helping them get higher rates of productivity growth than others?

So Romer looked at the role particularly of ideas; research and development perhaps facilitated by policies and institutions in countries to see if that could explain these differences and economic growth rates driven by technological change and productivity. That's the basic idea: ideas are different types of capital, different types of input. It's not just a matter of adding more machines and then running out of operators to push buttons; there are some natural limits too.

Growth is a matter not just of more physical capital like machines but of ideas that he called 'non-rival' and that people can use at the same time without diminishing supply. A common example is if one person is using Pythagoras' theorem, another person can use that same theorem or idea at the same time without excluding your use. In the case of 'rival' goods, if someone is using say a particular machine, then someone else can't also be using that machine; they're not this idea of non-rival goods such as ideas where people can use them simultaneously. You introduce this into a Solow-type model,[12] and it allows you to have what's known then as 'endogenous' growth. So that was Romer's big contribution that has been enormously influential.

ML: In other words, Romer brought technology and knowledge as drivers of economic growth explicitly into the conventional Solow model driven by capital and labour inputs. What about the classic innovation theory of Schumpeter with his focus on the role of the entrepreneur as driving innovation and growth as the disruptor, and of 'creative disruption' within the capitalist market economy?[13,14] How does Romer's view square with that theory of the entrepreneur as innovator?

KF: That's a great question. I should emphasise that an implication of Romer's model is that there is not enough innovation in an economy if left simply to market forces. That is, there's a 'market failure' argument that the market left alone does not produce enough ideas to be socially optimal, but if there was a central planner who could design things optimally, that central planner would want more ideas, produce more R&D, and then the market would provide. That's because there are things called 'spillovers', and in Romer's case these are 'positive spillovers'.[15]

A lot of this is generated by the fact that people making these new ideas and inventions are creating non-rival goods which other people can freely use: they provide a positive 'externality' that's not captured fully by the person who's created it. So even if there are patents and people are getting paid for it, there is still an externality; because the idea in Romer is that if there's a bigger stock of ideas out there, that's also going to facilitate the creation of more ideas and so you get this situation where there're never quite enough ideas provided, just through market forces. So you need some intervention by the government, some policies to help support the development of more research and development to get closer to the optimal amount of innovation and R&D.

The 'creative destruction' idea was raised in a paper shortly after Romer's seminal paper in 1990 by a couple of authors;[16] the study by Aghion and Howit has similarly been a very influential paper.[17] It is not in conflict with Romer's ideas. You can think of how ideas come about as being driven by this creative destruction, but with the Aghion and Howitt model, the difference is that there can be too much of the wrong type of innovation if you like. If so, if the innovation is just producing the same goods at lower cost then there's a negative externality towards the existing firms: if you get too much, you can have too much of that type of R&D and there can actually be the reverse effect to what you get from the Romer model.

ML: Is this the sort of discussion that's emerging about the so-called monopoly and pricing powers of the large digital platforms?[18]

KF: Not directly, but you raise a very interesting point – that having patents provides monopoly rents to the innovators. But even if you had complete patents and so these innovators were able to capture all the financial rewards from their individual inventions, their inventions still add to the overall stock of knowledge and that still provides an externality. The more ideas in total there are in an economy, the more ideas will be additional ideas forthcoming. Patents and monopoly profits to innovators such as these new digital companies don't fully capture the benefits, so there's still a role for government intervention.

ML: Left to its own devices, the marketplace for innovations might fail and would lead to an underinvestment in public goods such as research and development, in knowledge and in technology, and this might require institutional intervention.[19] So might it be fair to characterise Schumpeter's theory of innovation,[20] focusing on the entrepreneur as being pretty much a sort of *deus ex machina* external factor that pays little attention to questions of necessary institutional design and intervention?

KF: I wouldn't disagree with that. I think you know the Schumpeter way of thinking about how innovation comes about is not incongruous with Romer's ideas at all. I don't think that it's incongruous with the idea of there being a role for the government to play in supporting R&D.

KF: Perhaps we could look at this question of the significance of technology and innovation inside this 'black box', or within Romer's model. I'm not sure how Romer captures this technology factor as distinct from, let's say, the Solow model that focused on capital and labour. Economists talk about the impact of technology and innovation as measured by what's called 'total factor productivity' (TFP).[21]

Now, as I've said, it seems that through this era of blossoming digital technology – in just about every sector and through every home and business – we're not seeing the increases in productivity that seem to be required to drive economic growth and wealth. So, is there a problem here with measuring the impact of these new digital technologies as expressed through total factor productivity?

KF: That's an extremely good question. It's something which many of us are spending quite a bit of time trying to analyse and work out. You mentioned earlier the computer productivity paradox, namely, the productivity slowdown that occurred in the 1970s and 1980s in many industrialised countries.[22]

The first computer productivity paradox was in the 1970s and 1980s when Robert Solow coined the famous remark that 'you can see computers everywhere but in the productivity statistics'.[23] Then we had a boost in productivity in most industrialised countries[24] and in the US that was put down to finally seeing the benefits of the investment in computers, that workplaces had reorganised and learned how to use the computers better. When a new technology arrives, perhaps we initially don't know how to use it effectively and it takes some time to invest in complementary capital, reorganise our workforce, etc., so that we can better use that technology to raise productivity.

The US also seemed to have a lot of productivity growth in the production of high-tech computers which countries like Australia didn't have because we don't have a large computer-producing sector. But at the same time, Australia did have productivity growth around 1994 through 1996 and onwards into the early 2000s.[25] Many countries had this sort of 'upward bubble' if you like, or productivity growth.

In Australia, this was largely attributed to the benefits of microeconomic reforms. I think we're still debating whether that's true or whether Australia was just the same as other countries which didn't have microeconomic reforms yet had the same boost in productivity at that time.[26] But also, what's happened since then, from 2004 onwards, is there's been a productivity slowdown across all industrialised countries and these are countries with rather dramatically different industry structures. Countries with a lot of mineral resources, for example, like Canada and Australia, to countries with no mineral resources but large high-tech or larger high-tech sectors. It's not about the industry structure in these countries. So, what is it?[27]

At this very time, we see all this innovation around us – smartphones, all sorts of apps – that we're using freely, and which we feel maybe are enhancing our lives and we see the technology in the workplace. We have the productivity benefits of that. So, there are a number of theories. One is that we're just not measuring the digital economy.[28] A key part of productivity is measuring the value of outputs that's usually done by something like GDP.

Now, if we are taking a lot of photographs on our smartphone, we haven't purchased a separate camera anymore. So that transaction has disappeared from the national accounts, so it's disappeared from gross domestic product. Taking a photo on film and then taking it to be developed, etc. There's a price for that, but every marginal photo we take on our smartphone has a zero price. So all that activity that existed before and that appeared in GDP has disappeared. At the same time, we're doing more of the activity that we wanted to do, which is taking photos. So maybe we're just not measuring things appropriately; we need to change the way we think about how we measure free goods, in particular, the imputed price for these goods, the consumers' valuation for these goods.

The problem is, even if we try to address a lot of these measurement problems, we don't seem to be able to find enough extra output to get productivity up to its previous growth rates. So, it doesn't seem to be entirely a measurement problem. But we're unsure about what exactly it is. Is it that, as some people would have it, we've invented all the important things? Once we've got the combustion engine, we know how to fly, we've got internal plumbing, all this digital technology. These are just nifty little consumer goods which don't really impact on anything significant, so that's one view put forward by Robert Gordon.[29]

ML: As you say – on the one hand – we might not be measuring it and that might explain why the productivity and growth are perhaps not showing up; even though the technology is everywhere it seems, and increasingly. There is, as you've mentioned, Professor Robert Gordon at Northwestern Uni, who's run a very strong line, and many others have picked up on it that the technology today is just not as impressive as we think, and certainly not giving us the benefits of previous waves of technological change in electricity, steam power, etc. What do you feel is the substance of that argument?

KF: We can look back at cases through history such as the diffusion of electricity and personal computers, and how they had a delayed impact on productivity. One argument, particularly put forward by one of my co-authors, Eric Brynjolfsson at MIT, is that we're on the cusp of a remarkable new era of growth and we are still trying to work out how to best use these technologies so that we can enjoy the new levels of growth.[30]

I'm more of an optimist that that's what we're going to see and many economic historians seem to hold that view as well. As for the previous computer paradox, an example was given about the diffusion of electricity: If you had a water wheel powering your factory and an electricity grid suddenly appears, you don't turn off your water wheel because you've got a free source of energy coming from that. What happens is that the factory depreciates, wears out over time, and when it comes time to build a new factory, you don't have to build it next to the river. You can build it in the centre or closer to the centre of the city, closer to your labour market; you can plug into the electricity grid and don't need to build a water wheel anymore, so that it takes a while, right? People don't suddenly switch off old technologies just because a new one appears. There's a delay in diffusion.

ML: So there has always been a lag, hasn't there, in the diffusion and adoption and the showing up of economic impact of a technology wave. Is the implication of what you and your colleague Bryjnjolfsson are saying is that there's something essentially different about the nature of this particular wave of digital technology transformation that is making these lags longer or more complex? Or what's the underlying position here?

KF: I can't speak for Eric, but I would say that it's definitely more complex now. There's a lot of uncertainty in our companies and individuals. They're not sure which technology to adopt. There's so much changing so rapidly. In my own work I know, choosing a laptop and choosing software to use can be very confusing and sometimes we make the wrong choices and our productivity goes down temporarily when you think it should be going up because of all these wonderful new productivity-enhancing tools. It could be the fact that there's such rapid change, that it's taking companies and individuals a bit longer to work out the most effective way to utilise those.

ML: Yes, these new digital technologies are likely to take a lifetime to reorganise around, and I guess what we see is the disruption of existing industries and market structures and corporations as they try to transform the nature of their businesses and their business models with all that implies about how businesses are to be run in this new era. Those fundamental business models need to change. This all seems to be adding up, and suggesting that the way that we've thought about technology and innovation is perhaps changing very much in itself.

The traditional model of innovation was fairly straightforward, particularly as a guide to policy formulation. It was basically a linear, supply-driven model: invest in basic research, move through applied research and development, into production and through diffusion and adoption in the economy. This was a popular view in the post-war years and well into the 1960s and 1970s.[31] But is there something different, complex, iterative and adaptive going on with digital innovation?

KF: Well, that's a big question. I don't know if I have a ready answer. I think that where there are a lot of positive externalities, and possibly also negative externalities – negative externalities being things like simply confusion about what to invest in or investing heavily in the wrong technology – and having to backtrack on that and invest again. So that we don't get much insight with our typically puny models about what exactly is happening with the investment decisions at the firm level, and how effectively those decisions are being made. I don't think we have too much insight at this stage as to whether processes are changing, but certainly the role of externalities I think is becoming much more important.

ML: You mentioned early in the piece the idea of 'decreasing returns' to capital and labour investment. Maybe investment in current digital technology, knowledge and transformation is very much what might be called an 'increasing returns' phenomenon thereby fundamentally changing the nature of innovation. Did Romer himself measure, model and estimate 'total factor productivity' or come up with some new measure? Where are we at with measuring this technology factor of production in any statistical sense?

KF: Romer himself did not work on the measurement of total factor productivity. His work was more about being motivated by empirical facts to try and work out improvements to the standard growth model. And that was very valuable in terms of measuring TFP. Some of us are working on that very problem. It's still an extremely valuable concept. I think that the Australian Bureau of Statistics (ABS) does a great job in measuring productivity. They have annual productivity statistics by industry.[32]

There's interest and work going on around firm-level productivity as well given new datasets that are now becoming available. There's a lot of activity in this area, and I hope that we'll know more about the drivers of productivity and economic growth in the years to come.

One additional point I would like to mention is that new technologies can actually lead to 'stranded' capital assets whereby firms are left holding capital or too many of certain types of capital given the new technologies.[33] They can't get rid of that capital quickly and easily often. Say there's innovation in the accommodation sector. It is hard to get rid of just one corridor of rooms. For example, in the hotel, they have to wait until the hotel fully depreciates, and then move to new premises. There are these lags and adjustments and that could be a significant part of what is going wrong with the measured productivity growth.

In terms of policy and the role of the government, I should emphasise that this does not imply that an R&D tax incentive scheme is optimal by any means; it just says that there is potentially a role for government intervention to address the market failure. That could be investing, for example, in universities in Australia rather than investing in business research. I'm not making a case for more funding for business R&D support.

Conclusion

Economic theories of the drivers of economic growth that have traditionally focused on returns to increased inputs of capital and labour have been unable to account for increased productivity through technological innovation, generally treating 'total factor productivity' as an endogenous, residual driver and technology as a 'black box'.

More recently, further light has been shed on the importance of technology within traditional growth models with attention to factors such as the role of human capital, the adaptability of business organisations and the influence of government policies and institutions. It is now also more clearly understood that digital technology delivers 'increasing returns' to scale in contrast to decreasing scale economies in capital and labour drivers. Nevertheless, the measurement of these technological factors bearing on productivity has proved elusive and their accounting and incorporation into macroeconomic statistics such as GDP are a work in progress.

This work has been made more challenging in the digital technology era with the emergence of conventional economic growth models and statistics of a 'productivity paradox' wherein the products and services resulting from investments in new disruptive digital technologies are highly visible in business and daily lives but with little or no measurable impact or improvement in productivity or growth. This has led to a fundamental questioning of the value or otherwise of this wave of digital technologies by comparison to highly impactful previous waves of technological change, while others explore a range of explanations for the paradox. Possible reasons include delays in diffusion due to the inherent complexity and rapid rate of change in digital technologies, the restraining effect of 'stranded asset' investments, and the need for complex reorganisation of workforces and business models.

The difficulty of the search for definitive answers is compounded by the challenges of measuring the impact or 'imputed value' of these innovations given their non-rival character in consumption and their close to zero marginal cost and hence price of delivery. Ironically, new technology is also making it easier to generate and collect detailed data on productivity performance in the economy, which means we are likely to get a better handle on measuring productivity impacts.

Notes

1 Solow, R. (1956) A contribution to the theory of economic growth, *The Quarterly Journal of Economics*, 70 (1): 65–94
2 Nobel Prize (1987) *The Nobel Prize in Economic Sciences: Robert M. Solow* www.nobelprize.org/prizes/economic-sciences/1987/solow/facts/
3 Rosenberg, N. (1994) *Exploring the Black Box: Technology, Economics, and History*, Cambridge: Cambridge University Press
4 Nordhaus, W.D. and Romer, P.M. (2018) *Economic Growth, Technological Change, and Climate Change, A Scientific Background on the Nobel Prize in Economic Sciences*, 8th October www.nobelprize.org/uploads/2018/10/advanced-economic sciencesprize2018.pdf
5 Nobel Prize (2018) *The Prize in Economic Sciences 2018 – Popular Information* www.nobelprize.org/prizes/economic-sciences/2018/popular-information/
6 Romer, P. (1990) Endogenous technological change, *The Journal of Political Economy*, 98 (5): 571–602
7 Rotman, D. (2018) The productivity paradox: Why brilliant AI technologies are not leading to widespread growth and prosperity, *MIT Technology Review*, 18th June www.technologyreview.com/2018/06/18/104277/the-productivity-paradox/
8 Gordon, R.J. (2000) Does the new economy measure up to the great inventions of the past? *Journal of Economic Perspectives*, 14 (4): 49–74
9 Diewert, W.E. and Fox, K.J. (2019) Productivity indexes and national statistics: Theory, methods and challenges, in ten Raa, T. and Greene, W.H. (eds) *The Palgrave Handbook of Economic Performance Analysis*, pp. 707–759, London: Palgrave Macmillan
10 Australian Council of Learned Academies (ACOLA) (2014) *The Role of Science, Research and Technology in Lifting Australian Productivity*, Securing Australia's Future #4, Expert Working Group, June https://acola.org/wp-content/uploads/2018/08/saf04-lifting-australian-productivity-report.pdf
11 Professor, Kevin J. Fox, UNSW https://research.unsw.edu.au/people/professor-kevin-j-fox
12 Solow (1956), op cit
13 Schumpeter, J.A. (1934) *The Theory of Economic Development: An Inquiry Into Profits, Capital, Credit, Interest, and the Business Cycle*, Piscataway, NJ: Transaction Publishers
14 Schumpeter, J.A. (1942) *Capitalism, Socialism and Democracy*, New York: Harper
15 Romer, P. (1990) Endogenous technological change, *The Journal of Political Economy*, 98 (5): 571–602

16 See Aghion, P., Antonin, C. and Bunel, S. (2021) *The Power of Creative Destruction: Economic Upheavals and the Wealth of Nations*, Boston: Belknap Harvard Press
17 Aghion, P. and Howitt, P. (1992) A model of growth through creative destruction, *Econometrica*, 60 (2): 323–351
18 McIntosh, D. (2019) We need to talk about data: How digital monopolies arise and why they have power and influence, *Journal of Technology Law & Policy*, 28 (2): 185–121 https://scholarship.law.ufl.edu/cgi/viewcontent.cgi?article=1188&context=jtlp
19 Bryan, K.A. and Williams, H.L. (2021) *Innovation: Market Failures and Public Policies*, NBER Working Papers, No. 29173, Cambridge MA: National Bureau of Economic Research
20 Schumpeter (1934), op cit
21 Maudos, J., Pastor, J.M. and Serrano, L. (1999) Total factor productivity measurement and human capital in OECD countries, *Economics Letters*, 63 (1): 39–44
22 Erber, G., Fritsche, U. and Harms, P.C. (2017) The global productivity slowdown: Diagnosis, causes and remedies, *Intereconomics*, 52 (1): 45–50
23 Krishnan, M., Mischke, J. and Reemes, J. (2018) Is the Solow paradox back: Digitization isn't stimulating productivity growth – yet? *McKinsey Quarterly*, 4th June www.mckinsey.com/capabilities/mckinsey-digital/our-insights/is-the-solow-paradox-back
24 Erber et al (2017), op cit
25 Productivity Commission (2020) *Australia's Long Term Productivity Experience, Productivity Insights*, Canberra https://www.pc.gov.au/ongoing/productivity-insights/long-term/productivity-insights-2020-long-term.pdf
26 Ibid
27 Productivity Commission (2020) *PC Productivity Insights: Australia's Long Term Productivity Experience*, Canberra, November www.pc.gov.au/ongoing/productivity-insights/long-term/productivity-insights-2020-long-term.pdf
28 International Monetary Fund (IMF) (2018) *Measuring the Digital Economy*, Washington: IMF, 28th February www.imf.org/-/media/Files/Publications/PP/2018/022818MeasuringDigitalEconomy.ashx
29 Gordon (2000), op cit
30 Brynjolfsson, E., Collis, A., Diewert, W.E., Eggers, F. and Fox, K.J. (2020) Measuring the impact of free goods on real household consumption, *AEA Papers and Proceedings*, 110: 25–30 www.aeaweb.org/articles?id=10.1257/pandp.20201054
31 Godin, B. (2006) The linear model of innovation: The historical construction of an analytical framework, *Science, Technology, and Human Values*, 31 (6): 639–667
32 Rotman (2018), op cit
33 Green, J. and Newman, P. (2016) Disruptive Innovation, stranded assets and forecasting: The rise and rise of renewable energy, *Journal of Sustainable Finance & Investment*, 7 (2): 169–187

4 Entrepreneurs and Start-ups in the Digital Age

Profiles, Values and Paradigms

Interview With Nicholas Gruen

Introduction

What is the role of entrepreneurs in the innovation system of a country? What sort of people become entrepreneurs and what sort of business strategies do they adopt? In particular, Silicon Valley 'garage' start-ups have been the new wave of entrepreneurial change agents at the heart of the digital innovation process; and it's their vision, and their passion and commitment that builds the bridges between the opportunities of new technologies and markets, and their commercial realisation involving risk taking.[1]

It seems that in this age of digital technologies we have a wide range of new and, perhaps, different opportunities for start-ups; with perhaps different, and even lower, 'barriers to entry'[2] facing the new breed of young entrepreneurs to innovate successfully. Some have even argued that there has never been a better time for entrepreneurs, start-ups and the innovation process.[3]

Keywords: BAAD; barriers to entry; competition policy; corporate strategy; digital platforms; economic rent; entrepreneurs, increasing returns; innovation; leadership vision; lean start-ups; market risk; monetisation; monopoly; personal data; producers' surplus; SDG9; Silicon Valley; start-ups

Interviewee Profile

Dr. Nicholas Gruen (NG) is a policy economist, an entrepreneur and a commentator with particular expertise in innovation in the digital technology era. Nicholas is widely published and writes regular columns and essays, including for leading newspapers such as the *Financial Review*, *The Age* and the *Sydney Morning Herald*. He is the founder and CEO of Lateral Economics, a visiting professor at King's College London, Policy Institute and Adjunct Professor at UTS Business School.

Nicholas has also had a long career of being directly involved in digital start-ups as an entrepreneur, as a board member and as Chair with the successful San Francisco based, data analytics crowdsourcing platform called kaggle.com. On the policy side, he has been an adviser to governments and cabinet ministers and has chaired the Australian Centre of Social Innovation. He's

DOI: 10.4324/9781003280316-5

been involved with Innovation Australia, the Government 2.0 Taskforce, and he was a member of the major review of Australia's Innovation System. Dr. Gruen's formal background is in economics with a PhD from ANU and a law degree.[4]

The Interview

ML: Nicholas, what is your perspective on the role of new entrepreneurs and start-ups as change agents in the digital technology era?

NG: Well, it's really remarkable that even in the United States, where large firms have made innovation their business, with substantial investments in research and development – I'm thinking of companies like GE or IBM – that none of the big IT innovations came out of those firms. Now, in a sense you could say, for instance, that the 'graphical user interface' (GUI) innovation which Steve Jobs picked up from the Palo Alto Research Center (PARC) in Hewlett-Packard was done – not by some individual entrepreneur – but by entrepreneurial types within an existing company; its actual commercial realisation which would have seemed to many people in the industry as kind of cute but ho hum, was in fact a massively important innovation that was perpetrated by a brand new company. It was a company that started in a garage and this is true of every major digital innovation.[5]

There would have been far more money in IBM, GE, Honeywell and any number of dominant IT companies trying to find the next big thing; and every single next big thing was seized by a couple of kids.

ML: As you say, that is really quite a remarkable change in the profile of where innovation conventionally has come from, namely, the big corporations. What we seem to be seeing is the rise of celebrity stars and entrepreneurial leaders of the emerging, big new technology companies: Gates at Microsoft, Bezos at Amazon, Jobs at Apple and Zuckerberg at Facebook.

Impressively, they also took their garage start-ups to unprecedented global corporate leadership and valuations, and astonishing personal wealth in what has to be a record time: through the whole cycle of innovation.[6] Beyond that, too, they've become modern 'heroes' for the current generation of digital entrepreneurs. A big majority of millennials around the world, according to a Deloitte survey, want to join or establish a start-up venture as their preferred career choice.[7] Even in the *Sydney Morning Herald*, articles are being run, 'your child wants to be an entrepreneur'.[8] So, what is going on here?

NG: One thing I wanted to reflect on with the observations I just made about how each one of these big new innovations was from a start-up, was a converse observation which is to look at how dreary, and miserable life in these big companies is now. Yes, you get well paid, you get well looked after, but if you've got some get up and go, you will be killed off.

Now there's a book, in fact, it's a real pity it's a book. It's one of those books that was an article and was turned into a book and it should never have happened because all of the information you need is in the article. Some listeners will be familiar with the term the 'Innovator's Dilemma',[9] written intriguingly by a Mormon professor of management at Harvard, Clayton Christensen, in which he coined the expression 'disruptive innovation'. He showed that this pattern that I talked about of innovation which disrupts and, in many cases, simply 'blows up' the competitors and competing operations; for instance, Google blew up Alta Vista, HotBot and all the search engines of the time. He shows that in quite mundane things where there was technical progress, it's very common for a disruptive innovation to be incubated, not within the dominant companies which in principle have all the money to develop the new innovations, but within much more impecunious, much smaller, less rich start-ups.

The reason for this is, as Christensen suggests, that disruptive innovations typically are worse than the products and the technologies that they may disrupt. They're worse for a long period of time during which the start-up applies its ingenuity, its perseverance and its imaginative organisational capability to make it better.

The examples he uses are backhoes; the difference between backhoes driven by pulleys and cables, and backhoes driven by hydraulics is not that the companies that were dominant in mining and various industrial applications – who had all the money and profits to invest in R&D of hydraulic backhoes – didn't do that because when there were investing in projects within those companies, all the accountants would turn up and saying not making enough money on this, so we're going to kill it off.

It happened also in disk drives. He documents how all companies that ended up dominant in 3.5-inch floppy disks were new companies and they drove out of business all the companies making five-inch floppy disks a decade or five years before. How silly can you be if you're got a dominant market in five-inch disk drives that you don't have a good handle on and good research and development in this other market, which is less profitable but turns out to wipe you out, and that pattern repeats again and again.

Now, those examples are of high fixed costs areas where again incumbent firms – because there are large costs – you would expect the incumbent firms to have a bigger advantage but in IT digital technologies often the costs of these technologies are quite low. One of the main things that happen, if you look at say Facebook versus MySpace, for instance, is that Rupert Murdoch buys Myspace, he's got a lot more money than little old Mark Zuckerberg. Sounds funny now, but Mark Zuckerberg has got a vision for what this new technology can do socially, commercially and so on, which is what matters.[10] The Murdoch company is just thinking about how to put ads on this thing and optimise the amount of money it has invested there.

ML: Yes, that's a very different approach, driven by the new technology and those big corporations are pretty boring environments for most young people to contemplate. We have this ragtag group of young hackers, geniuses and geeks rather than those traditional big, well-funded, R&D-based corporations that have been making the breaks in this disruptive digital tech-based era.

You mentioned 'vision' and it seems to me this new breed of entrepreneurs is often seen as 'missionary' rather than 'mercenary'; they like to portray themselves as having a missionary purpose where they want to 'make a real difference'. They talk endlessly about making an 'impact' for the good of everyone and society.[11]

And their business strategies are actually quite different too. They tend not to operate by conventional business strategy approaches as per, say, Michael Porter's competitive structure and competitiveness.[12] They rather seem to weave 'stories' around what they're trying to do, and narratives that try to capture what they think is the essence of turning a mess of information and inventing big businesses out of their tidy stories, like Amazon.[13] They seem to build this, as I think you're saying, on the new technology base.

They are 'platforms' that people can access as start-ups from companies such as Amazon, Microsoft, Google, Oracle.[14] Each of those has a different basic paradigm of governance. So, it is a very different environment but it's also a bit of a random environment too in that it doesn't seem to me as structured from a corporate strategy point of view.

So, I wonder what you think about these interrelated roles of entrepreneurial vision, strategy and platforms as making things different and easier in the digital age for young start-up entrepreneurs to develop businesses.

NG: Well, let's go back a bit. I'm not sure about strategy. I think that there's only so much you can do to systematise something like strategy. I've written on strategy. I think an awful lot of strategy, for instance, the strategy retreats that one endlessly goes on in existing companies are a kind of anti-thinking. As for Michael Porter or anybody else, trying to generalise about how companies do strategy and should do strategy, I wouldn't get too excited. If I was trying to work out how to do strategy, I wouldn't be reading Michael Porter.

I've read about Jeff Bezos and he doesn't have any time for reading management books. He's hard driving, has a background vision, has a few basic ideas and he pushes as hard as he can on those ideas. Ideas like 'disagree and commit' but he's actually trying to encourage people to disagree with each other in a forceful but ultimately constructive way so that the best ideas can emerge. How many large corporations do you know which genuinely encourage other than some big blowhard at the beginning of the session saying everybody should be free to express their opinion? Give me a break. If you express a different opinion and express it strongly in most established corporations, you'll wreck your life.

So, a lot of these entrepreneurial people are quite loose with 'strategy'. Their strategy often focuses on very specific guiding ideas that they have. I love Warren Buffett who is a unique kind of entrepreneur. He says he's not very innovative: his job is to manage capital and to back people who will be innovative. Warren Buffett writes extremely amusing and very insightful letters to his shareholders every year before the annual meeting, the Woodstock for capitalists.[15,16]

One year, I think it's quite a long time ago. I've committed the words more or less to memory, where he says, I regretfully inform shareholders that your chairman, that's him, has made more than his usual number of colossal blunders this year. The company is, however, prospering well and we do have one enduring advantage over most other firms. We have no strategic plan.[17]

ML: Part of what seems to be going on here, Nicholas, is that more formal structures of strategy are abandoned with the new technologies and entrepreneurial approaches to innovation, and there's a certain randomness in the shape and directions in which they go. One of the issues that this gives rise to is the legitimacy of what these people are doing, because we're increasingly seeing questions asked about how these tech companies are behaving.[18]

It seemed in the early eras of industrial innovation it was turned very purposefully to social, comprehensive and politically inflected ends, a community of purpose. Then we had the industrial era of efficiency and competitiveness during the hot and Cold War eras governing corporate strategies. This was followed by the iconoclastic idea of the 1960s about technology and social purpose,[19] and post the 1960s and entrepreneurial idealism; it was like an outsider's view of technology and these current digital entrepreneurs seem to have picked up on some of that dreamy sentimentalisation, a new corporate idealism where they want to have a social impact and change the world for the better.

What motivates them?[20] Is it the money, the power, the desire to change the world? Because they're already running into trouble with some of that, aren't they, in terms of public responses to what they're doing and how they're behaving?[21]

NG: I can't give you the answer to that. I don't know whether they can give you the answer to that. The most successful entrepreneurs are certainly not motivated only by money: no great entrepreneur has ever got anywhere by sitting in their room and thinking how do I make more money? You can call it idealistic but I'm not really fond of this distinction between self-seeking and idealism, and most of our lives pass between those two extremes.

So somebody like Steve Jobs or Larry Page and Sergey Brin they're motivated by the 'aesthetics' of what they're doing, if I can use that term. Larry and Sergey were very proud of BackRub, the algorithm that they developed and offered to sell to Yahoo for $1,000,000 which was the foundation of Google Technology for generating better search results.[22] They got fonder and fonder of making money over time, as they made more, but they didn't have any ads on their sites for the first year and they didn't like ads. Now they're running a juggernaut where they're thinking a lot about making money, but at the same time they're trying to have moonshots. They're really captivated by doing amazing things and also by making a lot of money.

ML: Let's go along with what you say that they're driven as much by an 'aesthetic' sense, which I kind of like. That aesthetic sense is pretty free to roam over a pretty wide canvas with the new technologies as we're seeing, and yet it is striking to me that at this point we have cover stories being written in the Economist and elsewhere, where Google, Amazon and Facebook, all these big 'aesthetically driven' companies, maybe with some sort of idealism in mind, are accused of being BAAD,[23] namely, big, anticompetitive and addictive, and destructive to democracy. Its implications for competition policy are already starting to emerge, let alone on the privacy side, and the taxpaying side. We seem to be going through a bit of a reaction to this 'aesthetic', and an 'idealistic' motivation, or not?

NG: No, we're going through reaction to what's happened. The problem is that Facebook has become a 'vector', it provides a kind of Petri dish for all kinds of horrible things to live and thrive, and that wasn't a particular preference of Mark Zuckerberg or Facebook, but making money certainly was. I wouldn't accuse Facebook of being idealistic in a simple sense. Facebook's always had an aesthetic of what it was doing but making money is a huge driver at Facebook and they have been really quite like Bill Gates in Microsoft in putting that so far at the top of their priorities that they've run into a lot of flack now.

Gates is on record recently in media reports as 'Gates warns Zuckerberg and Google'.[24] Whether he did that or not, I don't know, but he reflected on the fact that he thought Microsoft overreached and ended up being tangled up in legal skirmishes, particularly in the EU ever since they ran Netscape out of business. But the problem is that in the case of Microsoft, it's not that hard for competition policy authorities to work out a remedy so they can start instructing Microsoft to not package Explorer in a way that is detrimental to Netscape and various other kinds of things. It's quite unclear, however, what the appropriate competition policy measure is for a product like AdWord that is an auction among people who want to advertise on Google.[25] It basically collects in theory all of the 'producer surplus', meaning basically, that it gets the most money that the monopolist can possibly get.

That isn't harming efficiency because anybody who wants to advertise on Google can. It's just a mechanism for creaming off a vast amount of 'rent' from Google. The point is that this is a constrained space. The constrained space is eyeballs; given we only might do two or three Google searches a day and there's only a certain amount of space, and there's nothing that's a competition issue; it's quite hard to think of things that the authorities can rule and regulate.

ML: I want to ask you about the technology base and approaches of these new start-ups, and particularly the idea of the 'lean start-up',[26] product development philosophy and methodology, which seems to be built on new digital technology that gets rid of the cloud of uncertainty around innovation. On the one hand, it seems to reduce market risk. Market risk arises because businesses can't really conceptualise, design and produce a product before they've correctly gauged the market. But the lean start-up approach built on technology deconstructs that high market risk into a plethora of low-stake gambles that you can test in real time on real-world customer: you do experiments, you can do it quickly, inexpensively and you can turn yourself around quickly on a dime and reorient to the market. Now that's totally reduced the market risk and surely that explains to a degree the proliferation of digital start-ups?

NG: Yes, absolutely. The simple bit of economic jargon is that' barriers to entry' have fallen very substantially. In the 1950s, for example, Elon Musk would not have been able to start-up a new car company because it required a vast amount of capital but now the market is sufficiently disaggregated and competitive that he can source say, brakes, and he can source lithium batteries, although he builds those now, and so on. And that's in a very expensive 'capital intensive' industry. But also, thanks to digital developments like Amazon Web Services[27] and so on, the digital platforms and online business services, and the ability to buy server capacity off the market, not by investing tens or hundreds of thousands or millions of dollars in servers yourself, you can launch new things, find out what works, what doesn't work; your entire business as a 'lean start-up' can be thought of as a sort of experimental spaceship in the market where you just go into the market able to test reactions, test things and gradually move towards success, at low cost and risk.

ML: Thank you, Nicholas. 'Barriers to entry' seem to have fallen in the face of these new digital technologies. It's not only the 'deconstruction' or 'dis-intermediation' of industry 'value chains', and 'digital platforms' and online business services, but it is also the digital 'open-source' software that's accessible and available. And, of course, the vast opportunities of 'big data' and data 'algorithms', all of which seem to open up a whole new accessible era of entrepreneurship and innovation in all sorts of directions and disciplines.

Conclusion

Entrepreneurs in the 'digital technology age' appeared as a 'new breed'. Their origins, characteristics, motivations and start-up business model paradigms stand apart from the dominant enterprises and their incumbent corporate executives' enterprises. The tech 'geek' garage start-ups of Silicon Valley disrupted the big corporate 'incumbents' who though successfully invested in research, development and technology fell to the 'innovator's dilemma' of sticking with the technology they knew well.

Traditional approaches to corporate competitiveness strategies were replaced by visionary, often idealistic leadership, missionary rather than monetary, communicated by way of compelling stories and narratives, loose with strategy but rooted in 'ideas', and tied to benign social outcomes like 'free information' and 'making a difference'. Many believed that there was never a better time to be an entrepreneur.

The process of 'digital disruption' was enabled by considerably lower barriers to entry of new tech players, including being able subsequently to build upon digital platforms, and big data algorithms, that required less capital to tap into as flexible 'services' in place of fixed 'infrastructure' and 'assets' to get going. The digital technology enabled the adoption of more flexible 'lean start-up' strategies based on rapidly repeated experimentation and learning that reduced 'market risk'. They adopted organisational forms, governance and cultures that have made them attractive 'models' and 'heroes' for new generations of youth who aspired to form or to join start-up ventures rather than become employees in large corporations.

The digital tech companies grew more rapidly than any previous generation of corporations reaching trillion-dollar valuations in unprecedented short order, exploiting the increasing scale economies of digital technology. The big tech paradigm form was the 'digital platform' with its seemingly uncontrollable 'market power'. Their arguably 'visionary' and 'idealistic' initial motivations were perhaps inevitably overtaken by a 'winner takes all' culture of monopolistic, anticompetitive behaviour that has increasingly raised social concerns about the ways in which their customers rights, data and privacy were being set aside in favour of their 'commoditisation' and 'monetisation', as well as concerns about their ability to lessen competition and ultimately innovation in the digital marketplace. The 'disruptive' start-up entrepreneurs have become the incumbent corporate 'titans'.

Notes

1 Berlin, L. (2018) *Troublemakers: Silicon Valley's Coming of Age: The People Who Put Silicon Valley on the Map*, New York: Simon & Schuster
2 Middleton, S. (2015) Five ways digital technologies are lowering barriers to entry, *Cognizant*, 12th November www.cognizant.com/five-ways-digital-technologies-are-lowering-barriers-to-entry
3 Wadhwa, V. (2015) Why there has never been a better time to be an entrepreneur, *Washington Post*, 20th April www.washingtonpost.com/news/innovations/wp/2015/04/20/why-there-has-never-been-a-better-time-to-be-an-entrepreneur/
4 The Interpreter, Nicholas Gruen, Lowy Institute www.lowyinstitute.org/the-interpreter/contributors/articles/nicholas-gruen
5 Meisenzahl, M. (2020) Starting in a garage is crucial to the origin story of many Silicon Valley entrepreneurs. Here are the modest beginnings of 5 tech companies worth billions today, *Business Insider*, 2nd April www.businessinsider.com/google-apple-hp-microsoft-amazon-started-in-garages-photos-2019-12
6 Vlastelica, R. and Bloomberg (2023) Apple becomes the first $3 trillion market value company, *Fortune*, 1st July https://fortune.com/2023/06/30/apple-history-3-trillion-market-value/
7 2018 Deloitte Millennial Survey Millennials disappointed in business, unprepared for Industry 4.0; Amanda, *One Theory about Why More Millennials are Finding Career Fulfilment at Tech Startups*, 10th October 2018 www.samplingculture.com, citing Deloitte 2018 Millennials Survey
8 Patty, A. (2016) Generation Y and baby boomers lead a boom in new entrepreneurs, *Sydney Morning Herald*, 3rd September www.smh.com.au/business/workplace/generation-y-and-baby-boomers-lead-a-boom-in-new-entrepreneurs-20160901-gr6pgy.html
9 Christensen, C. (1997) *The Innovator's Dilemma: When New Technologies Cause Great Firms to Fall*, Boston: Harvard Business Review Press
10 Sher, R. (2006) Start ups need to own the vision, *Silicon Valley Business Journal*, 22nd September www.bizjournals.com/sanjose/stories/2006/09/25/smallb4.html
11 Losse, K. (2019) The false promise of Silicon Valley's quest to save the world, *The New Republic*, 7th February https://newrepublic.com/article/153034/false-promise-silicon-valleys-quest-save-world
12 Porter, M.E. (2008) *Competitive Strategy: Techniques for Analyzing Industries and Competitors*, New York: Free Press
13 Wiener, A. (2021) Does tech need a new narrative?: Is Silicon Valley 'disruption' giving way to 'building'. What will be built? *The New Yorker*, 15th June www.newyorker.com/news/letter-from-silicon-valley/does-tech-need-a-new-narrative
14 Faster Capital (2023) *The Power of the Platform in Startups*, 23rd May https://fastercapital.com/content/The-Power-of-the-Platform-in-Startups.html
15 Darling, I. (2001) Woodstock for capitalists, *Documentary* www.imdb.com/title/tt0806213/
16 Cheng, E. (2017) Here's what it's like to attend Warren Buffett's 'woodstock for capitalists', *CNBC*, 6th May www.cnbc.com/2017/05/06/heres-what-it-was-like-at-buffetts-woodstock-for-capitalists.html
17 Buffett, W. (1998) We don't have any strategic plan, *Berkshire Hathaway Annual Meeting*, 4th May https://buffett.cnbc.com/video/1998/05/04/buffett-we-dont-have-any-strategic-plan.html
18 US Congress (2021) *Holding Big Tech Accountable: Targeted Reforms to Tech's Legal Immunity*, House Committee Hearings, 17th Congress www.congress.gov/event/117th-congress/house-event/114268?s=1&r=8
19 Turner, F. (2006) *From Counterculture to Cyberculture: Stewart Brand, the Whole Earth Network, and the Rise of Digital Utopianism*, Chicago, IL: University of Chicago Press

20 Guzman, J., Oh, J.J. and Sen, A. (2020) What motivates innovative entrepreneurs? Evidence from a global field experiment, *Management Science*, 66 (10): 4808–4819
21 O'Carroll, L. (2023) EU unveils 'revolutionary' laws to curb big tech firms' power, *The Guardian*, 6th September www.theguardian.com/world/2023/sep/06/eu-unveils-package-laws-curb-power-big-tech-giants
22 Google, *From the Garage to the Googleplex* https://about.google/our-story/
23 Florman, M. (2008) *The new Oligarchs: Good or BAAD?*, 13th February www.markflorman.com/the-new-oligarchs-good-or-baad/
24 Castillo, M. (2018) Bill Gates says Mark Zuckerberg 'owes me' for warning him about Washington DC, *CNBC*, 10th September www.cnbc.com/2018/09/10/bill-gates-thinks-zuckerberg-owes-me-for-washington-dc-warning.html
25 AdWords is Now Google Ads www.googleadservices.com/
26 Blank, S. (2013) Why the lean start-up changes everything, *Harvard Business Review*, May https://hbr.org/2013/05/why-the-lean-start-up-changes-everything
27 Amazon Web Services https://aws.amazon.com/what-is-aws

5 National Innovation and Competitiveness in the United States

At a Strategic 'Tipping Point'

Interview With Dr. Robert Atkinson

Introduction

The coming of 2021 saw the end of a very difficult and tumultuous year globally in 2020. It also saw the incoming Biden Administration in the United States of America confront the ongoing COVID-19 pandemic, climate change looming ever larger and many other issues, including particularly the geopolitical challenges posed by the arrival of China as a leading world power.[1] This time of crisis poses new strategic challenges to science, technology and innovation; and to America's historic global leadership in innovation capacity and competitiveness.

Keywords: cold war; crisis; disruptive innovation; endless frontier; entrepreneurs; financialisation; innovation ecosystem; lead adopter; leadership; mission oriented; national innovation system (NIS); offshoring; outsourcing; policy coordination; SDG9; SDG16; SDG17; semiconductors; strategic competition; tame problems; wicked problems

Interviewee Profile

Dr. Robert Atkinson (**RA**) is the founder and president of the Information Technology and Innovation Foundation (ITIF), in Washington, DC.[2] He's been described by the media in America, on which he appears frequently, as a 'tech titan'[3] and as one of the three most important thinkers about innovation in America. Dr. Atkinson's influential involvement over the decades in innovation policy is as an economist. He has been an advisor on innovation to the teams and administrations of Presidents Clinton, Bush, Obama and, with incoming President, Biden. He has written many books and reports[4,5,6,7] and is a highly sought-after public speaker and commentator.

The Interview

ML: Robert, what a moment for us to be talking about innovation from an American perspective. What is innovation and why is it particularly important to America at this time?

DOI: 10.4324/9781003280316-6

RA: Innovation is oftentimes too narrowly defined as scientific discovery, or maybe the development of some kind of new iPhone 14 or 20, or whatever we're going to get next. Yet innovation is broader than that. I would define it as the development of new technologies and then the business models and organisation models that go along with that, as those technologies are spread throughout society, whether on the production side of new industries or reorganised industries, or on the consumer side of how we live our lives.

ML: There has been a tendency among those involved with innovation, economics and policy, certainly historically, to think of innovation as a 'linear process'[8] where at the front end you push a bit of time and money into research, and research and development, and that somehow moves through a pipeline and funnels all sorts of products and good things for society in a linear 'supply push' model. Is that a useful way to think about innovation?

RA: It's certainly over simplified. That idea came about in the US from a famous report that the advisor to Franklin Roosevelt, Vannevar Bush, the president of MIT, came out with before the war ended in 1945; he talked about the 'endless frontier':[9] You put money at the beginning of the funnel into basic science and out come all these wonderful things. Who knows when, who knows what? But that's been pretty much debunked by innovations, and by science and technology scholars. It's a much more complicated system than simply 'supply push'. You also have 'demand-pull' innovation. There are also successive iterations in the innovation process that go back and forth, called 'feedback loops'. Societies, economies or governments have to think about what are known as 'innovation systems'.[10] In other words, all the components that work together to maximise innovation output.[11]

ML: How would you characterise the current American 'national innovation system' and its performance? In Australia, we are aware that our innovation performance keeps slipping rather remorselessly compared to other countries.[12] How's America been travelling in the international race and competition for innovation in recent years?

RA: At one level I don't put much stock in the rankings because many of them are basically opinion surveys. They're a little bit like looking at a star that has gone 'supernova'; at the start it looks like it's still there, but in reality it's blowing up. You just can't see it because it takes so long for the light to get to Earth, and so in some ways a lot of folks look at America in the past.

Sure, we had a great innovation system but our problem is that we have not kept that innovation system up to the level that it should be. For example, take government funding of research and development, scientific and engineering research as a share of GDP. It peaked in the late 1980s, and it's gone down pretty much every year since then. It's so low today that it is at levels before Soviet Russia's Sputnik in 1957.[13] At that point, there was a giant push because America wanted to compete with the Soviets and so we ramped up science spending for defense, for NASA and for other purposes, including energy. We've since let it slip and, and that's going to bite us, it is already biting us, it is already hurting us. There's some good signs on the horizon and maybe policymakers are beginning to address it but I'm not 100% confident that we're going to address it fully.

ML: It is difficult to measure and quantify innovation performance, particularly across countries, but what are some of the symptoms of a failing innovation system that you are concerned about?

RA: It's very hard really, because we don't have good internationally comparative measures of innovation output. We have input measures like the number of scientists or spending on R&D. We also have intermediate measures of patents or venture capital as inputs, but we don't really have outputs and goods measures. I'll give you a few examples that I think are troubling.

In the year 2000, the US ran a trade surplus in advanced technology goods. Today, we are running a trade deficit of around 130–140 billion dollars in those goods. Look at the number of major US firms that were for a long-time international leaders, who were dominant frankly, who are much weaker right now, or even bankrupt. General Electric has had serious problems. Hewlett-Packard, IBM and firms that were once seen as global innovation leaders are significantly weaker now. A lot of that gets covered up by the fact that America has some great Internet and IT firms: Microsoft, Google, Apple, Amazon, Facebook and the like; but even in IT if you look for example at semiconductors where the US was the unalloyed leader by far until recently, that's no longer the case.[14]

TSMC in Taiwan, a company that makes semiconductors for other firms, is clearly the global leader now in semiconductors.[15] Intel recently announced they were having problems going down to what's called 7 nanometres, really small and fast, and they were going to outsource some of their work to TSMC. That is extremely troubling and American policymakers have not fully woken up to that. I don't want to imply that we're the UK. I have a lot of colleagues in the UK, and I think the UK is doing a lot of really good work right now in innovation policy because they had to, having lost so many firms. They lost their innovation lead they had in the 1970s and 1980s and now they are struggling. We don't want to be in that situation, we don't want to go down that path, and I worry that unless we make some serious changes in effort and policy, we're going to move in that direction.

ML: You have referenced some major companies with concerning performances. They are operating in competitive markets driven by a profit motive. So, why are they not innovating for competitiveness, in response to market forces?

RA: That's the $64,000 question and I think there are a couple of major reasons. Clayton Christensen of MIT, now deceased, was one of the leading thinkers about business innovation and wrote about this troubling trend[16] and contrasted it with companies like Google or Amazon that are committed to what he would call 'disruptive innovation', high risk, high reward. His argument is that too many established American companies embrace 'incremental innovation', don't want to make big bets, want to play it safe. The problem is that playing it safe can only take you so far. It ultimately usually leads to decline because other companies in the world don't play it safe and some of those bets will pay off.

Second, corporate R&D in the US over the last two decades has dramatically shifted away from basic research and applied research towards development, and the reason is quite simple. Stock markets reward short-term thinking, they reward short-term investing and if you're a company and you're a CEO, you don't really want to worry too much about your value in five or ten years. Certainly, you do want to worry about your value in the next quarter, because that's what you get paid on. I think that investment incentives in the US have shifted the innovation system towards much too much conservatism and too much short-termism.[17]

ML: That observation seems to be questioning the 'business model' of these struggling corporations, but perhaps more importantly their 'corporate governance' behaviour. It points towards the broader systemic complexity of innovation. You talked about investment incentives and now we're talking about governance. But as you say, this might be contrasted with the very successful performance of the big IT companies with their birth as 'start-up' entrepreneurs and garage operations. The Gates and the Zuckerbergs who are world leaders are the biggest companies in the world. They seem to have a very different entrepreneurial-driven and governance approach to the more established major corporations, don't they?

RA: Yes, and I'll give you an example of the former. It was maybe 15 years ago that Hewlett-Packard was seen as probably the most successful, dynamic American technology corporation and their stock price was going through the roof. The CEO at the time, Mark Hurd, was lauded by everybody as a 'genius' because his stock price was so high but what he was doing was basically robbing the future of HP and putting it into the short term. It looked great at the time, but when you pull back the

'Potemkin village' curtain he was essentially gutting HP. The insiders at HP knew that and they couldn't fight back so HP is now a shell of its former self. Now compare that to companies like Amazon, Qualcomm or Google.

I was moderator on a conference panel with Clayton Christensen whom I mentioned earlier, with Paul Jacobs the CEO and son of the founder of Qualcomm; and Jeff Bezos, the CEO of Amazon. It was very clear that those two guys do not care about the short term; they care fundamentally about the long term. It was their company, it was their vision and it was their legacy. Certainly, Facebook with Zuckerberg and Google, with their CEO today still the founder, these founder-owned companies still have that 'aggressive' in the good sense of the term, longer-term disruptive vision. The more 'managerial'-driven companies where the CEO could be gone, next week, they're more conservative. They're more short term. In that sense, the fact that America has been able to continue to produce entrepreneurial giants is a real saving grace for us.

ML: Robert, how valid is it to consider those entrepreneurial founders of the big tech-based companies as sole 'genius' operators that operate by themselves and create their products by themselves without engagement in a broader innovation system or ecosystem?

RA: It is almost completely invalid. Look at a company like Google. But to be clear, all of these founders, including Steve Jobs and others are geniuses, they are risk-takers and we owe a lot to them in the US, there's no question about.

But in every single case, they relied upon a government-enabled ecosystem to help them initially. For example, Apple I believe got a Small Business Administration (SBA) loan or what's perhaps called the Small Business Innovation Research grant. It also built off some of the Xerox products such as a 'graphical user interface' (GUI) which was supported by government funding. The initial Google algorithm was developed by Larry Page working with his colleague on a National Science Foundation (NSF) grant towards their PhD dissertations at Stanford University.

The idea that somehow these people do this on their own is a mythology. They are part of and they take advantage of an overall 'ecosystem' that enables them to do this great work. Now, if we didn't have those people we would have a lot of innovation just sitting around on the side. But I don't want to make it sound like Mariana Mazzucato, for example, who is an innovation scholar and quite well known in Europe.[18] She is almost on the complete opposite side saying you do not need these entrepreneurs and that the governments are the innovators. I don't buy either the libertarian view that there is no role for government[19] or the sort of Mazzucato view that the entrepreneur's role is limited. I don't think either of those is the right way to think about innovation: it is a marriage if you will.

ML: In the cases of both traditional and big tech corporations, our discussion suggests that they're part of a broader 'national system of innovation'. This raises the question of the role of government in the innovation system in America. How has that been approached in recent years and how successfully?

RA: Historically, the US had at one time the world's greatest innovation system by far. It was put in place from the beginning of the Second World War (1939–1945) and in the 20 years after that it was globally dominant. I give you an interesting statistic: in 1963, the United States government spent more on R&D than the rest of the world combined, every and all other countries and businesses outside the USA. It's a phenomenal statistic when you think about it. That's why we were leading the world.

Another big reason we were leading the world was government demand for innovation. For example, I mentioned Intel: one of the reasons Intel was able to thrive was that nobody wanted to buy these chips at the beginning because they were super-expensive but the Air Force was saying we don't care how expensive they are, we need them for our missiles and we will pay the price. So Intel were able to sell them and then through volume and economies of learning they were able to bring the price down for the next ones.

In this way, historically the US government has played a big role just through demand, through purchasing things, not out of any industrial policy, but because we were big and we bought these things. That's a role that the government can play today. In the US, for example, we should be transforming our transportation system in our cities, our healthcare system and a number of other areas through information technology, 5G, AI, sensors, Internet of Things and more. If the government were a 'lead adopter' of those technologies, we could really move and drive innovation. I think that's true. The same is true for Australia as well. Governments should be thinking how can they help, how can they lead this innovation by using technology to solve the problems that they're trying to solve, that their citizens want them to solve.

ML: Yes, well, governments grapple, certainly here in Australia, with what sort of leadership or role they should play in innovation. We have endless committees of inquiry, reports, recommendations, white papers, but still as a country we struggle to achieve the sort of innovation and competitiveness that we often aspire to. What drives governments to take a leadership role in innovation? You've mentioned crises like wars. We're going through crises at the moment including the COVID-19 pandemic, global climate change and geopolitical turbulence in our region. Do crises create a certain sense of national purpose and mission on which innovation can be focused?[20]

RA: Very much so. There's a really excellent book by Mark Taylor at Georgia Tech University about why some countries are successful in innovation and why some are not.[21] One of his key arguments is that a sense of national crisis fosters innovation: you have to innovate. He uses the example of Israel that has to innovate because they're surrounded by enemies. He uses the example of Canada who doesn't have to innovate there because the US will protect Canada; they don't really have any existential threats on the planet so they don't have the same focus that we do. A place like Taiwan; boy, if they don't innovate they are toast. The US had that with the Cold War when we really saw that as an existential threat, rightly or wrongly.[22]

Since 1989 and the fall of the Soviet Union in 1992, we have taken our eyes off the ball. What's happening now though in the US is really interesting as you're seeing this bipartisan alignment of Republicans and Democrats in the Congress and it's got us started thinking again about being better at innovation. We have to have a better innovation policy because of the threat from China that is becoming seen as an existential threat, and it's leading to a lot of new policies.[23]

I'll give you two quick examples. A major component of the defense bill that just passed was to help reestablish and bring back semiconductor production to the US through well-funded advanced R&D in that area.[24] There's another bill called the 'Endless Frontier' Act that could be $100 billion oriented to ten key technologies like quantum computing, artificial intelligence and robotics.[25,26]

There's a new urgency, I think in the US, and it's still early, but we'll see where that leads.[27] So yes, absolutely, crises are important. But if there wasn't, the key thing I think in US innovation is that a lot of its success has been from its culture and I think a lot of foreigners don't understand that fully. The US is a highly entrepreneurial place. We like taking risks. We're always looking for the glass half full, not half empty.

New technologies are seen as 'good', they're not 'bad', and you compare that to Europe where an entrepreneur is seen as being second rate. People there would rather go work for the government or a big corporation. The Europeans really embraced the 'precautionary principle' approach to this new AI technology: we don't know but it might do something bad so we'd better slow it down. That really does give the US a leg up. So I think the big question for countries is, do you want to go down the European path or do you want to embrace more the innovation principle path?

ML: The development of Chinese capability in innovation and technology and its stated aspirations to be a superpower in technology in its current five-year plan suggests a major challenge and opportunity to which America might respond. As you say, Robert, America is putting a lot of money these days into defense,[28] space, AI, etc. How do you think the governance system in America can deliver on these challenges? Is the government sufficiently well organised and coordinated at the national level to deliver an effective response?

RA: Historically, we've done this through what are called 'mission-oriented' agencies, principally the Defense Department (DOD), the Department of Energy (DOE) and the National Institutes of Health (NIH). We've never really had a focused area on commercial, industrial, advanced technology competitiveness. We did put a few of those pieces in place back in the 1980s when we were facing the Japanese challenge.[29]

My first job in Washington was at one of those places, the National Institute of Standards and Technology (NIST), but we let some of those atrophy. I think it's interesting that now there's a lot of talk in Washington among think tanks in the defense community and I believe that in the Biden Administration those talks will be continued. We need better institutional mechanisms to coordinate a national 'Advanced Technology Strategy' that builds and integrates both defense technology needs and commercial technology needs.

Right now those tend to be dealt with in the White House at either what's called the National Economic Council (NEC) or more principally in what's called the Office of Science and Technology Policy (OSTP), and President-Elect Biden will appoint what's called the National Science and Technology Advisor.[30] So a lot of that will get played out there, but the next question is what agencies will really take that on and we'll see whether some of that gets assigned to the Department of Defense or whether some gets assigned to business in the Department of Commerce. But I do think we'll see a little bit more coordination and formal organisation in the next couple of years by the Biden Administration in this area.

ML: One of the issues perhaps is the 'silo' nature of bureaucracies and their programmes, missions and budgets on the one hand, and on the other, the realities of innovation and how it happens within business and society which is a more horizontal collaborative process. There was an attempt under President Trump to set up an Office of American Innovation?[31] How did that perform and what was the idea there?[32]

RA: President Trump, like President Obama, he had a Chief Technology Officer, Michael Kratsios,[33] who I think did an admirable job. Michael really was super good at focusing on this whole set of emerging technologies, quantum, AI and others, but he was a little bit hamstrung by the President's budget director, who was a very conservative free market type, didn't want to spend any money, and liked the best government as small government.

As you said, they created the Office of American Innovation and it was a very good idea, but ultimately, it was limited in terms of its scope, in its ambition. It never really became a priority for the President and I think for these things to work well you have to have at least some modest presidential backing and impetus.

I'll give you another example in the Obama Administration out of my think tank (ITIF) that we were instrumental in proposing essentially what you could call a '*Frauenhoffer*' system for the US.[34] The Germans have these 60 manufacturing institutes that are public–private partnerships between industry and universities, on a whole set of different manufacturing technologies. The Obama Administration set up this programme, now called the Manufacturing USA Institute system, made up of 15 of these institutes, and by and large they're very successful.[35]

They're not funded, perhaps as well as they could be now, but the White House in the National Economic Council (NEC) did make it a top priority. It really moved along, so I think you'll see that with the Biden Presidency. You'll see similar kinds of initiatives. He has a signature proposal that he ran on called 'Build Back Better',[36] which is an important initiative to expand federal R&D funding for certain key national priorities, particularly clean energy. I think you'll see a lot more in the next four years on clean energy innovation.[37]

ML: To what extent might some of the opportunities and challenges for new technology and innovation be characterised as 'wicked problems', rather different and more complex in nature than we are used to handling? Confronting the complexities of climate change and renewable energy seems to be one of them. How might governance approaches respond to such 'wicked problems' using perhaps a 'systems approach'?

RA: As I recall 'wicked problems' was a term from MIT back in the 1970s the idea being if we can put a man on the moon, why can't we solve poverty in the inner city?[38] That was the notion, so that a 'tame problem'[39] is an engineering problem that you can engineer and finally, say, put somebody on the moon.

But a 'wicked problem'[40] is super complicated with multiple causes. I actually think that climate is more of a 'tame' problem than a 'wicked' problem. At ITIF we have a robust clean energy innovation effort. Our view is that when we have very, very good batteries for grid storage, for automobiles, when we have even cheaper solar and wind, and a set of related technologies including industrial clean technology, it will happen and companies and organisations and consumers around the world will adopt these technologies. I don't want to make it sound like it's super easy: if you want to do this, for example, you have to seriously restructure electricity grids and that's not easy. But ultimately, unless we have those technologies we're not going to be able to do that.

On the other hand, 'wicked' problems would be, for example, like in the US pretty rampant levels of poor health. Some of that's going to be improved when, as we saw with the vaccine, the phenomenal RNA discovery, and gene editing. But some of the problem is just people not living the right way, smoking too much or eating too much or not exercising. I don't know how to solve such problems that require system intervention. To your point, we don't do a very good job on that; I don't think anybody does a really good job of thinking about how to intervene at a system level. My colleague John Kao, who's written a number of books on this, has done some of the best work on thinking about system innovation.[41] The key thing about fixing or addressing system innovation is you have to have some kind of body or organisation that takes responsibility for that and then tries to bring in everybody in the ecosystem and aligns the incentives and rewards so that we start to move in that direction. Until you do that it's 'happenstance' at best.

ML: The challenge for innovation in America has been described as entering a 'red zone'. In other words, a bit of a danger zone, an important potential 'tipping point', at least in the approach towards national innovation as a system. What frame of mind do you think the new incoming President needs to bring towards addressing this challenge?

RA: We've said that because in the US our politics are more extreme than Australian politics. You should be glad that you have the politics you have. Our politics are extreme in the sense that on the right or the Republican Party there certainly is a significant portion who are libertarians. Frankly, they just don't believe the government should play much of a role, that it's these lone brave entrepreneurs out of those Ayn Rand novels that do everything.

Then on the left, and this is somewhat of a new phenomenon, since Bernie Sanders ran in 2016 and then Elizabeth Warren, there is a growing sense among the progressive left that really we don't need innovation. That innovation is problematic, that it leads to overconsumption, that AI is going to kill jobs, that AI is racially biased. It's very troubling if you ask me, that big companies, particularly big tech companies, are inherently bad, and if we all just lived and worked at little mom-and-pop shops in the neighbourhood owned by workers and making organic cotton shirts, we'd all be great. I'm obviously exaggerating both of those positions, but they're both real and particularly on the progressive left it is an ascendant position.

I worry that those positions will end up saying we don't want innovation. We should regulate like the Europeans do. We should break up technology companies. We shouldn't fund the Defense Department R&D because who needs defense, while the reality is the way you get things done in the US because of our politics, a lot of it gets done through the defense bill, so if you want to fund R&D, quite a lot of it goes to the defense bill.[42] So I worry about that, but on the Biden campaign that I was involved in I headed up his advisory team on emerging technology policy and there's a lot of folks on that team who are very good, very sophisticated, and understand these questions quite well. I'm hopeful that once things get sorted out that you're going to see a new approach to innovation policy in the US that maybe you haven't seen since back in the late 1980s and early 1990s, which I think would all be all to the good, if we can get there.

ML: Thank you Robert Atkinson for winding up on a hopeful note but as you say, at the end of the day, the health of national innovation is very much caught up in the politics, culture and attitudes of people, the role of government and governance systems.

Conclusion

Innovation in America is at a political 'tipping point' having let slip its global leadership built up over previous decades. Many previously large and successful corporations lost their competitive incumbent positions to more entrepreneurial, risk-taking, disruptive tech-based enterprises. The national security crisis and competition of the Cold War years led to a surge of national investment in research, science, technology and skills, with the government taking the role of 'lead adopter' and carrier of technology risk in the name of national security. In more recent years, financialisation of business and innovation led to a short-term profit-driven focus at the cost of longer-term investment in basic research and development.

There is also a lack of recognition of the need for a 'systems-based' approach to promoting innovation premised on a complex ecosystem termed the 'national innovation system' that embraces a complex interaction of institutions, economics politics and technology, rather than a single-minded reliance upon either government research funding 'push' or private entrepreneurial leadership 'pull'. In confronting the emerging strategic and technological competition from China, there is an urgent need to rethink innovation policy, including drawing from past successful lessons from competition with the USSR in the 1950s and 1960s, and Japan in the 1980s and 1990s.

The American culture of entrepreneurial risk taking exemplified by the success of Silicon Valley tech companies is a big advantage over the precautionary, regulatory approach to new technology taken by the Europeans, with the UK possibly excepted. Neither government nor entrepreneurs can succeed alone. What is required is a national 'mission-oriented' approach that builds institutional capacity and coordination, behind national leadership at the highest level. Against the prevailing political currents of libertarianism and small government, there are signs that the Biden Administration may respond positively to the geopolitical-driven crisis in American innovation and strategic competitiveness.

Notes

1 Saric, I. (2021) Biden pushes for increased innovation to keep U.S. competitive, *Axios: Politics & Policy*, 28th April www.axios.com/2021/04/29/biden-us-innovation-research-global-competition
2 ITIF is a not-for-profit that was recognised as the world's top think tank on science and technology policy by the University of Pennsylvania's (2017) *Global Go To Think Tank Index*. See https://itif.org/publications/2018/02/02/itif-ranked-worlds-top-think-tank-science-and-tech-policy/
3 Attributed to Washingtonian Magazine (2011) see ITIF https://itif.org/person/robert-d-atkinson/
4 Atkinson, R.D. and Lind, M. (2018) *Big is Beautiful: Debunking the Mythology of Small Business*, Boston: MIT Press
5 Atkinson, R.D. and Ezell, S.J. (2012) *Innovation Economics: The Race for Global Advantage*, New Haven, CT: Yale University Press
6 Atkinson, R.D. (2006) *Why Conservative Economics Fails, Liberal Economics Falters, and Innovation Economics is the Answer*, Washington, DC: Rowman & Littlefield
7 Atkinson, R.D. (2005) *The Past and Future of America's Economy: Long Waves of Innovation That Power Cycles of Growth*, London: Edward Elgar
8 Godin, B. (2006) The linear model of innovation: The historical construction of an analytical framework, *Science, Technology and Human Values*, 31 (6): 639–667
9 Bush, V. (1945) *Science – The Endless Frontier, A Report to President Franklin D. Roosevelt on a Program for Postwar Scientific Research*, Washington, DC: USGPO www.nsf.gov/od/lpa/nsf50/vbush1945.htm
10 OECD (1999) *Managing National Innovation Systems*, Paris: OECD, 21st May www.oecd-ilibrary.org/industry-and-services/managing-national-innovation-systems_9789264189416-en
11 Atkinson, R.D. (2014) What is a national innovation system and why does it matter? *General Electric News*, 3rd July www.ge.com/news/reports/what-is-a-national-innovation-system-and-why-does-it-mat
12 Office of the Chief Economist (2017) *Australian Innovation System Report*, November, Canberra: Department of Industry, Science and Resources www.industry.gov.au/publications/australian-innovation-system-report-2017
13 Anderson, G. and Moris, F. (2023) *Federally Funded R&D Declines as a Share of GDP and Total R&D*, National Centre for Science and Engineering Statistics (NCSES), National Science Foundation (NSF), 23–339, 13th June https://ncses.nsf.gov/pubs/nsf23339
14 Williams, A. and Khan, H. (2021) *A Brief History of Semiconductors: How the US Cut Costs and Lost the Leading Edge*, Employ America Research Report, 20th March www.employamerica.org/content/files/2022/06/A-Brief-History-of-Semiconductors.pdf
15 Soo, Z., Tao, L. and Ho, C.K. (2019) Taiwan became top chip manufacturer with US help. Can it stay there? *South China Morning Post*, 11th September www.scmp.com/tech/tech-leaders-and-founders/article/3026766/taiwan-became-top-chip-manufacturer-us-help-can-it
16 Christensen, C.M. (1997) *The Innovator's Dilemma: When New Technologies Cause Great Firms to Fail*, Boston: Harvard Business Review Press
17 Knowledge At Wharton (2016) *The Pitfalls of the 'Financialization' of American Business, Book Review of Rana Froohar's Makers and Takers: The Rise of Finance and the Fall of American Business*, 28th June https://knowledge.wharton.upenn.edu/article/pitfalls-financialization-american-business/
18 Mazzucato, M. (2013) *The Entrepreneurial State: Debunking Public v Private Sector Myths*, London: Anthem Press
19 Feeney, M. (2020) A Libertarian Vision For Technology, *Libertarianism*, 31st March www.libertarianism.org/essays/libertarian-vision-for-technology

20 Kibasi, T. (2021) Mission economy by Mariana Mazzucato review: The return of the state, *The Guardian*, 20th January www.theguardian.com/books/2021/jan/20/mission-economy-by-mariana-mazzucato-review-the-return-of-the-state
21 Taylor's book introduces the new theory of 'creative insecurity'. See Taylor, M.Z. (2016) *The Politics of Innovation: Why Some Countries are Better Than Others at Science and Technology*, New York: Oxford University Press
22 Centre, S. and Bates, E. (2019) *Tech-Politik: Historical Perspectives on Innovation, Technology, and Strategic Competition*, Centre for Strategic and International Studies (CSIS) Brief, 18th December www.csis.org/analysis/tech-politik-historical-perspectives-innovation-technology-and-strategic-competition
23 Tan, H. (2023) China has a 'stunning lead' over the US in the research of 37 out of 44 critical and emerging technologies, new study finds, *Business Insider India*, 3rd March www.businessinsider.in/tech/news/china-has-a-stunning-lead-over-the-us-in-the-research-of-37-out-of-44-critical-and-emerging-technologies-new-study-finds/articleshow/98382844.cms
24 Hawkins, M. (2023) Bid to accelerate US chips permitting passes Senate as part of defense bill, *Bloomberg News*, 28th July www.bloomberg.com/news/articles/2023-07-27/bid-to-accelerate-us-chips-permitting-passes-senate-as-part-of-defense-bill
25 This bill was superseded by the United States Innovation and Competition Act (USICA) which was passed in 2021. www.congress.gov/bill/117th-congress/house-bill/2731
26 Lopez, G. (2021) How congress wrecked its own science bill, explained in 600 words, *Vox*, 4th June www.vox.com/2021/6/4/22518923/endless-frontier-act-innovation-competition-act-china-congress
27 Holland, M. (2023) Tech competition with China remains top of mind for U.S., *TechTarget*, 21st March www.techtarget.com/searchcio/news/365532997/Tech-competition-with-China-remains-top-of-mind-for-US
28 Amyx, S. (2020) The technological innovation challenges in defense, *Forbes*, 14th July https://scottamyx.com/2020/07/15/forbes-the-technological-innovation-challenges-in-defense/
29 Lohr, S. (2011) Maybe Japan was just a warm-up to the rivalry with China, *The New York Times*, 21st January www.nytimes.com/2011/01/23/business/23japan.html
30 Lane, N. (2022) I was a presidential science adviser – here are the many challenges Arati Prabhakar faces as she takes over President Biden's science policy office, *The Conversation*, 6th October https://theconversation.com/i-was-a-presidential-science-adviser-here-are-the-many-challenges-arati-prabhakar-faces-as-she-takes-over-president-bidens-science-policy-office-188273
31 Mervis, J. (2017) Trump's White House science office still small and waiting or leadership, *Science*, 11th July www.science.org/content/article/trump-s-white-house-science-office-still-small-and-waiting-leadership
32 McCormick, R. (2017) New White House office aims to help run government like a great American company: Office of American innovation has already met with Tim Cook, Elon Musk and Bill Gates, *The Verge*, 27th March www.theverge.com/2017/3/27/15069482/white-house-office-of-american-innovation-apple-tesla
33 Resnick, B. (2018) Trump's de facto science adviser is 31 and has no science training, *Vox*, 14th February www.vox.com/science-and-health/2018/2/14/17012322/trump-ostp-science-adviser-michael-kratsios
34 Comin, D., Trumbull, G. and Yang, K. (2012) *Fraunhofer: Innovation in Germany, Harvard Business School Case Number: 9-711-022*, Boston: Harvard Business School, 6th January
35 Slack, M. (2014) *Manufacturing Innovation Institutes: Putting America at the Forefront of 21st Century Manufacturing*, Blog Archive from The White House President Barack Obama, 25th February https://obamawhitehouse.archives.gov/

blog/2014/02/25/manufacturing-innovation-institutes-putting-america-forefront-21st-century-manufactu

36 *The White House's Build Back Better Framework* www.whitehouse.gov/build-back-better/

37 German, B. (2020) Biden features energy R&D in economic push, *Axios: Energy & Environment*, 10th June www.axios.com/2020/07/10/biden-energy-promises-2020-campaign

38 Rittel, H. and Webber, M. (1973) Dilemmas in a general theory of planning, *Policy Sciences*, 4 (2): 155–169

39 Kreuter, M.W., De Rosa, C., Howze, E.H. and Baldwin, G.T. (2004) Understanding wicked problems: A key to advancing environmental health promotion, *Health Education Behaviour*, 31 (4): 441–454 https://pubmed.ncbi.nlm.nih.gov/15296628/

40 Kreuter et al (2004), op cit

41 Kao, J. (2007) *Innovation Nation: How America is Losing Its Innovation Edge, Why It Matters, and What We Can Do to Get it Back*, New York: Free Press

42 US Defense R&D expenditure of US$55 billion (2017) was four times the combined total of all the other OECD countries and accounted for 80% of total OECD Defense R&D spending. See US Congressional Research Service (2020) *Government Expenditures on Defense Research and Development by the United States and other OECD Countries: Fact Sheet*, 28th January https://sgp.fas.org/crs/natsec/R45441.pdf

6 Innovation Policies in Australia

The Divisive Politics and Administration of Systemic Transformation

Interview With Roy Green

Introduction

What are the settings in Australia's National Innovation System (NIS)[1,2,3] and how do they provide for an innovative, productive and competitive economy? What are the systemic barriers to productivity and innovation growth, and what is the political and policy path to cultural transformation?

Keywords: advanced manufacturing; direct grants; innovation; long-term strategy; mission focus; moonshot thinking; National Broadband Network (NBN); National Innovation System (NIS); renewable energy; SDG 4; SDG 9; STEM; tax incentives; technology foresight

Interviewee Profile

Emeritus Professor Roy Green **(RG)**, Deputy Vice Chancellor, UTS, Former Business School Dean, PhD Cambridge, has a long and distinguished career in many aspects of innovation policy research, administration and advising with particular interests in how companies manage innovation on the one hand; and on the other, how governments set the framework and environment for innovation in the country through their policies. He's been involved in many boards and committees of inquiry, government reports on innovation. He's been associated with the CSIRO, OECD and the EU; and as an expert advisor to ministers and the Australian Senate 2015 Innovation Systems Inquiry.

The Interview

ML: How do you see Australia's standing and performance on innovation in this globally competitive day and age compared to what other countries are doing?[4]

RG: We're not performing badly; let's say that at the beginning. But we're not performing as well as we could or as well as we should. One of the most widely cited statistics about Australia's performance is that we have a very strong performance in our research output, the production of ideas through our universities through the CSIRO and other research

DOI: 10.4324/9781003280316-7

institutions. We rank very well there, sometimes in the top ten or very close to it, but the efficiency or effectiveness with which we turn those ideas into commercial outcomes is lacking. That's where we fall right down to the bottom of the table around the seventies and eighties in rank and this is also mixed up with our poor record in university/business collaboration.[5]

So those elements hang together and we could say, to some extent, that the reason is the culture and the sense of complacency that we have in Australia after some 27 years of uninterrupted growth. There's no other economy in the world with a record like that, and so no one who has not experienced adversity is likely to say that it is going to face us in the near future or that we urgently need to reposition or that, look here is the 'burning platform';[6] if we don't change, we're going to jeopardise future jobs and growth.

Some people are saying that, and in the recent report by Innovation and Science Australia (ISA),[7] we're certainly sending out the call to that effect but it's not a call that is resonating in government, in politics generally, or indeed with the wider population. The government found that to its cost, in a sense in the 2016 election; when people in marginal electorates were told by the Prime Minister that innovation was important, they reacted differently than he might have expected.[8] They saw innovation as technological disruption that meant that they might not have a job in the future, and the focus was seen as a negative one on universities, technology, start-ups and so on. It didn't connect with people's reality which does require innovation and experiences innovation all the time in our current industries. But it didn't say that these industries – in order to survive into the future – need to think about how they not only develop technology themselves but adapt to technologies that others also create.

ML: Yes, as you say, perhaps we have slipped into a bit of complacency in recent times, although I think it's probably fair to say that Australia has had a long history of perhaps not being fully up to the mark when it comes to innovation, as distinct from research. That distinction you've made, and it seems that our rankings on global scales are continually falling, so it was pretty gratifying, I thought, when Malcolm Turnbull took over in 2015 that he spoke in such glowing and positive terms about the role and contribution that innovation and technology and science could make to the productivity, the competitiveness, the growth and the well-being of the Australian economy. And yet, as you say, kind of strangely, he's been very silent on innovation since the campaign. You don't even hear the word innovation pass his lips anymore.

RG: No, under his predecessor, Tony Abbott, the word innovation was removed from the name of the Department of Industry and Innovation; the word Innovation disappeared,[9] after a period of Labor government when innovation was promoted, not perhaps as heavily as we might like, but it was certainly part of the government policy framework.

Under Tony Abbott though, everything that the previous government had done had to be undone and innovation was one of those things, so you could almost measure the lift in spirits in the science, innovation and research community when Malcolm Turnbull took over and told everyone there was no more exciting time to be an Australian, you might recall.

While not much seems to have happened, the point is, he touched on the *zeitgeist*, which was that after an unprecedented mining boom, people did recognise in the population that we did need to change and we needed to prepare for an uncertain future which was not going to depend on a high 'terms of trade'. We saw the dollar dropping. We saw that we needed to make up for the gap in our export revenues that would be left by a decline in commodity prices. We've seen a few spikes in the price of iron ore and coal since then, but the trend remains the same. The International Energy Agency (IEA) and other reliable forecasters would argue that over time, our reliance on commodities will provide us with 'diminishing returns'; and that, in general, the world will move beyond fossil fuels to renewable forms of energy.

ML: It does now seem that the political rhetoric of the day which invokes concepts of productivity and competitiveness is important but it seems to reduce those to ideas of decreasing the costs of labour and capital. For example, the justification for the huge corporate tax cut that's being proposed is that it's somehow going to boost our competitiveness by a 'race to the bottom' on tax rates.[10] Meanwhile, labour and wages are also being held down, and this is a very time when generally around the world people recognise that if you want to be competitive in the future, you have to increase productivity through skills, technology and innovation.

Perhaps we could turn to our next point that the government, through its agency the ISA, an 'independent' group, released a report earlier this year on a future agenda called *Australia 2030: The National Innovation Report* with 30 recommendations.[11] What is that report and what is it trying to say about what needs to be done to enhance innovation?

RG: It's important to go back to the way in which this report was foreshadowed by Malcolm Turnbull. In 2015 when he took over, he released a kind of Innovation Report Mark One, the National Innovation and Science Agenda,[12] which was designed to set up the prospect of doing a long-term strategic review of where we were placed as a nation and what levers we needed to pull to get to where we needed to go in a post-mining boom economy.

That was clearly the agenda that was established at that time and it prompted a great deal of enthusiasm and interest. But, as I said earlier, it came a little unstuck in the election campaign because it hadn't gone further by that point. It was meant to encompass the transformation of our existing industries in a way that made people feel less insecure about future job growth.

Be that as it may, the government nevertheless did push ahead with its Mark Two, which was not so much a set of policies at this stage, but a review which would look at where we wanted to be in the future and a couple of years later, probably way past the initial deadline. The new Innovation and Science Australia (ISA) body was a sort of semi-independent advisory body, a part of government but also with its own independent board led by Chair Bill Ferris with a long track record in innovation, entrepreneurship and venture capital. The Deputy Chair was Alan Finkel, the Chief Scientist and a number of prominent individuals from business.

The idea was that this report would provide relatively independent advice back to the government along those lines, and it has done it to that extent but because the momentum has dropped in the area generally, it hasn't got very much attention. Its proposals are not as ambitious as one might have hoped, partly because of the constraints provided by the government. One can only suspect that the board was told, look don't expect too much more spending in this area. Try to 'cut your cloth' when you make your proposals to keep them realistic. You can imagine the discussions behind the scenes there, and of course, they did want their proposals to be picked up by the government, so they've kept them relatively modest. They do contain a couple of 'national missions' sometimes called 'moonshots'.[13]

ML: I think, generally, you feel that there are a number of things they got right in their report. Like emphasising the importance of innovation to our continuing social and economic environment and well-being, and criticising some of the fragmented institutions and activities we have in this domain, including federal-state activities, and even recognising a role for government in settings for innovation.

RG: I would have liked the group to have picked up the shortcomings in our institutional structures which are not everything but they certainly make it either easier or more difficult to implement policy. At the moment, we have about $10 billion as a country going into research and innovation from the taxpayer that is spread across 13 separate portfolios of government, and 150 separate budget line items.[14]

We have review after review suggesting ways of consolidating this to get a more coherent picture. Given we are a small economy, we only do 2% of the world's R&D, we are not going to be excellent at everything.

How do we focus our resources to get the best return from areas of current and potential competitive capability and competitive advantage? They didn't go that far unfortunately.

They did, however, focus on a couple of areas which are important to us and the most important and most controversial area I guess is the fact that over a third of our innovation spending is in the form of an R&D tax concession and this is something that's grown dramatically over recent years. It's 90% of R&D spending. It's the highest proportion of a tax incentive version as opposed to direct targeted funding in total expenditure of any OECD comparable countries with only one up there with us, and that's the Netherlands.

Most other countries balance their portfolio of spending in such a way as they encourage innovation and R&D via direct targeted funding.[15] We rely on a tax concession, which means in the view of the Board that this is a lot of expenditure that is wasted on 'business as usual' activities. We should really be targeting a lot of our expenditure towards business transformation which is not just technology, but it could also be new business models or high-performance work and management systems; or new systems, new forms of systems integration connecting with global value chains, as well as the more traditional types of R&D based on new technologies and the adaptation of technologies from elsewhere.

They made a suggestion to switch the balance towards more targeted funding, and they also put in there a possible 'premium' that would attach to the R&D tax concession where innovation and research were conducted together with universities. So that was a positive step, but it's just one of a series of measures which weren't related as well as they could have been in the context of a transformation of our entire system.

ML: And yet at this time, so many of our global competitors that we hear about in the context of the tax competition, in Europe and Asia, are very busy, focused and supporting national innovation strategies with highly targeted policies based on competitive advantages and the provision of infrastructure items.[16] What are the areas that we are good at, that deserve targeting and that perhaps weren't made enough of in this so-called 'strategic plan' and recommendations?

RG: We know that we're good at certain areas of technology, digital technologies, medical technologies, agribusiness technologies, and we're good at adapting technologies to new business models that we developed here in Australia in a range of industries, including advanced manufacturing.[17]

Even though many would say that we're hopping out of advanced manufacturing, it is still a growing area to some extent at the expense of traditional mass production manufacturing. But it's based on our increasing participation in global value chains, so it's not just services, but manufactured goods that as well as mining technologies that do propel us forward in the research and innovation space and could do much more than we do currently.

But these are just my guesses if you like, about the areas that we're good at. The point is we've never done within Australia a systematic technology or knowledge 'foresight' exercise.[18] Many countries do this and they do them on a regular basis. They ask themselves the questions: what are we good at and what could we be good at in the future – in order that we allocate our limited public funds together with private funds to those areas where we think we can get the best comparative or competitive advantage as a nation.

Small countries in particular do this. The northern European countries, some of the East Asian countries,[19] even the US has had a go at this as part of what they called the Advanced Manufacturing Partnership a few years ago,[20] and it requires a lot of research which is not a short-term exercise.

You take a year or two in doing these things but because our governments have such a short-term focus, no one has felt any great incentive to develop longer-term thinking.

ML: Australia has a long story, hasn't it, of scepticism about so-called planning exercises, targeting exercises and 'picking winners' in this way. While those might well be a good way to go, it seems to me there are a couple of blindingly obvious areas in which the government has an important role that's recognised overseas but in which nothing happens here.

For example, the whole energy, renewable energy and climate change area which is a leading driver globally of new sustainable technology and innovation and products and services,[21] and in which, for example, a country like China is hugely driven by innovation.[22] Then there is also the so-called National Broadband Network (NBN) public infrastructure which should be the platform for all enterprises and individuals to innovate with the new digital technologies in forming new businesses.[23] Australia's world rankings on broadband connectivity compared to other countries are worse than even our overall innovation performance ranking.[24] Yet both these sectors are judged beyond the scope of the report. Why?

RG: You might say there's no coincidence or accident there either. When I referred to the fact that the Innovation and Science Australia board in its 2030 strategy identified national missions,[25] those national missions left out two things which most people would regard as quite important. One was energy – renewable energy technologies and energy efficiency that wasn't there; and nor was super-fast broadband.

I guess you could only interpret that as a political issue because had the board being given a complete scope to identify areas in an independent and impartial way you would think that energy policy and all the related measures to mitigate climate change and to assist the transition from fossil fuels would have been high on their agenda, along with super-fast broadband which is already a supposed goal of government. But it's proved so embarrassing over the last few years as we dropped down the digital connectivity scale around the world, we were up there around number 10 or 11 with 4G and so on.

And now as other countries have rolled out optical fibre not just to the area, but to the home and the business we have dropped down into the thirties and forties in rank.[26] I think we're somewhere below Oman. Now it's a really serious challenge which the government doesn't want to draw attention to.

These are fundamental changes that will be crucial to our future productivity growth which is another factor that needs to be taken into account in innovation policy. The key driver of productivity is innovation, both of the technology type of innovation and non-technology innovation, including management capability. Until we get that right, we're not going to be prepared for a post-mining boom economy.

Productivity underpins growth. It underpins our living standards and we've seen wages growth stagnate in the last few years as the top comes off our mining boom and their terms of trade go into retreat somewhat. The changes that we make must both improve the supply side in terms of our technological and skills proficiency but also the demand side. There's some recent research on this recently published by some American academics indicating the importance of the demand side as well, so wages growth is not just a result of higher productivity, it also drives productivity and that means having a workforce that is paid enough to create demand.[27] As far as corporate tax cuts are concerned, this is a very lazy way to try to achieve these objectives. It's $65 billion, which could more productively be spent in a targeted way on building our research, education and innovation capability, but it's going to be a concession to companies who will have choices about how they spend it, and it may be spent in productive investment, but it can also be spent in share buy-backs, dividends and executive salaries.[28]

ML: It can indeed, and as you say, perhaps it's not even a matter that the government is not actually doing much. One is tempted to conclude that what they are doing seems to be almost going in the opposite direction to the sorts of things you've been talking about that are needed to drive innovation, productivity and competitiveness.

RG: That is exactly the problem, and it was certainly shown up by the 2030 report which made some very sensible and positive suggestions to a government that perhaps wasn't listening as carefully as it should because it is going off in the other direction. We're up to now the sixth Innovation Minister under the Abbott and Turnbull Governments, over a period of five years or so. It's Michaelia Cash and not many people would even know this is our

Minister for Jobs and Innovation.[29] Jobs were thrown in just to give the impression that something was happening that might result in a positive outcome for workers but Minister Cash gave a speech the other day in which she said: what we need in this area is business certainty, and I'm going to provide it by doing exactly nothing in this space, and I'm not making this up.

ML: Roy, what is your opinion on where we stand with a key element of skills building for innovation, namely the debate over science, technology, engineering and maths (STEM) education, and what we're doing about it, because it seems that student numbers are continuing to turn well away from that focus?

RG: I guess this is one of the more disturbing parts of our research and innovation ecosystem, which will depend on the skills we develop for the future. In the PISA international rankings of school education proficiency,[30] we're falling compared with other countries, including countries to the north of us in East Asia, and we have to ask ourselves, why is this the case?[31]

There's been a lot of emphasis on focusing students on STEM subjects, it's very important and we should certainly do that but it isn't just about STEM skills. The skills of the future are also going to be those broader boundary-crossing skills in areas of critical thinking and resilience, adaptability that require students to go beyond the more specialised areas of scientific knowledge. This is where the humanities is also very important and it's where design thinking is important.[32]

How do we imagine a future and indeed one where the jobs that currently exist may not exist and certainly won't exist in their current form in five or ten years' time? There is no established career ladder in large organisations in the way that there was in the past, so we need to prepare students for a very different type of future and many of the students, not only businesses but the students themselves, want this.

At UTS for example, we did a survey of our students and found that 40% had an interest in starting a business of their own, creating their own jobs, and so we've had to and we're pleased to do this, shift the focus of our teaching activities towards some entrepreneurship skill building.

How do you develop a new venture? Can we give you an experience in a co-working space? Can we connect you up with venture capital if you've got an idea that can be commercialised, and students are really gravitated to this? Those that don't start a business and join an existing one will nevertheless also have entrepreneurial skills, which are valued a lot more highly now than simply managerial skills in the context of large organisations. So, there's a big change going on in our education system.

ML: I wish I could feel a degree of optimism that our political system and culture might pick up on some of this in the near future, but I'm not sure from what we've been saying here tonight, that's going to be immediately forthcoming.

Conclusion

Effective innovation and technology change for productivity, growth and jobs requires a functioning national innovation system (NIS). All parts of an innovation ecosystem need to act in concert across a range of inter-acting institutions in research, science, technology, education, skills, entrepreneurship, commercialisation and markets, across businesses, industries, sectors, government and society.

In Australia, over a long period, the innovation policy and institutional components and linkages neither are effectively linked nor operate in the required degree of collaboration, cooperation and alignment of purpose or vision. Australia's long-term loss of international standing in international rankings of innovation and competitiveness speak to an inability to rise to the systemic national innovation challenge.

Australia's inability to capitalise on its strong research base with successful business and industry development through commercialisation, particularly in technology- and manufacturing-based industries, is symptomatic of an underdeveloped national innovation ecosystem. A case in point is the weak linkages between publicly funded research and private enterprises and industry. The education and training system is a poor performer by international standards and displays a similar lack of effective linkages to skills required for future technology- and knowledge-based jobs, including developing and supporting entrepreneurial business culture and skills, and STEM education.

A very substantial national budget for Science, Research and Innovation (SRI) activities falls across over a dozen ministerial portfolios and well over 100 budget lines. A lack of interest in forward-looking technology 'foresight', vision and long-term strategy and coordination might lend coherence and purpose to the elements of the national innovation system.

Various attempts to transform the economy to a high-value, high-skill economy, including in the context of post-mineral boom cycles, have failed politically both at the highest levels of government and within the community, to capture sustained interest and commitment. There has been no shortage of analysis, reports and recommendations, but there has been over decades much vacillation and temporising, not to say politicisation and playing on community fears of change.

Changes to and even reversals of policy, as with organisational and ministerial reshuffles and renamings, are all too frequent, lacking coherence and consistency. Key innovation policies involving tax incentives and direct grants become political playthings, while recommendations for 'mission' focus on key strengths are set aside on ideological grounds. The sorry handling of the development of a national broadband network (NBN), the fate of the manufacturing sector and the reluctance to embrace renewable energy all illustrate the politicisation and the inability of politics and culture to come to grips with the challenges and opportunities of new technology and innovation.

Technology, politics and society are misaligned on innovation and raise the question of whether Australia even has a functioning 'national innovation system' that is 'fit for purpose'.

Notes

1 Nelson, R.R. (ed.) (1993) N*ational Innovation Systems: A Comparative Analysis*, New York: Oxford University Press
2 OECD (1997) *National Innovation Systems*, Paris: OECD www.oecd.org/science/inno/2101733.pdf
3 Webster, E. (2009) Does Australia have a 'national innovation system'? *Australian sEconomic Review*, 42 (1): 84–87
4 According to the Global Innovation Index (GII), *From the World Intellectual Property Organisation (WIPO) in Geneva, in 2022 Australia Ranks 24th Among 48 High-Income Group Economies* www.wipo.int/edocs/pubdocs/en/wipo_pub_2000_2022/au.pdf
5 Ibid
6 Paris, J. (2013) Real leaders never say 'burning platform', *Operational Excellence Society*, 2nd July https://opexsociety.org/body-of-knowledge/real-leaders-never-say-burning-platform/
7 Innovation and Science Australia (ISA) (2017) *Australia 2030: Prosperity Through Innovation: A Plan for Australia to Thrive in the Global Innovation Race*, Canberra: Australian Government www.industry.gov.au/sites/default/files/May%202018/document/pdf/australia-2030-prosperity-through-innovation-full-report.pdf
8 Koziol, M. (2016) How Malcolm Turnbull's innovation agenda failed to take flight, *Sydney Morning Herald*, 15th July www.smh.com.au/politics/federal/how-malcolm-turnbulls-innovation-agenda-failed-to-take-flight-20160714-gq5dwu.html
9 Bogle, A. (2013) Australia's new PM Nixes science minister post at worst possible moment, *Slate*, 20th September https://slate.com/technology/2013/09/tony-abbott-nixes-australia-s-science-minister-post-cuts-climate-change-research.html
10 Jericho, G. (2021) The race to the bottom on cutting company tax rates has failed, *The Guardian*, 18th April www.theguardian.com/business/commentisfree/2021/apr/18/the-race-to-the-bottom-on-cutting-company-tax-rates-has-failed
11 ISA (2017), op cit
12 Turnbull, M. (2015) National innovation and science agenda, *Media Release*, 7th December www.malcolmturnbull.com.au/media/national-innovation-and-science-agenda
13 Mazzucato, M. (2020) *Mission Economy: A Moonshot Guide to Changing Capitalism*, New York: Penguin Random House
14 Department of Industry, Science and Resources (DISR), *Science, Research and Innovation (SRI) Budget Tables 2022–23*, Canberra: Australian Government, 28th April www.industry.gov.au/publications/science-research-and-innovation-sri-budget-tables-2022-23
15 See the table "Tax incentives play a key role in the business R&D support policy mix" in OECD's, *Tax Incentives for R&D and Innovation* www.oecd.org/innovation/tax-incentives-rd-innovation/
16 Park, T. and Kim, J. (2020) *Innovation Policy in Asia*, Manila: Asian Development Bank www.adb.org/sites/default/files/institutional-document/575671/ado2020bp-innovation-policy-asia.pdf
17 See CSIRO's, *Advanced Manufacturing Roadmap* www.csiro.au/en/work-with-us/industries/manufacturing/advanced-manufacturing-roadmap

18 OECD (2021) *Workshop on Re-Imagining the Future: The Role of Foresight and Anticipatory Governance in STI-Led Transitions*, S&T Policy 2025, 6th April www.oecd.org/sti/inno/workshoponre-imaginingthefuturetheroleofforesightand anticipatorygovernanceinsti-ledtransitions.htm
19 Shin, T., Hong, S.K., & Grupp, H. (1999) Technology foresight activities in Korea and in countries closing the technology gap, *Technological Forecasting and Social Change*, 60 (1): 71–84
20 NIST (2011) *President Obama Launches Advanced Manufacturing Partnership*, 24th June www.nist.gov/news-events/news/2011/06/president-obama-launches-advanced-manufacturing-partnership
21 Garnaut, R. (2019) *Superpower: Australia's Low-Carbon Opportunity*, Melbourne: LaTrobe University Press
22 Purtill, K. (2021) The world is hungry for solar panels: Why did we stop making them? *ABC News*, 18th September www.abc.net.au/news/science/2021-09-19/solar-panels-why-australia-stopped-making-them-china/100466342
23 Quiggin, J. (2013) NBN: We would have been better off without privatisation, *The Guardian, Opinion*, 2nd August www.theguardian.com/commentisfree/2013/aug/21/national-broadband-network-elections
24 Ross, D. (2019) Australia plunges to 62nd place in global internet speed rankings, *Australian Financial Review*, 30th April www.afr.com/technology/australia-plunges-to-62nd-place-in-global-internet-speed-rankings-20190430-p51ifx
25 ISA (2017), op cit
26 Ross (2019), op cit
27 Storm, S. (2020) Demand-side secular stagnation of productivity growth, *Institute for New Economic Thinking*, 30th January www.ineteconomics.org/perspectives/blog/demand-side-secular-stagnation-of-productivity-growth
28 The Australia Institute (2018) *14 Reasons Why the Case for a Company Tax Cut for Big Business Has Collapsed*, 27th March https://australiainstitute.org.au/post/14-reasons-why-the-case-for-a-company-tax-cut-for-big-business-has-collapsed/
29 Cash's tenure as Minister was nine months from December 2017 to August 2018. See Baldassarre, G. (2018) Senator Michaelia Cash named new minister for jobs and innovation in cabinet reshuffle, *Startup Daily*, 20th December www.ssstartupdaily.net/topic/senator-michaelia-cash-named-new-minister-jobs-innovation-cabinet-reshuffle/
30 See OECD's, *PISA* www.oecd.org/pisa/
31 Carey A. and Hunter, F. (2019) Alarm bells: Australian students falling behind in maths, science and reading, *Sydney Morning Herald*, 3rd December www.smh.com.au/politics/federal/alarm-bells-australian-students-falling-behind-in-maths-science-and-reading-20191203-p53gho.html
32 Strauss, V. (2017) Why we still need to study the humanities in a STEM world, *Washington Post*, 18th October www.washingtonpost.com/news/answer-sheet/wp/2017/10/18/why-we-still-need-to-study-the-humanities-in-a-stem-world/

7 Efficient, Effective and Integrated Economy-Wide Climate Change Policy

Economics and Politicisation

Interview With Ross Garnaut

Introduction

What are the economics of climate change and how we might transition in an innovative and cost-effective manner to renewable energy technologies and a sustainable future? On 8th October 2018, the Intergovernmental Panel on Climate Change (IPCC) brought down its report on where we stand with reaching the 1.5 degree target,[1] which now looks like it's going to be hit and overshot, whether we like it or not; and the short time frames that we still have remaining to even get to our 2.0 degree target.

On that very same day, the Nobel Prize committee announced the award of its 2018 Prize in Economics to American economist, Professor William Nordhaus of Yale University.[2] The Nobel Committee citation for Nordhaus is for his contribution to 'integrating climate change into long-run macroeconomic analysis',[3] and for his associated advocacy of a policy of carbon pricing for long-term sustainable economic growth.[4]

Keywords: cap and trade; carbon price; carbon tax; Carbon Pricing Mechanism (CPM); Carbon Pollution Reduction Scheme (CPRS); carbon trading; Emissions Trading Scheme (ETS); endogenous economic growth; externalities; Great Barrier Reef; greenhouse gas emissions; integrated climate models; Intergovernmental Panel on Climate Change (IPCC); market failure; Nobel Prize Economics; public goods; SDG 11; SDG 12; SDG 13; spillovers; sustainable economic growth

Interviewee Profile

Professor Ross Garnaut **(RG)**, AO, is Vice Chancellor's Fellow and Professorial Fellow of Economics at the University of Melbourne, and was for many years a highly distinguished professor of economics at the Australian National University (ANU). In recognition of his lifelong and manifold contributions to public policy in Australia, he was awarded the Order of Australia (AO).[5] He has held many very influential positions, including as Australia's Ambassador to China and as Principal Economic Adviser to Prime Minister Bob Hawke during Australia's major structural economic reforms of the 1980s.[6]

DOI: 10.4324/9781003280316-8

Ross wrote the landmark 2008 report for Prime Minister Kevin Rudd, *The Climate Change Review for Australia*,[7,8] and as a result of that report and its recommendations, Australia adopted a climate pollution charging system, effectively a form of carbon pricing which was, unfortunately, subsequently scrapped by Prime Minister Tony Abbott.

The Interview

ML: What does the Nobel Prize citation for William Nordhaus mean when it says that he 'integrated climate change into macroeconomic analysis'? Haven't economists taken account of and analysed the economics of the environment before his work?

RG: No doubt his contribution wasn't the first to take environmental impacts into account. In fact, the economic principles of doing that have been with us for a long time, 100 years ago with the Cambridge economist, Pigou. In his important book *The Theory of Welfare*,[9] Pigou said that in a market economy, if some economic actors are damaging other economic actors, it could only work efficiently if you taxed the costs that some people were imposing on others.

It was always recognised that this had a very ready and important application in the case of environmental costs. Even the high priests of free market liberalism like Hayek and Friedman recognised the importance of taxing environmental 'externalities' where some activities were imposing environmental costs on the rest of society.[10]

What Nordhaus did was apply these principles specifically to the case of climate externalities and he did some extensive modelling of the long-term impacts of the costs and benefits of mitigating climate change. He was a pioneer in those applications of the general principle of 'negative environmental externalities'. He became an advocate of a 'carbon tax' at fixed price on carbon pollution.

He pointed out that it was a pretty good tax independent of its environmental benefits; at a time when there's some difficulty in raising enough taxation to cure our budget problems and to provide needed 'public goods' this was an efficient form of tax. So you might do it even without the environmental externalities, but certainly, once you realise the importance of the external costs of carbon pollution, you might do it for two reasons. One was the public finance reason, and the other was the efficient application of constraints on pollution.

His modelling showed that on his assumptions of a relatively modest rate of carbon tax, you could bring the cost of climate change mitigation into line with the benefits of climate change mitigation. His was not the last word on these things, but it was an important step along the path to where we are now in thinking about these issues.

ML: What exactly is it that Nordhaus 'integrated assessment models' are integrating into economics and how does he do that?

RG: He looked at all the costs of carbon pollution, of generation of greenhouse gases and traced those into all of their economic effects.[11,12] If you burn a lot of coal and each extra tonne adds to the effects, then you do change the climate through well-known mechanisms in atmospheric physics.

Carbon dioxide is a greenhouse gas. If you have a high proportion of it in the atmosphere, then it traps more of the heat that comes from the sun and is reflected from the surface of the earth that warms the atmosphere, eventually that warms the seas, and the surface of the earth as well. That has costs. It disrupts a lot of existing economic activity over time. It leads to expansion of the oceans and a rising of the sea level. It leads to melting of the ice caps and ice in glaciers on mountains, and that raises the sea level, and that disrupts economic activity in low-lying areas. It makes the rate of evaporation higher and in areas of agriculture where water is scarce and valuable; it reduces the amount of water available for agricultural use.

The warmer climate will have more energy and climate systems, and so extreme weather events will become more extreme, we will have more extreme heat waves, we will have more extreme storms, and therefore there will be costs of engineering infrastructure to withstand these, more fierce events.

In warm or hot climates like Australia, mortality rates rise when there are more heat waves. Bushfire events will be more severe; they'll be associated with economic loss and with the death of humans.

Nordhaus through the use of 'integrated assessment models' found a way of adding up all of these costs recognising the cost to the economy. The integration part was looking at how through putting a tax or a price on carbon pollution you could, at some cost to the economy, reduce the environmental damage.

The endpoint of the analysis was to have the tax high enough to balance the economic cost of mitigating climate change and of restricting carbon pollution with the economic benefits of avoiding all of that disruption. That's how you integrated the taxing of externalities with taking into account the damage those externalities were doing to the economy.

ML: You seem to be saying that a key part of the integration was that Nordhaus, as an economist, brought on board his modelling processes the physics and the chemistry; both of the carbon cycle and climate systems alongside an economic growth model?

RG: Yes, and he didn't do that all by himself of course. A lot of work had been done on those physical systems, atmospheric systems, biological systems, by other scientists, and the integrated models distilled the wisdom of those other sciences and turned them into economic impacts. In my big review of climate policy for all of the State Premiers and for the Prime Minister, which I presented to the Premiers and the Prime Minister in 2008, I applied those approaches in a lot of detail; rather more detail than others had done specifically for the Australian case.[13]

ML: Economists have long looked at the sources and drivers of economic growth, particularly in the long run and across different countries, and the standard model at least when I was at university, was the Solow model. Is anything that Nordhaus is contributing when he brings in these integrated climate change issues in any sense adding to, changing or rewriting the Solow economic growth model?[14,15]

RG: Bob Solow, who I'm pleased to say is still in good mind and good heart in his nineties,[16] would feel very comfortable with what Nordhaus has done. The framework that Solow used for modelling long-term economic growth looked at the very basic building blocks of economic activity, capital, labour, other resources, and took into account productivity growth.

An integrated assessment model of the kind that Nordhaus has helped to develop adds to that; it is just recognising that part of the impact of economic activity is not simply on prices in markets, but is on environmental amenity, and that impact on environmental amenity itself has an economic impact. So, it's really adding a new dimension to the analysis without changing its structure.

ML: Some critics of markets regard environmental problems as examples of what are called, technically at least, 'market failure'[17] and there seems to be disenchantment too these days, not only with markets but also with capitalism generally. In a 'market failure' system, as I understand it, the market mechanism under-prices certain resources as being external to the responsibilities of the user, and therefore leads to the wrong price signals for those who want to invest their capital and their knowledge in improving technology, innovation and productivity. The market doesn't send the right signals. How does that work in the context of carbon pollution and climate change?

RG: I would have to be very careful how one uses these terms. There's huge value in an efficiently operating market economy. The market can do a lot of things that central planning and other methods of control and allocation can't do; the prosperity we currently enjoy, the process of global development that's lifted billions of people from poverty over the past half century, all of that depends on the power of market exchange.

But markets will only deliver a maximum of the economic welfare, of amenity, if the prices of goods and services reflect their true costs to society. Sometimes costs imposed by some activities in the production of some goods exceed those that are reflected in markets because there are what economists call 'external costs'.[18] If we make a megawatt hour of electricity from burning coal, then the market will pick up the cost of digging up the coal and putting it into the generator, and then of building and operating the generator, and the cost of building the wires to transmit the power to the factory where it's used, or the home where it's used.

There's another external cost that the market doesn't pick up. It's the cost of carbon dioxide from burning the coal going into the atmosphere changing and disrupting the climate with some of the effects I mentioned earlier; the warming of the planet will raise sea levels, it will disrupt agriculture, we will have more bushfires and other extreme weather.

If you want the market to deliver economically efficient outcomes, then you've got to tax the external costs, or else you have to regulate the activities that are generating the external costs. The market failure is the failure of the market to pick up all of the costs that are generated by an activity and you can correct that by imposing a price on the externality. You can calculate and Nordhaus was one of the first who attempted to do so, the cost that the burning of that tonne of coal imposes on the rest of society around the world through its effect in changing the climate.

If you make your tax equal to that cost, then you can let the market determine whether people use their solar energy or coal and how much electricity they use. If you don't have the tax on the externality, if you don't correct the market failure in that way, then the market won't give you an economically advantageous outcome.

ML: In other words, the market won't send the right signals to those who need to invest in this particular case of these negative 'spillovers' that you're mentioning. The damage done by carbon that isn't priced directly won't give the correct signals to invest in the technology to either rebate or replace those damage costs with innovation and new technology.

RG: That's right. We will under invest in low emissions, local pollution activities and over invest in high pollution activities and we won't get an economically optimal outcome. Nordhaus was focused on economic costs and benefits but there are non-economic effects of carbon pollution as well, that are extra reasons for action.

I'll give an example that I discussed at some length in my major report ten years ago. If we destroy the Great Barrier Reef, and sadly it looks as if it's going to be difficult to save much of the Reef the way we're going,[19] then it will be a big economic cost imposed through markets. There will be less tourism with far fewer tourists interested in going to Port Douglas, Cairns, Bundaberg and other places along the North Queensland coast. One can consider that to be an economic market failure. The failure to tax carbon will have led to an excess of economic activity, generating carbon pollution and that will have done economic damage. The market won't have led to a good outcome, but Nordhaus was just calculating the economic effects.

There will also be the destruction of the Great Barrier Reef which, of itself, will have some costs that are important to people independently of that economic cost. Lots of people would think it's a bad thing in itself for that natural wonder of the world to no longer exist.

Let's be clear that the Nordhaus analysis focused on economic costs and benefits. There are other non-economic costs of failure to deal with climate change.

ML: It's hard to believe that your landmark and monumental piece of work on the climate change review was more than ten years ago and yet here we are in 2018, still as a country, and arguably as a world, not really tackling them in a very effective and efficient manner. You advocated a carbon pricing or taxing mechanism, referred to as a 'Carbon Pollution Reduction Scheme' (CPRS).[20] Meanwhile, Nordhaus has been advocating what's called a 'Cap-and-Trade' approach.[21] What's involved in these notions and do they differ?

RG: What I advocated was really a 'cap-and-trade' scheme and Nordhaus also was an advocate for a carbon tax, a fixed price on carbon. The effects of a 'cap-and-trade' scheme and a 'carbon tax', in some circumstances, can be very similar. In a cap-and-trade scheme, you work out how much carbon you can afford to put into the atmosphere without causing excessive damage through climate change. One can argue about how much damage we should tolerate.

The recent IPCC report said that even with 1.5 degrees of warming there would be very great damage, for example, much damage to the Great Barrier Reef.[22] Prior to the focus on 1.5 degrees, in the last few years, including from the IPCC, it had been generally accepted that we should aim for holding the temperature increase to three or possibly 2 degrees above pre-industrial levels.

Realisation that the costs will still be pretty high at 2 degrees has led to increased focus on 1.5 degrees. Say you had settled on the objective of 2 degrees and, economically, you can settle on that number by looking at how much it would cost to hold that and how much benefit you could get from holding climate change to a 2-degree temperature increase and balance the two up and give you an economically optimal level of abatement. Once you take the non-economic costs and benefits into account, you'd probably be more ambitious in trying to restrict climate change.[23]

Say, the agreed objective is 2 degrees. The science can tell us how much carbon we can put into the atmosphere to have a reasonable chance of holding temperature increases from pre-industrial levels to 2 degrees. That can be expressed as a certain amount of tonnes of carbon dioxide and or its equivalent in other greenhouse gases.

Once we know that number, the public authorities can issue permits and say it is illegal to emit carbon dioxide unless you have one of these permits. You could sell those permits by auction and the government issuing them would get a lot of revenue or you could give them away for free which gives a bit of a 'free kick' to the polluting businesses. But if the regulation of the system stops you from putting carbon dioxide into the atmosphere unless you have a permit, then that limits the increase in carbon in the atmosphere to the number of permits.

ML: So it's a combination of a regulation to effect the total amount of emissions and the introduction of a market mechanism beneath that allows people to trade those who want to trade and pay for the right to pollute within that limit, and the price will accordingly go up in the market and provide relevant reduction and mitigation incentives. This question of terminology, between a 'tax' and a 'price' has led to all sorts of political issues. A variation of your scheme was introduced for a couple of years and then scrapped by Prime Minister Abbott who referred to it as a new 'tax' and focused on the costs of electricity thereby imposed.[24] Surely, it doesn't have to be talked of as a 'tax' in any strict sense. The government doesn't have to collect revenue. Couldn't it just set a cap and then through trading of permits between businesses, establish a price in the market without the government even being involved except by determining and issuing the permits?

RG: I was describing an Emissions Trading Scheme (ETS) which is also known as a 'cap-and-trade' scheme and the government could give out the permits for free or it could sell them by auction. The effects on the price of goods and services, the price of electricity or price of anything else is not affected by whether the permits are given out free or sold. It's a market price in either case, whether they're auctioned or not.

The people who receive the permits whether from an auction or receive free from the government will charge the scarcity value of that permit, if they generate electricity using coal, for example. The fact that the permit is scarce gives it a value; if they're getting it for free, it will mean that the value of that permit goes to the polluting business and that business will pass on the cost to consumers anyway, so the consumer will pay in the long run.

ML: Nevertheless, this has been a highly toxic political issue that we still haven't resolved here; and of course, America backed right away from a 'cap and trade' in part because it's seen as another tax grab for revenue by governments.

RG: I've just been describing the emissions trading schemes, and it actually has no effect on the prices of goods and services whether the government collects a revenue or not. In one case, the price is paid by the consumer and the money goes to the government; and in the case of the system we had in Australia, the government then gave that back as increased in to social security and cuts in income tax so that no

Australian on average or lower than average incomes was worse off as a result.

If you just gave the permits free to the businesses that emit the carbon, that would mean there was a transfer from the consumer that paid for the electricity to the electricity generator. That would increase the profits of the generator above what it would otherwise be, and make the consumer poorer compared with the case where the revenue is collected by the government and given back in tax cuts.

Now, the alternative approach as Nordhaus discusses both in his work – and I discussed both in my Climate Change Report – is a fixed carbon price where instead of setting the price in the market, the government makes an estimate of the price of carbon that's necessary to hold temperature increases to 2 degrees and just sells off permits.

The economic effect of that is very similar to a 'cap-and-trade' scheme, an emissions trading scheme with the government auctioning off the permits, but one cannot be quite so certain that you'll hold carbon pollution to the desired level because the calculation of what price is necessary might be wrong.

What we had in Australia, for two years from July 2012 until June 2014, was a system that had the structure of an emission trading system 'cap and trade' but with a fixed price for the first two years. If Tony Abbott and Clive Palmer, whose votes were essential for the repeal in the Senate, hadn't abolished the carbon price; then from 1st July 2014 we would have had integration of the Australian trading system with the European trading system. The Australian carbon price would have been set in an international market, and it actually would have been lower than the price in the first two years.

Conclusion

In analysing environmental issues, economists have long agreed that due to the nature of the negative impacts on others external to the source of pollution these so-called 'negative spillovers' or 'negative externalities' constitute a case of 'market failure' whereby the market price system does not reflect the true overall costs of environmental damage.

This results in an overproduction of pollution and underinvestment in pollution control investment in equipment and abatement from the point of view of economic efficiency in the marketplace. The efficient economic response is to internalise these negative externalities by imposing a cost on pollution in the form of a 'tax' per unit of harmful emissions.

There are different views among economists about the best design of carbon pollution charges. These have been central in the decades-long debates about tackling carbon emissions from fossil fuel burning that contributes to man-made climate change and global warming. Two approaches have been argued. First, a carbon tax rate that is set iteratively until overall emissions are regarded as at an agreed target level. Alternatively, a 'cap-and-trade' approach that sets the overall target level of emissions and leaves the price of emissions to be set in a market.

A further refinement in instrument design is the approach by Nordhaus who advocates for carbon taxes in the context of his Nobel Prize-winning work on 'integrated climate assessment models' that take account of the interactions between the environment; and its range of physical systems, and across the economy. His model seeks to optimise that relationship, by determining a carbon emission charge that balances the respective costs and benefits of climate mitigation. There is also disagreement among economists about the level and rate at which carbon prices/taxes need to increase to meet global temperature targets.

The economic debate over emissions charges, prices or taxes fuelled a super-charged and highly politicised public debate over decades resulting in very limited application of carbon taxes across different jurisdictions. In Europe, this resulted in a system of carbon trading and hence carbon market price. In Australia, an emissions trading scheme (ETS) advocated by Garnaut as a carbon pollution reduction scheme (CPRS) operated successfully for a couple of years only to be abandoned politically. Finally, in America, a proposed 'cap-and-trade' form of ETS promoted by Nordhaus never did get off the ground. As in Australia, an effective response to climate change was consequently delayed, if not completely set aside. A far less efficient and effective combination of regulatory and incentive measures was put in place.[25] It was based on unambitious overall decarbonisation targets that needed to be applied administratively on a complex sector-specific rather than whole-of-economy basis market-based carbon price.

Notes

1 The Report emphasised strongly that we are already seeing the consequences of 1 degree C of global warming and that limiting global warming to 1.5 degrees C would require 'rapid and far-reaching' transitions in land, energy, industry, buildings, transport, and cities. See IPCC (2018) *Summary for Policymakers of IPCC Special Report on Global Warming of 1.5 degrees C Approved by Governments*, Incheon, Republic of Korea, 8th October www.ipcc.ch/2018/10/08/summary-for-policymakers-of-ipcc-special-report-on-global-warming-of-1–5c-approved-by-governments/

2 The award was made jointly to Professor Paul Romer of New York University, but our focus here is on the work of Professor Nordhaus. See Nordhaus, W.D. (2018) Climate change: The ultimate challenge for economics, *Nobel Prize Lecture*, 8th December www.nobelprize.org/uploads/2018/10/nordhaus-lecture.pdf

3 Royal Swedish Academy of Sciences (2018) *Prize in Economic Sciences*, 8th October www.nobelprize.org/prizes/economic-sciences/2018/press-release/

4 Rabe, B.G. (2018) The economics – and politics – of carbon pricing, commentary, *Brookings Institution*, 25th October www.brookings.edu/articles/the-economics-and-politics-of-carbon-pricing/

5 University of Melbourne (2017) Professor Garnaut among Australia's best in Queen's birthday honours, *Faculty of Business and Economics Newsroom* https://sbirthday-honours

6 They were wide-ranging microeconomic reforms that Australia put in place. It was a sustained and comprehensive program of trade liberalisation and other structural reforms that freed up markets, promoted competition and generally sought to ensure that prices did their job of signalling costs in relative returns. See Banks, G. (2005) *Structural Reform Australian-Style: Lessons for Others?* Productivity Commission Chair Presentation to the IMF and World Bank, Washington DC and OECD, Paris www.oecd.org/australia/39218531.pdf
7 Garnaut, R. (2008) *The Garnaut Climate Change Review: Final Report*, Port Melbourne, VIC: Cambridge University Press
8 See the follow-up: Garnaut, R. (2011) *The Garnaut Review 2011: Australia in the Global Response to Climate Change*, Cambridge: Cambridge University Press
9 Pigou, A.C. (1920) *The Economics of Welfare*, London: Macmillan https://oll.libertyfund.org/title/pigou-the-economics-of-welfare
10 McMahon, J. (2014) What would Milton Friedman do about climate change? Tax carbon, *Forbes*, 22nd December www.forbes.com/sites/jeffmcmahon/2014/10/12/what-would-milton-friedman-do-about-climate-change-tax-carbon/?sh=3d4497ec6928
11 Nordhaus, W.D. (2008) *A Question of Balance: Weighing the Options on Global Warming Policies*, New Haven, CT: Yale University Press
12 Nordhaus, W.D. (2015) *The Climate Casino: Risk, Uncertainty and Economics for a Warming World*, New Haven, CT: Yale University Press
13 Garnaut (2008), op cit
14 Solow, R. (1956) A contribution to the theory of economic growth, *Quarterly Journal of Economics*, 70 (1): 65–94
15 Acemoglu, D. (2009) The Solow growth model, in *Introduction to Modern Economic Growth*, Chapter 2, Princeton, NJ: Princeton University Press
16 Solow was born in 1924
17 'Market failure' is, in economic terms, the inefficient distribution of goods and services in the market where individual rational economic decisions do not lead to rational outcomes for society, resulting in either too much or too little investment from a social efficiency perspective. See Caplan, B. Market failure theory as reproach to government practice, *EconLib* www.econlib.org/market-failure-theory-as-reproach-to-government/
18 'Externalities', in economics, are unpriced effects of production or consumption activities in the market and can be either negative as in the case of pollution or positive as in the case of education; not all of the benefits or costs are captured by the producer or the consumer of an activity. See. Caplan, B. Externalities, *EconLib* www.econlib.org/library/Enc/Externalities.html
19 Thompson, P. and Hoegh-Guldberg, O. (2021) The great barrier reef is a victim of climate change – but it could be part of the solution, *The Guardian*, 26th July www.theguardian.com/environment/commentisfree/2021/jul/26/the-great-barrier-reef-is-a-victim-of-climate-change-but-it-could-be-part-of-the-solution
20 Also known as the Emissions Trading Scheme (ETS), the CPRS was not legislated but was subsequently implemented by the Gillard Labor government in 2011 as the Carbon Pricing Mechanism (CPM) until repealed by the Abbott Coalition government in 2014. See Climate Alliance (2016) *Carbon Pollution Reduction Scheme (CPRS) Background*, Blog, 21st January www.climatealliance.org.au/blog/2016/carbon-pollution-reduction-scheme-cprs-background
21 Stavins, R.N. (2019) *Carbon Taxes vs. Cap and Trade: Theory and Practice, Harvard Project on Climate Agreements*, Discussion Paper ES 2019–9, November https://seors.unfccc.int/applications/seors/attachments/get_attachment?code=TJQGYTI096K3J33ANM1HDWYEU51VRXNC
22 Intergovernmental Panel on Climate Change (IPCC), *The Special Report on Global Warming of 1.5 degrees C* www.ipcc.ch/sr15/

23 This article discusses the controversy over the rate at which carbon taxes need to be increased based essentially on differences related to the discount rate used to value sfuture costs and benefits: Komanoff, C. (2014) Is the rift between Nordhaus and Stern evaporating with rising temperatures? *Carbon Tax Centre*, 21st August www.carbontax.org/blog/2014/08/21/is-the-rift-between-nordhaus-and-stern-evaporating-with-rising-temperatures/

24 Taylor, L. (2014) Tony Abbott hails demise of 'useless, destructive' carbon tax, *The Guardian*, 17th July www.theguardian.com/environment/2014/jul/17/tony-abbott-hails-demise-of-useless-destructive-carbon-tax

25 Albanese, A. (2022) Australia legislates emissions reduction targets, Prime Minister, Minister for climate change and energy, *Media Release*, 8th September www.pm.gov.au/media/australia-legislates-emissions-reduction-targets

8 Climate Change Energy Transition

Modelling, Scenarios and the Political Economy of the 'Tragedy of the Commons'

Interview With Warwick McKibbin

Introduction

On 8th October 2018, the same day that the Intergovernmental Panel on Climate Change (IPCC) brought down its latest dire special report on climate change and how the world is actually not progressing too well towards the targets of 1.5 degree centigrade, let alone 2 degrees,[1] the Nobel Committee awarded the prize in economics for 2018 to Professor William Nordhaus for Yale University. The Committee's citation was for his contribution 'for integrating climate change into long-run macroeconomic analysis' and for his associated advocacy of a global policy of carbon pricing for long-term sustainable economic growth.[2]

Keywords: Climate change; carbon price; climate bonds; DICE model; hybrid models; Kyoto Protocol; emissions permits; emissions targets; energy transition; market failure; public goods; RICE model; scenarios; SDG 11; SDG 12; SDG 13; SDG 17; tragedy of the commons

Interviewee Profile

Warwick McKibbin, AO,[3] (**WMcK**) is Professor of Economics at the Crawford School, Australian National University (ANU), Canberra, and Director, Center for Applied Macroeconomic Analysis.[4] He is internationally renowned for his contributions to global economic modelling and climate change policy. Warwick is also associated with many international organisations, including the Brookings Institution, Washington, and as a founding Fellow, Lowy Institute, Sydney. He has been a member of the Board of the Reserve Bank of Australia (RBA) and also Advisor to the Prime Minister's Science Engineering & Innovation Council (PMSEIC), among many other positions. In particular, he has written the book *Climate Change After Kyoto: Blueprint for a Realistic Approach*,[5,6] and his research project for the ANU's Climate Change Institute is: Macroeconomics, climate change and energy.

DOI: 10.4324/9781003280316-9

The Interview

ML: Warwick, what is Nordhaus' contribution to integrating climate change into long-run macroeconomic analysis and forecasting?

WMcK: The first very important contribution Bill made was in the early 1970s where he redefined the concept of economic welfare and how you measure 'well-being', which was arguing that it's not just how much we produce in the economy, but it's the quality of the environment. Subsequently, he invented two of the major economic models that look at the links between the economy and climate, and the feedback of climate back into the economy. One is called DICE,[7] and the other one is RICE.[8] Bill pioneered both the way in which we think about measuring economic well-being as well how we might go about modelling it.[9]

ML: What did Nordhaus contribute to the measurement of economic well-being and how was that an advance on what economists had been doing about the environment?

WMcK: Most economic models focus on what we can measure and so the idea of gross domestic product (GDP) or the 'value added' in the economy is a very narrow definition of what people value. Bill's argument was that you need to take into account environmental benefits, the quality of the environment, a range of activities which are very hard to measure, but because you can't measure them doesn't mean that they're not important. He was one of the pioneers in that area and it's now broadly developed into the field of 'ecological economics'.[10]

Bob Costanza,[11] who's a colleague at the ANU, was at the forefront of developing that idea of thinking more broadly about the economy and economic welfare. There're various ways of measuring the value of the environment.[12] One way is to do surveys, and another is to see how much people are willing to pay to use national parks. My own research is more focused on the costs and benefits of climate change specifically.

ML: Could you explain the significance of Nordhaus's integrated assessment models?

WMcK: I've been involved with the IPCC working along the lines of the work of Bill Nordhaus. In the early stages, people were looking at just the economics of climate policy, the economics of environmental policy. The economists were working in one area, scientists in another and engineers designing energy systems in yet another. The problem was that the climate issue is so encompassing that you needed to get all of those groups into a framework to work out not only their own expertise but also the interlinkages. What Bill Nordhaus did in the DICE model was to build in the impact of emissions from economic activity through the long-term concentrations of CO_2 climate greenhouse gases and, then feeding that back into the economy and the interaction between the economy and the energy system. It was quite a simple concept to do a very complex task and even now there is a debate about how useful integrated assessment models are.

My decision not to build an integrated assessment model was because I thought we didn't even know enough about the economics. So the modelling that I did was a much more detailed economics-energy interface, leaving the climate story to the climate scientists to feed into my framework and give informative feedback to them. I prefer to have a much more complex economics framework, whereas what Bill was able to do is still controversial because some of these issues are very complicated. To make them simple enough for an all-encompassing model you have to cut corners. His work did change the way in which people thought about the whole issue of climate policy and the economics of transitions from a carbon-based system to a non-carbon-based system, and so it is a significant contribution.

ML: The Nordhaus integrated model sounds like it's a multi-disciplinary exercise with a combination of physics, chemistry as well as economics where he links a carbon circulation model to a climate model and an economic growth model. Your modelling doesn't straddle those three spheres, so what is your approach to the integration of the systemic disciplinary insights and interactions?

WMcK: Our argument is about what determines the level of emissions in the economy. Early on in the IPCC process when we were doing model comparisons, lots of people took GDP economic growth rates as given and fed them through an energy model and that would tell you the level of emissions. Our work suggested that actually, no, that's not the right way to think about this. What determines economic growth and what determines your energy system are happening at the same time. Some sectors in the economy are growing very quickly, but they're not energy intensive and other sectors are growing more slowly in their energy intensiveness. The ratio or the relationship between energy use and CO_2 emissions and GDP will be determined simultaneously, and so you can't just take the economics and feed it to the engineers, and you can't just take the technology and feed it in separately. You have to do the whole thing simultaneously.

Economic growth can come from a variety of different inputs, from energy usage, the productivity of labour or new technology. Technology may be saving on fossil fuel use or it may be using fossil fuels, so you need to go down into the deep economic structure to understand if you're going to change the relationship between measured GDP and energy use, and CO_2 emissions. You have to know the structure of the economy. The fact is that some manufacturing sectors use a lot of energy while services don't use very much. When you're doing these long-term projections you need to model the composition of the economy and how it changes, in response to government policies, market changes and demographic changes. The economics is quite complicated, the modelling of the economy in Bill's models is very simple and economists can criticise the model for not getting the economics right. The climate scientists would probably criticise it because he simplified the climate science too much, and the chemists could probably criticise it for that reason. You do have to simplify to build a model in many different dimensions. The results of the model are interesting, but I think from a policy point of view you still need to have all the various groups working together and talking to each other to come up with an integrated framework.

ML: Do you believe that it's a quixotic endeavour that Nordhaus embarked upon or do you believe that over time it might be the way that things will develop?

WMcK: It was important that Nordhaus did that because it showed the interdependence, some very important insights, and the feedback loops involved. Again, there's a debate about how quickly the emissions and concentrations will feed into temperature. In my model, it's 80 or 100 years into the future before there is serious feedback, and so we were more focused on the short-term policy framework for changing the structure of the economy rather than trying to get the environmental feedback on the economy as a core part of our focus. It's very important that it's there, but you can't build a model that's complicated enough to be able to answer some of the deep policy questions, but still simple enough to understand the issues well.

ML: You mentioned that you're focused on an economic model. The modelling of economic growth has a long history, and one of the conventional approaches is the Robert Solow approach.[13] I notice that this Nobel Prize award to both Nordhaus and Romer citing them as integrating, on the one hand, knowledge and technology; and, on the other, the natural world or the environment, into standard economic growth models. To what extent did the models that you're working with reflect those features, as distinct from the traditional Solow capital and labour drivers?

WMcK: One thing I would suggest is that the person who should have won the Nobel Prize with Bill Nordhaus was Marty Weitzman from Harvard,[14,15] because Marty actually was a leader before Bill in thinking about climate policy and how to deal with environment–economy interactions. Paul Romer should have won the prize next time on economic growth, with Robert Barro, who is also a professor at Harvard.[16]

So, I was actually betting on a Nordhaus-Weitzman combined award. I worked with both of them in terms of exchanging ideas. They were very closely related, and Marty actually predates Bill in terms of some of the early environmental work. Having said that, the Romer work is important for the climate debate because we just don't understand the way in which technology evolves in our modelling framework: we go back to a more classical growth framework in various versions of ways in which technology can impact on the economic outcomes, but we don't model the endogeneity of that, or the way in which technology responds to incentives.

We analyse 'scenarios'.[17] We say, these are the bits of the system we understand and we feed in drivers like assumptions about population growth, and it will tell us what will happen to emissions, what will happen to energy use. Then we do a different scenario about how the future might evolve. We do four or five different future scenarios and then we look at the emission profiles under those different worlds. Then we define various types of policy interventions and see how those profiles will change. We're not trying to forecast the future because that is a very difficult thing to do on the time frames that matter. But we are trying to understand the key sensitivities, the key drivers and the policies that are likely to have the biggest impact in terms of biggest emissions reductions at lowest economic costs.

ML: You've made mention of the utility of these models, including yours, for policy prescription on climate change measures. Nordhaus wrote on policy aspects, presumably based on his model work, and in a pretty accessible way, in his well-known book *Climate Casino.*[18] He talks about the environment and climate as a 'public good' and which he instances, as an example of 'market failure', that somehow requires government intervention. How do you see his policy analysis and prescriptions?

WMcK: I agree completely with Bill's framework. The obvious thing you need to do, and I think people get this wrong, is they think if we deal with the energy system, we solve the problem. In fact, most of the CO_2 emissions and all greenhouse gas emissions in any economy don't come from electricity generation. They're coming from broad economic activities like agriculture, like transportation and a whole range of uses, so what we want to do from an economic point of view is change people's behaviour in how energy or how CO_2 emissions are created in their system and how people use energy as well as produce energy.

You really need to change the behaviour of many, many people and firms in the economy, not just a couple of electricity generators. That's a general proposition and the only way you can do that from an economics point of view, because there are so many decisions that are being made you cannot regulate each decision, is to change the price of carbon in the system so that when people look at the costs of their activity that they bear, then they will change their behaviour. So Nordhaus would argue for a carbon tax or a carbon pricing mechanism. The subtleties are you might use a different pricing mechanism in different countries because of the structure of the economies and the political situations. But pricing carbon in his view and in my view is the foundation of any of the policy changes. Whether there's technological innovation or a whole range of other government interventions for getting a price on something that you don't want.

ML: Why can't the market find and respond to an appropriate price without intervention? What's leading to this 'market failure'?

WMcK: The 'market failure' is that my own behaviour not only affects what happens to me but also leads to CO_2 emissions which will affect what happens to you. My individual actions end up changing the environment or changing the climate, and that's not being taken into account in my own decisions. There's no market that's pricing the quality of environment and the idea of pricing carbon is to put a price on something which is impacting on the economy or impacting on individuals so that they can then take that price and 'internalise' it. In this way, they take that price into account when they're making their decisions because now their own actions will affect the system, and the system will affect back on their own actions, and so it creates a market that's otherwise missing.

ML: What considerations are involved in trying to estimate a proposed carbon price for policy purposes? Do the models help with that?

WMcK: They do help actually. There are two general approaches theoretically, in the literature. One is a carbon tax where you tax people who emit carbon and that tax optimally would rise over time because we're trying to get the emissions to fall over time. The alternative approach is to say that to emit a unit of carbon, a company needs to have an emission permit, and these emission permits are issued by the government and people who emit have to buy one, in which case the market will determine a price.

These are two different approaches because, in one case, you're setting the price path for the tax; in the other case, you're setting an emissions target and the market will give you a price that will be changing over time. The third approach that Peter Wilcoxen and I invented is called a 'hybrid', which is in between the two of those approaches,[19] and which we made when we were modelling the Kyoto Protocol around 1997 for a volume that Bill Nordhaus edited. We made the observation that if we did ten 'scenarios' of the IPCC model comparison people had asked us to run and we took those 'futures' of the world and imposed the Kyoto Protocol as it was being negotiated, the world 'blew up' eight out of ten times.[20]

This was because the amount of 'adjustment' that was needed by countries buying and selling permits across borders, the changes in exchange rates and trade, were so great that our model couldn't solve it. We discovered that under different 'futures'; in two of the futures that we considered the Kyoto Protocol worked, but eight out of ten times it didn't work. As a result, we decided to come up with a framework that works in our model ten out of ten times, and that also would work in other people's models, in case their world was different than ours. That's how we came up with the 'hybrid'.

ML: What does your modelling show about the impact of these various interventions on the growth of the economy and on innovation in the economy, and does it bear any relationship to any estimates of the economic damage costs?

WMcK: It depends very much on the 'future' that you project in the scenarios. We did a study for the Abbott Government (2013–2015) of what Australia's target should be going into the Paris negotiations. We looked at four different 'future' targets under one assumption about economic activity in the future, and we modelled 26% to 28% as our average approach, so that's the target the government took.

Given the scenarios that we fed in, that would cause a roughly 1% lower level of GDP by 2030, which is a very small change in the growth rate between now and 2030. That's less than the environmental damage that a lot of people have forecast would impact in a global system. The key difference here though is you've got to be careful because Australia's actions alone have very little impact on the climate; where economic costs were going to be probably from an Australian point of view, larger than the avoidance of damage if Australia acted alone.

The key here is that Australia has to be part of a global framework so that then the 'public good' aspect will swamp the short-term economic costs for a country like Australia, but it has to be a coordinated, clear and sustainable approach. Because any country like Australia acting alone doesn't in itself have much impact on the climate.

ML: Despite what appears to be a broad consensus in mainstream economics that a carbon pricing mechanism of some sort or other is the way ahead, the political situation in trying to get action on climate change is 'toxic'. It's not only toxic within individual countries, including Australia and America where it is stymieing action but on a global scale it might be viewed as a manifestation of what is called the 'tragedy of the commons' – that no individual country has much incentive to do anything in the way you've been suggesting for Australia, unless everyone else does it. And if no one else does it, basically we end up destroying the 'public good' that is a healthy global environment. Is that correct?

WMcK: That's right, but I think there is a solution, and that's what we've been arguing for a very long time. The first issue is to get away from the idea that we have to have a precise target and all countries have to have the same sort of target. This is not a good strategy because the actual emission reductions in a world where you cut emissions where it's cheaper to do so would have some countries cutting a lot with other countries not cutting very much.

At Kyoto and Copenhagen, people argued for targets without acknowledging the costs, and the costs are what politicians and the public worry about. The way to think about climate change is not in a targeting framework. It's to say how much are we willing to pay as an insurance mechanism against the uncertainty of climate change. That uncertainty is a real cost to the economy. Even if you don't believe in climate change, if you're a complete sceptic, you cannot argue that there isn't uncertainty about whether climate change is going to be costly or not, or uncertainty about the policy frameworks of governments, which have real economic costs if you keep changing them.

Australia is a classic example. In the study I did for the Abbott Government, I slipped in an appendix which looks at the cost of Australia not taking action and what it does to the cost of capital in energy generation alone. That uncertainty has a bigger economic cost than the policy of taking action, so doing nothing is not the right strategy. Doing something that enables low-cost reductions and ramping up if needed as an insurance premium is the way in which you can take the 'tragedy of the commons' and make it in the interests of every country to take action. If every country takes action, the 'commons' effect will be much more handled at an aggregate level. We can get around it if we get away from this idea of extremes, nothing or absolute shutting of the economy: the reality is in the middle and we can design policies to solve this 'tragedy of the commons'.

ML: That all sounds rational in regard to climate change, but the reality of 'political economy', globally and within countries, in respect of renewable energy technologies is a case of 'disruptive technologies' encountering formidable walls of opposition from existing vested interests that have a lot at stake in not seeing any solution adopted, at least for the moment.

WMcK: That's exactly right Michael. That's why the 'hybrid' approach that Wilcoxen and I've written about seeks to create 'constituencies' within an economy that find it in their own financial interest to not block the policy. We have a system of creating rights to emit carbon, which are very valuable, and are given out to carbon-intensive businesses and households. If they act to destroy the carbon policy, those assets will go to zero in value and their balance sheet would be better sustained by encouraging the policy rather than opposing it.

We've designed economic instruments that can be thought of as 'climate bonds',[21] that encourage corporations and oppositions to actively support the policy, because you have to have a policy that's bipartisan. Until you get bipartisan support, nothing will work but once it's bipartisan, you can lock in the constituencies using financial encouragement so that they no longer oppose it. That's one of the strengths of our approach in that it deals with the political opposition as well as the economic incentive.

ML: All strength to your 'hybrid' approach Warwick, because we seem to be a long way both domestically and internationally from any sort of bipartisan approach to resolving the political economy of climate change transition. You've mentioned 'scenarios' a number of times and the one now looming is an overshooting of the 1.5 degree target which will lead to all sorts of disruption around the globe. As usual, the rich will adapt and the poor won't be able to. It's not actually a very attractive global scenario is it?

WMcK: Well, it's not, but my focus over the last five years has been on developing countries, particularly China, Brazil and India.[22,23,24] This is where the ideas that Wilcoxen and I have put together can have a real impact, if we can get ten of the main countries, that's 90% of global emissions.[25] You have to leave Trump's America out to the side for the moment, but there's still a great opportunity to put in place good policies in many of these countries where their future investments in all sorts of energy use and energy generation haven't been made yet. You can encourage them to move in a direction which makes the costs of their adjustment so much lower.

There are options out there, and it would be ideal if Australia led the way by building demonstration models of how you can actually implement this policy, as we have done domestically with Reserve Bank monetary policy and with Productivity Commission microeconomic reforms.[26,27] These institutions have been powerful in making the argument and having it widely accepted by developing long-term frameworks that support economic growth. We can do that to help solve the climate change problem. However, America is really the key problem right now because it is the second biggest emitter in the world and it needs to be 'inside the tent' at some point.

Conclusion

Economics can provide a framework for climate change transition policies that enable sustainable long-term economic growth. This has been demonstrated by the Nobel Prize-winning work of William Nordhaus and his development of economic models that integrate growth economics with the insights of physical sciences and the global climate cycle. Such models provide for important feedback loops between emissions levels, environmental damages and economic growth. However, the inherent technical complexity of the systems they integrate and the technical simplifications necessary to enable feasible modelling has led to alternative models that rely on building a range of 'scenarios' to provide the feedback loops and sensitivity testing within the interrelated systems, and that more explicitly recognise the varying industry structure relationships between emissions and economic activity across all sectors of the economy.

Valuing the environment by taking account of costs imposed by producers and consumers on others but not priced in markets is a central idea to the economic approach. Balancing the environmental costs of climate change against the costs of mitigation can be achieved at lowest cost by taking account of the emissions levels recommended by science and establishing property rights for polluters up to those limits. These market-based economic solutions involving a 'carbon price' internalise previously unpriced external costs on others of polluters' activities, thereby changing behaviour across the economy. However, 'toxic' political 'status' has effectively hindered effective, sustainable climate action along these lines particularly from vested interests in the electricity and fossil fuel-based sectors that will carry most of the mitigation costs.

This resulting policy 'paralysis' that confronts the globe with the 'tragedy of the commons' can be overcome by a 'hybrid' approach that moves away from policy based on setting overall targets and a single carbon price. The real financial costs and business risks imposed by climate and policy 'uncertainty' on the cost of capital in different economic sectors and indeed countries can be treated as' polluters' 'insurance' for their assets in the form of 'climate bonds'. These would create 'constituencies' with direct financial stakes of self-interest rather than imposed costs, thereby transforming the 'political economy' of opposition to more draconian 'all or nothing' approaches to policies for climate change transition that involve carbon pricing and setting emissions targets and prices.

Notes

1 IPCC (2018) *Summary for Policymakers of IPCC Special Report on Global Warming of 1.5°C Approved by Governments*, Incheon, South Korea, 8th October www.ipcc.ch/2018/10/08/summary-for-policymakers-of-ipcc-special-report-on-global-warming-of-1–5c-approved-by-governments/

2 Royal Swedish Academy of Sciences (2018) *The Sveriges Riksbank Prize in Economic Sciences in Memory of Alfred Nobel 2018: William D. Nordhaus and Paul M. Romer* www.nobelprize.org/prizes/economic-sciences/2018/popular-information/
3 Economic Society of Australia (2016) *Australia Day Honours List* https://esacentral.org.au/latest-news-item/15640/australia-day-honours-list/?type_fr=4
4 Officer AO (Order of Australia) *For Distinguished Service to Education as an Economist, Particularly in the Area of Global Climate Policy, and to Financial Institutions and International Organisations* https://esacentral.org.au/365/images/McKibbon.pdf
5 McKibbin, W. and Wilcoxen, P.J. (2002) *Climate Change Policy After Kyoto: A Blueprint for a Realistic Approach*, Washington, DC: Brookings Institution Press. See also Commentary, 1st March, Brookings Institution Press
6 See also McKibbin, W. and Wilcoxen, P.J. (2002) Climate change policy after Kyoto: A blueprint for a realistic approach, *Commentary*, 1st March www.brookings.edu/articles/climate-change-after-kyoto-a-blueprint-for-a-realistic-approach/
7 Dynamic Integrated model of Climate and the Economy (DICE) model
8 Regional Integrated Climate-Economy (RICE) model
9 Nordhaus, W. (2020) *Scientific and Economic Background on DICE models,* 3rd February https://williamnordhaus.com/dicerice-models
10 This is an interdisciplinary, solutions-based studies concerned with sustainability and development, rather than efficiency and growth. See Nelson, A. and Coffey, B. (2019) What is 'ecological economics' and why do we need to talk about it? *The Conversation*, 5th November https://theconversation.com/what-is-ecological-economics-and-why-do-we-need-to-talk-about-it-123915
11 Emeritus Professor Robert (Bob) Costanza is an American-Australian economist. He is a founder of the trans-disciplinary field of ecological economics and sustainability and also chairs Public Policy at the Crawford School, Australian National University https://crawford.anu.edu.au/people/visitors/robert-costanza
12 Guijarro, F. and Tsinaslandis, P. (2020) Analysis of academic literature on environmental valuation, *International Journal of Environmental Research and Public Health*, 17 (7) April: 2386 www.ncbi.nlm.nih.gov/pmc/articles/PMC7178272/
13 Acemoglu, D. (2009) The Solow growth model, in *Introduction to Modern Economic Growth*, pp. 26–76, Princeton, NJ: Princeton University Press
14 Wagner, G. and Weitzman, M. (2015) *Climate Shock: The Economic Consequences of a Hotter Planet*, New Jersey: Princeton University Press
15 Roberts, S. (2009) Martin Weitzman, virtuoso climate change economist, dies at 77, *New York Times*, 4th September www.nytimes.com/2019/09/04/business/energy-environment/martin-weitzman-dead.html
16 Professor of Economics, Robert J. Barro, Harvard University https://scholar.harvard.edu/barro/home
17 Zenghelis, D. (2018) The role of modelling and scenario development in long-term strategies, *World Resources Institute (WRI) Expert Perspectives*, April www.dimitrizenghelis.com/publications
18 Nordhaus, W. (2015) *The Climate Casino: Risk, Uncertainty, and Economics for a Warming World*, New Haven, CT: Yale University Press
19 McKibbin, W., Morris, A. and Wilcoxen, P. (2009) *A Copenhagen Collar: Achieving Comparable Effort through Carbon Price Agreements*, Washington, DC: Brookings Institution, 28th August www.brookings.edu/articles/a-copenhagen-collar-achieving-comparable-effort-through-carbon-price-agreements/
20 The text of the Kyoto Protocol, sets binding targets for 37 industrialised countries and the EU to reduce greenhouse gas emission to an average of five per cent against 1990 levels, over five years, 2008–2012. See the UN Framework Convention on Climate, *What is the Kyoto Protocol* https://unfccc.int/kyoto_protocol

21 First issued in 2007 as AAA rated by the European Investment Bank (EIB) and World Bank (IBRD) they have grown exponentially to the landmark $1 trillion in cumulative issuance by the end 2020. They are fixed-income financial instruments used to finance with climate solutions projects. See the Climate Bonds Initiative www.climatebonds.net/about/what-we-do

22 McKibbin, W. (2005) *Global Climate Change Policy Beyond 2012*, Op-Ed, Washington, DC: Brookings Institution, 23rd November www.brookings.edu/articles/global-climate-change-policy-beyond-2012/

23 McKibbin, W. (2004) *Climate Change for India*, ASARC Conference, ANU, 27th-28th April https://crawford.anu.edu.au/acde/asarc/pdf/papers/2004/WP2004_03.pdf

24 McKibbin, W. and Liu, W. (2015) China: Ambitious targets and policies, in *COP21 at Paris: What to Expect – The Issues, The Actors, and the Road Ahead on Climate Change*, pp. 48–52, Washington, DC: Brookings Institution www.brookings.edu/wp-content/uploads/2015/11/cop21atparis.pdf

25 McKibbin, W., Morris, Adele C. and Wilcoxen, P. (2005) Pricing carbon, in *COP21 at Paris: What to expect – the issues, the actors, and the road ahead on climate change*, pp. 14–18, Washington, DC: Brookings Institution www.brookings.edu/wp-content/uploads/2015/11/cop21atparis.pdf

26 Kelly, P. (2000) *The Politics of Economic Change in Australia in the 1980s and 1990s*, Address to Reserve Bank of Australia (RBA) Conference www.rba.gov.au/publications/confs/2000/kelly-address.html

27 Berger-Thomson, L., Breusch, J. and Lilley, L. (2018) *Australia's Experience with Economic Reform*, Australian Treasury Working Paper, October https://treasury.gov.au/sites/default/files/2019-03/p2018-t332486-economic-reform-v2.pdf

9 The Innovative 'Circular Economy' as a Sustainable Business Model

Design and Transformation Challenges

Interview With Sami Kara

Introduction

The notion of a 'circular economy' might sound esoteric but be assured that we're all caught up in it every day in our homes, our jobs and our lives.[1] It's a topic more commonly, but more narrowly referred to as waste management and recycling and is also associated with the term 'zero-waste' economy.[2]

We have, for some time, been diligently separating our household waste streams and placing them in various coloured bins for pick up and recycling by our local councils who charge us for the service in our rates. However, we've now come to realise that this waste recycling stream is not perhaps working as well as we thought, or delivering what it should.

It has been described as being in a state of crisis around the country,[3] in all the Australian states and by local governments as a broken system. The fact is that we've been exporting a lot of our waste to neighbouring developing countries including China,[4] and Indonesia, and now they've told us that they've had enough and are refusing to take our waste streams anymore. We are now faced with the question of what we are going to do with all the waste that we generate.

And there's a lot of it. Four and a half million tonnes a year. Waste management is a big industry, with a turnover of $15 billion, some 20,000 people working in it directly and hundreds of companies; but they don't seem to have the capacity to cope with the waste stream here in Australia.[5]

So what's going on? There seem to be many business opportunities and available technology. How should we be approaching and innovating to handle our waste management streams more efficiently, effectively, and sustainably? How can enterprises build sustainable competitive advantage by using less? The answer lies in the idea of the 'circular economy' and the decoupling of growth from resource use and waste.[6]

Keywords: Circular economy, design engineering; innovation; life cycle engineering; linear economy; material separation; recycling; SDG 9; SDG 12; SDG 13; sustainability, waste management; whole-of-life cycle; zero waste

DOI: 10.4324/9781003280316-10

Interviewee Profile

Professor Sami Kara (**SK**), University of New South Wales (UNSW), Sustainable Manufacturing and Life Cycle Engineering, School of Mechanical and Manufacturing Engineering, is a specialist and widely published engineer,[7,8] with 30 years' experience in the waste management stream in industry, research and tertiary education. He has worked with many companies and is the founder of the Life Cycle Engineering Research Group, UNSW, that delves deeply into these matters.

The Interview

ML: How have we reached this dire point of crisis with our inability to handle our waste streams including, in particular, the recycling stream that we've all put so much time and energy and money into in recent times?

SK: There are many stakeholders involved in this whole process and you need to look at it as an 'end-of-life' product management rather than just recycling, because recycling is only one means of waste management. Ultimately, waste management is a business. For instance, if you have a manufacturing business, you buy material, invest in your factory, produce something and then hope that the customer will pay at the end so that you can recover your expenses and make a profit.

Whereas if it's a waste management business, you are actually paid at the beginning. So what you need to do is come up with strategies to utilise that waste. Otherwise, if you just send it to landfill sites it's going to cost you money. Whether or not a company recycles a material depends on the recycled material market and costs; if the market is flooded with recycled material, you have to come up with alternative strategies to manage that waste. At the moment, a common problem in developed countries is that material separation and recycling is fairly costly and the cheapest alternative is to send it where the waste management's cost is lowest.

ML: So that's why we've been exporting this material since it is scarcely economical to do otherwise. Even so, the industry has been struggling as reported, on ABC Television's Four Corners and elsewhere.[9] We even ship the stuff across state borders; rather than to bury it in New South Wales, we take it across to Queensland. This does not sound like a system that is well conceived and operated either from a business point of view or from a government regulatory point of view, does it?

SK: Again, it's purely economics driven so that if landfill cost in one of the states is cheaper than that in another state then the companies shift their waste disposal to the cheapest state. This is no different to sending our waste to developing countries where the treatment is cheaper. It's the same market mechanism at work.

ML: Yes, but it's not actually creating any value and utility, let alone environmental sustainability, is it?

SK: These are two separate issues here that need to be looked at carefully: the economic utility and the sustainability aspect.

In terms of economic utility, whether we separate our waste and then collect it, and then go to a recycling centre, even if the product is recycled, what needs to happen is that there is an end-user for the recycled material. Take plastics, for instance, recycling it means turning into a granulated raw material and then hoping that there's going to be an end-user who is going to take this raw material and turn it into product again.

But that's an overly simplified assumption because depending on the waste material type there is a 'degradation' process, meaning that if it's a plastic it may or may not be the same as the virgin material. Even for highly recycled materials such as aluminium and steel there could be contamination problems. So, if you are a manufacturer and want to utilise these recycled materials you need to go back to square one and start designing products to take into account these uncertainties in the recycled material properties.

There are a number of ways to tackle this issue from my background in design engineering. You can design to take account of material degradation. For instance, if the recycled material property is lower than the virgin material, you need to come up with a different design to compensate so that you can provide structural integrity to the product. Otherwise, there are going to be consequences functionally and the product may not fulfil its role. So, it's OK if at the front end we can separate the material for recycling; but if there is no user for that material, the loop actually is not closed. We are then spending an awful lot of resources of time and money to collect and recycle material from the waste stream but it is not fed back to the materials stream to be reutilised.

ML: From what you're saying we're confronting both a challenge and an opportunity that runs across all sectors of the economy, all arms of manufacturing and a whole range of different materials. This is a big idea that we need to confront about the sort of technologies and business models that we're using to try to optimise from both an economic and business point of view, and an environmental and energy point of view.

The concept of the 'circular economy' appears to embrace this idea in a new unified theory which reconciles business and growth with environment and sustainability. It's described as potentially 'disruptive' across all these industries and stakeholders.[10] It seems to represent a transition from what we've been ***discussing:*** a traditional 'linear economy' with companies that 'make, use and dispose' or 'take, make and waste'; but it's not a closed loop.[11] So what is this idea of the 'circular economy'?

SK: It's not new and has been around more than 50 years under different names, such as 'cradle to cradle',[12] 'performance economy', 'biomimicry', 'industrial ecology', 'closed-loop systems'.[13,14] The main concept is systematically designing out waste and pollution from products and keeping the products and materials in use as long as possible while regenerating the natural environment.

ML: And that would apply not only within one manufacturing enterprise but also across the sector and the broader economy?

SK: This is an interesting point that you're making, because some of the concepts such as 'closed-loop' systems were developed, for instance, during the late 1990s by companies like Fuji, Xerox and Ricoh who called it 'Ricollect'.[15] They developed their own understanding of 'circularity' as literally keeping the materials and product in use as long as possible with the main aim of minimising what went to landfill. The biggest difference is that it was a bottom-up approach coming from the company perspective, whereas this 'circular economy' is more of a top-down approach with huge political backing behind it. The essence of 'circular economy' is closing the material and product loop, and hoping that it will prevent primary production.

ML: As you say, this has got a strong top-down political element. For example, the EU put in place an action plan with funding for various activities, such as a zero-waste strategy where different communities and clusters of businesses can recycle stuff around between themselves.[16] At heart, this seems to involve a disruption to the business models at the enterprise level. As you were saying, where they've got to rethink right from the early stages of creativity of product and service design, through manufacturing, marketing and communication, right out to price and supply. Is this what you call 'life cycle engineering'?

SK: That's correct. The products need to be designed for the entire 'life cycle', not for one particular stage. You opened the conversation making an analogy that the 'circular economy' is effectively a recycling issue. There are a number of strategies under the circular economy from designing products for longer use or longevity, reusing the product, reusing the components to need, manufacturing, repairing and then recycling.

Recycling for material content and energy comes as a last step in this cycle. To achieve this from the technology perspective, we need to design products with that in mind. Products need to last longer, once they come to 'end of life', we need to be able to dismantle it easily so it needs to be designed for ease of recycling. That's essentially about engineering for the 'whole-of-life' cycle.

ML: So, it is the whole 'value chain' that an enterprise, a manufacturer or sector has to re-engineer and their business models in the sense of how and where they're going to make their investments and returns? Does this concept extend to the manufacturer's responsibility for the product both in use by consumers or in the market, and even beyond that onto the 'waste' stream?

SK: That's correct. Let's step back to the 'big picture' and ask what the 'circular economy' is trying to address. We have two pressing issues: limited resources and environmental pollution. From an environmental perspective the earth's 'carrying capacity' is limited in terms of the amount of pollution load it can carry. On the other hand, we have limited resources to provide for the material needs of society. For instance, the United Nations predicts a global population of around 10 billion by 2050. If everyone wants to have a lifestyle similar to us, and pollution is already a serious concern, the question arises from a 'circular economy' perspective, how much can we produce? Can we produce small enough amounts of pollution to stay within the earth's 'carrying capacity' as well as providing enough goods and services using limited resources to sustain society's lifestyle? That's the big-picture question.

ML: There do seem to be big business opportunities in these challenges. It is estimated that as early as 2030 there is a global industrial market for recycling, waste management and design of $4.5 trillion.[17] As we have discussed, realising this scale of opportunity in individual companies across many sectors requires that they completely reconfigure their business models and their value chains. How much innovation beyond business model innovation is involved? Do we have, even now in Australia, the technologies needed to give effect to these concepts, or are we even short on technology?

SK: It is a very good question to look globally at how many products incorporate a design mentality from the entire product life cycle perspective. The Fuji Xerox 'One-Shot' camera is a perfect example of product design with this concept in mind. People buy it, use it and when they are done with it, it goes back to the company who pulls it apart, repairs, refurbishes and reassembles it for use again. But when you look at most other products that we are using, we have a long way to go. The main issue is: can we find a way to achieve one-to-one replacement for primary materials, recycled materials or products? Product demand is growing with population and affluence so we need to develop technologies that have a one-to-one displacement. Otherwise, we also create new business opportunities for the recirculated products and that leads to even more material consumption and environmental impact. That is a criticism of the 'circular economy'.

ML: From what you're saying, there are significant technology challenges on the materials and manufacturing process side to realise a circular economy on a global scale. Taking recycling as a particular dimension rather than an equivalent of the circular economy, here now in Australia we've got private-sector investment in some technology stock. But now we need to suddenly start doing something domestically with all this waste that we've been shipping offshore. Have we got the technology, the skills and the investment or do we need to pile lots of money into research and development, innovation and new capital equipment to tackle this crisis . . . and opportunity?

SK: Michael, if you take recycling as a purely technical or technological problem, whether it's an 'open-loop' system or a circular 'closed-loop' system, we still need to use the same recycling technology to enable that. The real issue is that once we recycle the material and convert it to a recycled, raw material to be used for other applications, is there enough economic value and a customer willing to pay for it and to make the recycling economically viable? That's the key issue.

ML: So, there are indeed technology and research challenges and opportunities but essentially what is lacking is a market that will allow the private sector to develop profitable and sustainable businesses handling waste streams. The Council of Australian Governments (COAG) federal and state ministers met and discussed waste management issues. The Prime Minister announced a $20 million programme.[18]

From what you're saying, the key issue to be tackled is what might be called 'market failure': that in the normal commercial market the way it's constituted and priced, and with the existing regulatory frameworks we can't sustain commercially viable businesses to handle the waste stream in the sustainable ways that we're talking about?

SK: That's true. Recycling is just one stage in multiple life-cycle life stages of a product. From an economic perspective, a customer has to be willing to pay for recycled products. From a technology perspective, the recycled material needs to be a substitute for the virgin material; recycled aluminium versus virgin element aluminium needs to be one-to-one comparable.

With growing demand for materials and products, this market situation is complicated by society's perception of the use of recycled or remanufactured products as substitutes or alternatives to the original. Government backing and support is fine and in a free market economy, government intervention can act as a catalyst: but to maintain the market mechanism there needs to be customer demand to which businesses respond at all stages of the product life cycle. At the recycling stage, that means a downstream customer, a manufacturer, a building industry. Whatever their business, they need to create demand for recycled products to sustain the recyclers.

ML: So how does this happen? It doesn't seem to exist at the moment, which is why presumably we now face some sort of crisis because we can't ship out our waste. As we've discussed, companies need to reconfigure their value chains, their technology and their business models. So why aren't they? On the other hand, in waste markets is there a direct role for government procurement? For example, in purchasing recycled plastics for use in road construction and maintenance? Is there a role for governments as a customer to create markets? It certainly doesn't address the full range of market opportunities you're talking about though, does it?

SK: What is required is reduced environmental impact with less production and less consumption. But we are not talking about sacrificing living quality; we tend to confuse lifestyle goals with living standards. Our lifestyle is highly wasteful consumption in greater quantities whether needed or not. At the core of this discussion, we should not miss the big picture, which is the reduction of the environmental impact by aiming for less production.

ML: What are the incentives or barriers in the way of what sounds like a sensible proposition that you're putting about minimising environmental impact? Is the answer in government action to effect this shift and not just through procurement? Historically, regulations have driven huge technological and business model innovations, such as motor vehicle safety, emissions and fuel efficiency standards.[19] Otherwise, is it going to happen with our waste streams?

SK: Government regulations can play a catalyst role, but in the meantime, what needs to happen is that companies need to come up with technology solutions to enable such a concept and society needs to be educated.

ML: Education is fine. We can all watch the ABC's television shows and Craig Reucassel's popular presentations about how we should all be recycling stuff and his gathering heaps of plastic bottles in Martin Place.[20,21] That's all education, but where's the real incentive for business to change the way it does business in the ways we've been talking? Will it come from everyone's watching shows like this and then buying all the right products and sending all the right signals to businesses?

SK: Of course, it's not only the societal element that I hope is right. To move from a linear to a circular economy there needs to be business benefits for the companies to become involved as well, and eventually someone is going to pay for it.

Conclusion

The idea of the 'circular economy' poses a challenge and an opportunity for sustainability through innovation. There is a long history of such ideas and practices under a variety of names such as 'closed-loop', 'cradle-to-grave', 'whole-of-life' product cycle, etc., variously adopted by individual enterprises. Latterly, governments have promoted such ideas and intervened in a number of ways with policies, programmes, regulations, funding and incentives. A systematic approach to the circular economy or zero-waste economy involves a variety of stakeholders from consumers through to businesses who need to completely rethink their 'lifestyles' and their 'business models', respectively. Products need to be reconceived and redesigned to minimise the waste stream and environmental impacts at every stage in the 'whole-of-life' product cycle: design, manufacture, distribution, repair, recycling and re-use.[22] Consumer education can change perceptions and behaviour to more sustainable practices.

Exemplifying the challenges, one component of the life cycle attracting popular attention involves recycling at the end of product life. Left to market mechanisms alone this, neither effectively designs for minimal use of materials, their efficient recovery and re-use nor creates adequate price signals in the market to incentivise business value chain reconfiguration or investment in viable waste management businesses.

There is 'market failure' in waste management with no effective market demand for recycled materials as recently evidenced by the glut in global recycled product markets. The main challenge for technology and design is: can we find a way to achieve one-to-one replacement for primary materials, recycled materials or products? Product demand is growing with population and affluence so we need to develop technologies that have a one-to-one ratio displacement. Otherwise, we also create new business opportunities for the recirculated products and that leads to even more material consumption and environmental impact. That is a criticism of the 'circular economy'.

Notes

1 This is a practical guide from one of the 'fathers' of the 'circular economy': Stahel, W.R. (2019) *The Circular Economy: A User's Guide,* London: Routledge

2 This article describes the consumer movement to produce no waste at all, sending nothing to landfill based on five principles – refuse, reduce, reuse, compost and recycle: Mangla, A. (2020) Zero waste movement: A closer look, *Yale News*, 1st October https://yaledailynews.com/blog/2020/10/01/zero-waste-movement-a-closer-look/

3 Morton, A. (2020) Australia's recycling crisis: Is the government's $190m on new infrastructure worth it?, *The Guardian*, 6th July www.theguardian.com/environment/2020/jul/26/australias-recycling-crisis-is-the-governments-190m-on-new-infrastructure-worth-it

4 Gellerman, B. (2019) How a new policy in China has led to a recycling crisis, *WBUR*, 19th March www.wbur.org/news/2019/03/19/recycling-massachusetts-china-effect

5 IbisWorld (2023) *Waste Treatment and Disposal Services in Australia, Market Research Report*, 13th July www.ibisworld.com/au/industry/waste-treatment-disposal-services/5024/

6 Lacy, P., Long, J. and Spinder, W. (2019) *The Circular Economy Handbook: Realising the Circular Advantage*, London: Palgrave Macmillan

7 Abdoli, S. and Kara, S. (2020) A modelling framework to support design of complex engineering systems in early design stages, *Research in Engineering Design*, 31, January: 25–52

8 Hauschild, M.Z., Kara, S. and Røpke, I. (2020) Absolute sustainability: Challenges to life cycle engineering, *CIRP Annals*, 69 (2): 533–553

9 This report exposed the hidden, big business, waste industry of rubbish and where it ends up:

Ferguson, S. (2017) Trashed, Four Corners, *Australian Broadcasting Commission (ABC) TV*, 7th August www.abc.net.au/news/2017-08-07/trashed/8770146

10 Kirchherr, J., Bauwens, T. and Ramos, T.B. (eds) (2023) Special issue: Circular disruption: Concepts, enablers and ways ahead, *Business Strategy and the Environment*, 32 (3) March: 1005–1188 https://onlinelibrary.wiley.com/toc/10990836/2023/32/3

11 Taylor, L. (2020) What is the linear economy and why do we need to go circular? *Planet Ark, Australian Circular Economy Hub*, 14th October https://planetark.org/newsroom/news/what-is-the-linear-economy-and-why-do-we-need-to-go-circular

12 These authors argue against the conventional 'cradle to grave' model involving 'reduce reuse recycle' or 'downcycling' in favour of a system of 'lifecycle development' or 'upcycling' initiated in the 1980s: Braungart, M. and McDonough, W. (2009) *Cradle to Cradle: Remaking the Way We Make Things*, London: Random House

13 Winkler, H. (2011) Closed-loop production systems – a sustainable supply chain approach, *CIRP Journal of Manufacturing Science and Technology*, 4 (3): 243–246

14 Wallace, T. (2022) Closed loop production: Sustainability across the supply chain, *The Future of Commerce* www.the-future-of-commerce.com/2020/01/23/closed-loop-production/

15 Graedel, T.E. and Lifset, R.J. (2015) Industrial ecology's first decade, in Clift, R. and Druckman, A. (eds) *Taking Stock of Industrial Ecology*, pp. 3–20, Berlin: Springer

16 European Commission (EC) (2020) *A New Circular Economy Action Plan: For a Cleaner and More Competitive Europe* https://eur-lex.europa.eu/legal-content/EN/TXT/?uri=COM%3A2020%3A98%3AFIN

17 Alves, B. (2023) Waste management market value worldwide 2022–2030, *Statista*, 12th May www.statista.com/statistics/246178/projected-global-waste-management-market-size/

18 Morton (2020), op cit. This article reports the commitment to change laws covering 'product stewardship' which are meant to ensure manufacturers and retailers take responsibility for the products they sell once they become waste.

19 Cohen, S. (2013) *The Impact of Regulation on Automobile Innovation, Sustainability: State of the Planet*, Columbia Climate School, 17th April https://news.climate.columbia.edu/2023/04/17/the-impact-of-regulation-on-automobile-innovation/

20 This is a program series hosted by Craig Reucassel. See: ABC Education (2022) War on waste with Craig Reucassel, *ABC TV*, 12th December www.abc.net.au/education/digibooks/war-on-waste-from-waste-to-resource/101750678

21 Spring, A. (2018) War on waste returns: Craig Reucassel dishes dirt on recycling crisis, *The Guardian*, 25th July www.theguardian.com/environment/2018/jul/23/war-on-waste-returns-craig-reucassel-dishes-dirt-on-recycling-crisis

22 The work by Levitt is a classic formulation: Levitt, T. (1965) Exploit the product life cycle, *Harvard Business Review*, November https://hbr.org/1965/11/exploit-the-product-life-cycle

Section II

Climate Change and Energy Resources

10 Renewable Energy Development

The Costs of Policy Uncertainty and Lack of Political Stability

Interview With Giles Parkinson

Introduction

Renewable energy technologies are having a deeply disruptive impact, particularly on electricity markets around the world.[1] This is a moment of remarkable transition from fossil fuel-fired power stations into renewable energy sources of solar and wind power in particular; conventional coal-fired power stations are closing and powering down, and here in Australia we're embarking on this potential transformation.[2] The electricity industry experienced a similar moment of 'Electric Ambiguity'[3] in an earlier 'fledgling' era of its development: a moment at which its fate and pathway for the future were contested and decided upon. In the late eighteenth century, a 'War of Currents' was fought on the choice between an industry based either on alternating current (AC) or on direct current (DC) with Tesla and Edison as the respective proponents.[4] It was a protracted and vitriolic debate that challenged large, vested interests. But eventually, the 'ambiguity' was resolved in the favour of alternating current and the future path of the electricity industry was set. . .until now.

Driven in large measure by responses to climate change and global warming trends and forecasts, governments around the world (including in Australia) are actively concerned about this transition to renewable energy supplies.[5] For example, over the last decade or so, global public investments in energy research and development have substantially increased, particularly since the low levels in the mid-1990s and in the early 2000s.[6]

In 2016, OECD governments invested in the order of $17 billion, with many countries adopting specific strategies, including incentives for adoption, and putting in place new institutions and regulations for facilitating the transition to renewables. Technologies have developed rapidly, including for battery energy storage, while the price of renewable energy generation has fallen remarkably and continues to do so.[7]

Keywords: dispatchable power; distributed generation; smart grids; dis-intermediation; base load; electric ambiguity; war of currents; behind the meter; big battery; virtual power plants; SDG 7; SDG 11; SDG 12

DOI: 10.4324/9781003280316-12

Interviewee Profile

Giles Parkinson (**GP**) is the founder and editor of the authoritative and widely read online renewable energy newsletter 'renew economy'[8] and is an influential and high-profile commentator on the development of renewable energies in Australia. He is a distinguished career journalist, including as business editor and deputy editor of the *Australian Financial Review*.[9] He has written for *The Bulletin*, *The Australian* and many other publications.

The Interview

ML: Giles, what's been happening in recent times with innovation of renewable energy technologies, particularly with respect to the economics of renewable energy with solar and wind generation costs, and the positioning of renewable energy in the global energy mix and markets?

GP: The biggest development is the quite astonishing cost reductions to which you've alluded. The cost of solar has come down about 70% in the last five years, and down 98% since 1975. Wind energy costs have also fallen quite dramatically. It basically means that across the globe, the cheapest form of bulk energy for new construction is undoubtedly wind and solar which are now challenging the incumbent power generators on cost.

Storage technology is also emerging, so we're starting to think again about pumped hydro, which is an old, well-understood technology but with a new value in the electricity system because we've got more variable renewable energy coming into the market. We're also seeing battery storage costs coming down quite sharply as the technologies develop rapidly. They're expected to fall even further and to follow roughly the cost curve that solar has taken. Some big batteries are appearing in the main grid, for example, the Tesla big battery in South Australia, which has been a really exciting development showcasing its speed, accuracy and versatility.[10]

It's a completely new way of thinking about the grid from the old style 'analogue' systems, with their 'centralised' generators, big networks, and customers at great transmission distances; compared to this new really smart 'distributed' digital system where power generation is happening everywhere and all over the place.

You're seeing the emergence of what's called 'behind the meter' generation referring to households and businesses who see the economic advantage in having solar generation on their rooftops – an advantage in Australia that is amplified by the very expensive grid prices. Globally, most serious analysis, including by the major agencies talk of this big transformation towards wind and solar, and particularly to this 'behind-the-meter',[11,12] distributed generation system involving rooftop solar, storage battery and demand management.[13] That should account for probably 45% or 50% of our electric energy supply in Australia within the next few decades.

This exciting development is potentially upending the conventional electricity market and its business model. Control and influence are shifting out of the hands of the big incumbents and to the consumers, the households and businesses. There are also new business models and technology providers emerging. Although their ultimate form is as yet unclear, what we are seeing is a last thrashing death rite of the incumbents who are trying determinedly to hinder and delay this transition for as long as they possibly can, so they can make as much money while they still can.

That's one of the reasons that we have such ridiculously high prices for our electricity as in the ACCC (Australian Competition and Consumers Commission) report.[14] It has been known for years but it was great to see it finally came out in one report, that consumers are being ripped off by network companies, by wholesale generators on the wholesale market, and at the retail level. But this has been previously lost in the confusion and complexity of the billing process and statements.

Some people simply try to blame the introduction of renewables. That's not the case because the ACCC's assessment talks about bringing costs down but trying to unravel this is a complex business. Over many, many years, the incumbents have hidden behind that complexity to charge people like wounded bulls. I'm not sure that it's going to get any less complex, but I think that what it should do is get us smarter, cleaner, greener and cheaper electricity sometime very soon.

ML: Although forms of renewable energy have been around for a while, in a sense this wave of renewables' transformation seems to have taken people, including the experts, by surprise. I understand that historically the International Energy Agency (IEA) was very cautious on renewable energies and was predicting a 'golden age' for gas, which didn't actually transpire and now seems to be a little passe in strategic terms. Yet, in its 2017 review, the IEA commented on 'the remarkable progress in falling costs in renewables and particularly solar, and remarkable gains that have been made by solar in the world markets for energy'.[15] Apparently, solar power grew by 50% on a global basis in 2016 and by 2022 is going to contribute 30% of global energy production. Why has this apparently 'snuck up' on people so much, or hasn't it?

GP: Well, it certainly snuck up on people like the IEA because they're a very conservative organisation that believes almost entirely in fossil fuels. There are very amusing graphs that predicted the take-up of solar; some go up quite sharply, some in a moderate way and some almost go flat line, and that was the IEA forecast.

Even though they've adjusted them upwards since then, they still can't bring themselves to get really excited about it. Interestingly enough, it was Greenpeace that was most accurate and some other more progressive analysts also got closer to the mark. So, it has taken people by surprise. Even in Australia, the cost of installation per megawatt (MW) for large-scale solar was until only recently probably more than twice what it is now, and it's still falling really rapidly. That has taken people by surprise.

The IEA now actually admits that by 2050 solar will be the largest single source of generation across the world; most people think that will probably be a great deal earlier.[16] The likes of Bloomberg New Energy Finance is predicting that for Australia it'll be 86% wind and solar by 2050 and about 64% wind and solar across the world.[17] They make the point that this is not a climate action policy but just a result of economics. If you think of all the new electricity we need for growing populations and economies, these cheaper new renewable sources are what they say will replace the existing ageing power stations, and account for the new generation capacity over the next few decades, basically on economic grounds.

ML: There's certainly been a lot of technological innovation and development in the design and production of solar photovoltaic panels. Big innovations are also happening around the application of digital technologies and electronics for the taking, storage and distribution of this renewable energy and its integration for stability, reliability and affordability into existing grids. What is that story?

GP: You are talking about 'inverters' and 'battery storage' in regard to application of electronics; inverters are pretty exciting because they can take energy output and they can do different things with it. They can either use it instantly, they can put it in the box and store it for later, or they can interact with the grid to keep a reserve in times of peak demand, and they also can provide all these different sorts of network services.

We're starting to see that with the Tesla Big Battery installed by Elon Musk in South Australia,[18] and we've also seen it with trials for what's called 'virtual power plants'.[19] This is the idea that lots of different households and businesses with their individual solar panels will start putting in battery storage soon if they haven't already done so. Using technology and the Internet, these will become linked and they can act together to provide power when it's needed, or these network or grid services dealing with changes in frequency, for instance, and in any system problems they can be used and aggregated, and this is lightning fast.

If you think about the system we've got now, let's go back to this analogue version versus digital transformation. These things are incredibly fast, and that's what we've seen with the Tesla Big Battery in South Australia. They're responding in milliseconds to disturbances in the network, and addressing them, which is much quicker than we've seen with the traditional generators. The grid operators and owners need to think completely differently about the way they design and manage the grids. A lot has been said about renewables that de-stabilise the grid but they don't really; it is actually a matter of looking at the grid in a different way. As with so many great technological transformations, for example, from the horse and cart to automobiles, we had to think completely differently about the modes of transport.

The same is going to happen in this shift from large, centralised fossil fuel generators to more distributed energy systems which combine cheap bulk energy that comes from wind and solar, 'dispatchable generation',[20] which could come from batteries and pumped hydro or solar, thermal or even a little bit of gas that will stay in the system towards the end.

And these 'smart technologies'[21] can do all sorts of different things about storing energy, responding to system faults or even things like 'demand management'.[22] There's so much of the electricity that we use at the moment which we don't necessarily need to be running all the time. So if there is a peak in the system, rather than switching on the dirtiest and the most expensive piece of machinery that we can find, which is what we've been doing for the last 50 years with these diesel peak generators, why don't we get smart and dial down voluntarily some load that is not needed now? That could be done by adjusting air conditioners by 1 degree or it could be by a manufacturer who doesn't need to have everything switched on at the same time at certain times of day.

ML: We do hear in the public debate about the need to maintain 'base load'[23] and the importance of big coal-fired base load stations to cope with the unreliability and lack of stability and storage with renewables and particularly solar. It does seem though, that what's being transformed here is the very concept and nature of an electricity grid and how it actually works. As you say, it's a big shift, and in part that's being driven through the application of digital technologies to that process. Are the terms 'smart grid' and 'smart metres' and 'demand management', at the heart of this transformation of the electricity sector?

GP: Yes, and that's what the big debate is about. The political debate is centred around the need for base loads meaning some coal-fired generators and things like that. It's a term that we're going to get used to not hearing very much in the future, hopefully, because it really just defines the old analogue system.

We used to have these baseload coal generators trundling on through the night, that were very inflexible and couldn't be switched off, and to keep them going we had to split or shift all sorts of production. That's why a lot of manufacturing works throughout the night, why all the hot water systems switch on at 1:00 o'clock in the morning. We don't need to do that now we've got cheaper wind and solar, and particularly with solar coming into the system. We should be switching all those hot water heaters not already being heated by solar, and if they've got the electric boosters or they're just on electric then that should be done in the middle of the day. Or we could mix and match to times when there's enough supply so you're really just thinking about a system.

Michael Liebreich from Bloomberg New Energy Finance is visionary on base costs renewables and dispatchable energy.[24] It means taking the cheapest source of power, wind and solar and generating as much as you can when you can, then throwing that into the system effectively as your 'base' for use. It is then made 'dispatchable' at the time it is needed, at peak demand and things like that.

All this can be done by real-time demand response and storage and things like that. That's the way you construct and operate the system by throwing in wind and solar as the cheapest form of electricity with storage and dispatchability to meet changing demands. While it sounds complicated it's probably no more so than what we've been doing now with these inflexible machines trundling away but with these incredible variabilities in demand.

Demand changes all the time, it goes up and down, as you can just imagine with the different millions of people switching on lights, switching off lights, switching on fridges or off, or whatever else they're doing, air conditioner use that changes through the day, that's managed even now. There's no reason why this new more flexible system can't manage at least as well, particularly with the advantage of these very fast-responding technologies using digital software.

ML: Australia has pretty high penetration rates for photovoltaic solar panels up on household roofs but apparently half the power, more or less that is generated isn't used by the houses, but is available to be sold at the moment into the grid and market to retailers at five to seven cents a kilowatt-hour (KWh), whereas the retailers are selling it at about 30 cents, apparently claiming that this is due to the costs of transferring electricity across vast distances on the grid. I understand that, for example, digital technology-enabled peer-to-peer trading and energy management can achieve the process much more effectively of selling electricity to neighbours using power ledgers, etc. Is that another aspect of the renewables transformation that we're talking about?

GP: Absolutely, yes. What we're seeing is that most of the impediments to transformation in the system are not physical, they're not engineering, they are institutional. The electricity utilities have learned that they can 'clip the ticket', effectively taking a fee everytime an electron goes somewhere. You're absolutely right. Some people are getting paid five or six cents for their electricity exported from their rooftop solar that they're not using while the same electrons throughout the system can go next door, where your neighbour will be charged say 30 cents or possibly even more per kWh for that same electricity. The utilities are always talking about the difficulties and the costs, and they never talk about the benefits of having more rooftop solar distributed around the grid, particularly paired with storage. It's really quite frustrating that we saw that in the ACCC 2018 report.[25]

ML: All this technological innovation and falling prices that we've been discussing has driven in the United States a booming solar industry which has been growing at quite a pace.[26] Solar energy in the United States creates more jobs than any other industry adding jobs at a rate 17 times faster than the overall growth of jobs in the US economy, and in 2016, one in every 50 new jobs was created in the solar sector. On projections, this will be the fastest growing occupation over the next ten years according to the US Bureau of Labor Statistics.[27] More than half of these jobs (50–55%) are in installation, very decentralised installation work, and only about 14–15% are in the manufacturing side. It's the biggest source of jobs in absolute terms and growth in the US energy industry, second only to oil and gas. What's happening to jobs in solar in Australia?[28]

GP: I don't know that we've seen quite such a dramatic increase in Australia and what we see never lasts more than a few years. It's because of the frequent changes in policy that we've had, a bit of a 'roller coaster' or a 'solar coaster' as some people in the industry call it. While I can't recall the exact number, there's been thousands of jobs created here.

ML: I've seen figures that suggest that in financial year 2016 that there's been a 27% collapse in the number of jobs within the solar energy sector since 2010/11.[29] I think as you're implying this might be tied to government policies or lack of them, at the very time when this is the source of huge job creation globally and potentially also in regional areas because of the decentralised nature of a lot of this installation and other work.

GP: Work done by the Climate Council has also pointed out that Australia has missed out in that renewable energy jobs boom simply because of the precarious nature of those jobs.[30,31] So those jobs number you referred to from 2011/12 was at the height of what was then the premium feed-in tariffs and did go through to 2016.

I think it's recovered in the rooftop solar industry quite significantly since then, and we're now starting to see the rollout of large-scale solar, so I'd say it was rebounding with a surge in installations, but it's a bit difficult to say what's going to happen over the next couple of years because the policy uncertainty continues. There is a lot of construction at the moment for large-scale wind and solar across the country to meet the Renewable Energy Target (RET), but that expires in 2020.

After that there is great uncertainty because the proposed policy replacement, the National Energy Guarantee (NEG), does not seem capable of attracting any new investment because the emissions targets are so weak. The industry will then have to depend on household and corporate buyers to invest in new projects, either on the household or on large-scale wind and solar, if they want to reduce costs.

ML: It is certainly interesting to see how very dependent this growth is on government policies, for better or for worse. US President Trump with his trade policies was imposing big tariffs on imported Chinese solar equipment, which is rather ironically feared to threaten growth of the solar industry and up to 23,000 jobs in America. Neither will it improve the competitiveness and innovation of their own solar industry.[32]

GP: No, well, that's probably exactly right. Tariff wars are quite crazy, and I don't think it's just affecting the solar sector; it's affecting water bottles, automobiles and even Harley-Davidson is talking about shifting its manufacturing to Europe because of the tariffs that are going to be imposed on imports to Europe in retaliation against America's tariffs.[33]

ML: In Australia, how important is the proposed National Energy Guarantee (NEG)[34,35] likely to be in securing an innovative future for the growth of the renewables sector and for the associated growth of jobs and innovation of companies? Aren't federal and state ministers meeting as the Council of Australian Governments (COAG) due to decide the final design for this new policy shortly?

GP: It's a bit of a worry to tell you the truth. The NEG is basically the fourth or fifth best policy choice. We had a carbon price that was working fine but we got rid of that. The renewable energy target (RET) expires in 2020. We rejected an Emissions Trading Scheme. We rejected the Clean Energy Target. So now we're going back to the NEG. All this apparently, for the sake of having a bipartisan policy that is not really bipartisan policy anyway. It is a mechanism which may or may not work.

The issue with the NEG is that it's unclear how it's going to work. The details have not been sorted out. The ACCC, for instance, raised concerns that it might actually reduce competition rather than increase it, which would be disastrous for consumers. Under the Coalition government policy,[36] it basically won't do anything. In fact, it could be worse than doing nothing because the electricity emissions targets for the sector under the current Coalition government, which they refused to adjust, are basically going to be met by 2020 from the Renewable Energy Targets previously set in place. Also, inciting any new investment based on emissions is not going to happen under a NEG, let alone innovation in the whole system of electricity production and distribution.

> The consideration for state governments who will vote shortly on the proposed NEG is: do we adopt this as a mechanism that we can ramp up subsequently in terms of emissions or do we reject it because we think it might actually do harm? The way it's framed will act as a handbrake on and an impediment to new investment for this transition. That is what they've got to weigh up. It's an extraordinarily rushed timetable alongside a history of changing rules and regulations in this sector in Australia and characterised by incredibly slow change and a lack of policy certainty and stability.

Conclusion

In an historic moment of 'electricity ambiguity', renewable energy technologies are deeply disrupting the electricity industry around the world in a transition away from fossil-fuelled power generation to sustainable renewable energy sources. The costs of renewable solar and wind technologies and equipment have fallen dramatically as a result of substantially increased investments in research and development and innovation, backed by governments. They are now the cheapest sources. Policy changes have been driven by growing concerns about the need to act on global warming and climate change and have included setting carbon prices and emissions targets, alongside regulations and new institutions, as well as incentives to adoption by consumers and business.

The rapid fall in costs of the new technologies has been accompanied by development of new more efficient and effective battery technologies and associated digital technology-based smart systems for use in the electricity grid to stabilise the delivery of dispatchable energy, matching renewable supply to user demand patterns. In the process, the conventional providers and their business models have been disrupted and dis-intermediated allowing a new model of distributed power generation and distribution. These developments have opened significant new employment opportunities, including in regional areas.

In the case of Australia, the large existing vested interests in the industry based on fossil-fuelled power generation have resisted the transformation that would see their significant assets stranded and their business models over-turned. The importance of government policies for both facilitating or hindering has been highlighted by the Australian experience. In particular, the highly contested space of climate change policy emissions targets and carbon pricing has led to protracted debate and stop-start policies that create uncertainty and lack of policy stability required by new investors in the renewable energy sector. Despite the election in May 2022 of a new Labor government substantially committed to the transition to renewable technologies, policy contention undermining investor confidence with political divisiveness,[37] and continuing 'culture wars'[38] have continued.

Notes

1 Green, J. and Newman, P. (2016) Disruptive innovation, stranded assets and forecasting: The rise and rise of renewable energy, *Journal of Sustainable Finance and Investment*, 7 (2): 169–187
2 PwC Australia (2014) *Utility of the Future: A Customer-Led Shift in the Electricity Sector – An Australian Context, Report*, April www.pwc.com.au/industry/energy-sutilities-mining/assets/utility-of-the-future-apr14.pdf
3 Coughlin, M. (2017) *Electric Ambiguity: Renewable Energy Innovation and the Fate of an Industry*, PWC Australia, 10th October www.pwc.com.au/digitalpulse/electric-ambiguity-renewable-energy-innovation.html
4 Lantero, A. (2014) *The War of the Currents: AC vs DC Power*, US Department of Energy, 18th November www.energy.gov/articles/war-currents-ac-vs-dc-power
5 Churchill, S.A., Inekwe, J. and Ivanovski, K. (2021) R&D expenditure and energy consumption in OECD nations, *Energy Economics*, 100, August: 105376
6 International Atomic Agency, *Public Energy Technology RD&D Budget 1975–2000* www.iea.org/reports/key-world-energy-statistics-2021/rd-and-d
7 International Renewable Energy Agency (2020) *How Falling Costs Make Renewables a Cost-Effective Investment*, June www.irena.org/news/articles/2020/Jun/How-Falling-Costs-Make-Renewables-a-Cost-effective-Investment
8 Renew Economy Online https://reneweconomy.com.au
9 Australian Financial Review www.afr.com
10 Parkinson, G. (2020) *Tesla Big Battery in South Australia Delivers Stunning Windfall Profits*, 24th September https://reneweconomy.com.au/tesla-big-battery-in-south-australia-delivers-stunning-windfall-profits-77644/
11 Sioshansi, F. (2018) Electricity's future: Mostly behind the meter, *Energy Post EU*, 5th October https://energypost.eu/electricitys-future-behind-the-meter-distributed-generation/
12 Cory, K. (2020) *Behind-the-Meter Projects: Overview*, US Department of Energy Office of Indian Energy Policy and Programs, 26th August www.energy.gov/sites/default/files/2020/08/f77/1_Cory-NREL.pdf
13 St. John, J. (2020) 5 Major trends driving the US$110B distributed energy resources market through 2025, *Green Tech Media*, 22nd June www.greentechmedia.com/articles/read/5-takeaways-on-the-future-of-the-u.s-distributed-energy-resources-market
14 ACCC (2018) *Restoring Electricity Affordability and Australia's Competitive Advantage, Final Report on the National Electricity Market*, 11th July www.accc.gov.au/about-us/publications/restoring-electricity-affordability-and-australias-competitive-advantage
15 IEA (2017) *World Energy Outlook 2017: A World in Transformation, Report*, International Energy Agency, November www.iea.org/reports/world-energy-outlook-2017
16 As of July 2023, the IEA predicts solar to overtake coal as the largest single source by 2027 www.iea.org/energy-system/renewables/solar-pv
17 Izadi, A. (2017) *Renewable Energy Market Outlook*, Presentation to 5th Northeast Asia Energy Security Forum, 12th December www.unescap.org/sites/default/files/Session%201-2.%20Ali%20Izadi-Najafabadi_BNEF.pdf
18 Clean Energy Finance Corporation (CEFC) (2021) *SA Big Battery a Game Changer*, November www.cefc.com.au/where-we-invest/case-studies/sa-big-battery-a-game-changer/
19 Australian Renewable Energy Agency (ARENA) (2021) *What are Virtual Power Plants and Why Do They Matter?* 8th February https://arena.gov.au/blog/what-are-virtual-power-plants-and-why-do-they-matter/

20 Taylor, A. (2021) Dispatchable capacity is important while technologies evolve, *Australian Financial Review, Opinion*, 23rd September www.afr.com/companies/energy/dispatchable-capacity-is-important-while-technologies-evolve-20210920-p58ta5

21 Neagu, B.C., Grigoras, G. and Ivanov, O. (2019) The optimal operation of active distribution networks with smart systems, in Ustun, T.S. (ed) *Advanced Communication and Control Methods for Future Smartgrids* www.intechopen.com/chapters/68122

22 Bhalshankar, S.S. and Thorat, C. (2016) *Integration of Smart Grid with Renewable Energy for Energy Management: Puducherry Case Study*, Paralakhemundi: International Conference on Signal Processing, Communication, Power and Embedded Systems (SCOPES) https://ieeexplore.ieee.org/abstract/document/7955498

23 Needham, S. (2008) *The Potential for Renewable Energy to Provide Baseload Power in Australia*, Research Paper, Parliament of Australia: Department of Parliamentary Services, 23rd September https://core.ac.uk/download/pdf/30686614.pdf

24 Liebreich, M. (2017) Keynote conference presentation, *Bloomberg New Energy Finance Summit*, 25th April https://assets.bbhub.io/professional/sites/24/2017/04/2017-04-25-Michael-Liebreich-BNEFSummit-Keynote.pdf

25 Australian Competition and Consumer Commission (ACCC) (2018) *Retail Electricity Pricing Inquiry – Final Report*, June www.accc.gov.au

26 The Interstate Renewable Energy Council of the USA (IRECUSA), *Reports Over 230,000 Jobs in the Sector in 2022* https://irecusa.org/programs/solar-jobs-census/

27 According to the US Bureau of Labor Statistics, demand for wind turbine technicians is projected to grow at 44% and solar photovoltaic installers at 27%, between 2021–2031 www.bls.gov/ooh/fastest-growing.htm

28 Farr, M. (2018) Renewable energy could offer up to 60,000 Australian jobs, *News.Com.Au*, 21st November www.news.com.au/finance/work/careers/renewable-energy-could-offer-up-to-60000-australian-jobs/news-story/18ddf975618ae782fc94aa39b763dcfb

29 The ABS reports that there were nearly 27,000 jobs in 2018–19, with a 27% increase over 2017–18, and 120% over 10 years. From Australian Bureau of Statistics (ABS) (2020) *Employment in Renewable Energy Activities*, 6th April www.abs.gov.au/statistics/labour/employment-and-unemployment/employment-renewable-energy-activities-australia/latest-release

30 The Climate Council estimates around 28,000 jobs by 2030. From Climate Council (2016) *Renewable Energy Jobs: Future Growth in Australia*, 16th June www.climatecouncil.org.au/resources/renewablesreport/

31 Scully, J. (2020) Climate council unveils plan to create 15,000 renewable energy jobs in large scale projects, *PV-Tech*, 21st July www.pv-tech.org/australias-climate-council-unveils-plan-to-create-15000-renewable-energy-jo/

32 Lybrand, H. (2021) Biden wants millions of clean-energy related jobs. Can it happen?, *CNN Politics*, 2nd February https://edition.cnn.com/2021/02/01/politics/joe-biden-green-energy-jobs/index.html

33 Rappeport, A. (2018) Harley-Davidson, blaming EU tariffs, will move some production out of US, *New York Times*, 25th June www.nytimes.com/2018/06/25/business/harley-davidson-us-eu-tariffs.html

34 Potter, B. (2018) Explained: How the national energy guarantee works, *Australian Financial Review*, 13th April www.afr.com/politics/explained-how-the-national-energy-guarantee-works-20180413-h0ypih

35 Murphy, K. (2018) Turnbull's national energy guarantee could have 'no meaningful' emission reduction, *The Guardian*, 17th April www.theguardian.com/australia-news/2018/apr/18/turnbulls-national-energy-guarantee-could-have-no-meaningful-emission-reduction

36 The Coalition Government lost power to a Labor Government in May 2022. See Doyle, M. (2022) Labor, Anthony Albanese make history with 2022 federal election victory, *ABC News*, 21st May www.abc.net.au/news/2022-05-22/labor-anthony-albanese-history-federal-election-victory/101088062
37 Parkinson, G. (2023) Gas lobby launches new scare campaign on electrification, saying it will break the grid, *Renew Economy*, 3rd August https://reneweconomy.com.au/gas-lobby-launches-new-scare-campaign-on-electrification-saying-it-will-break-the-grid/
38 Brown, A. (2023) Coalition says inverters in rooftop solar systems are national security risk, *Renew Economy*, 22nd July https://reneweconomy.com.au/coalition-says-inverters-in-rooftop-solar-systems-are-national-security-risk/

11 The National Energy Guarantee (NEG)

Frustrated Reductions in Electricity Emissions and Dirty Party Politics

Interview With Chris Dunstan

Introduction

Former Australian Prime Minister Malcolm Turnbull was described as 'obsessed about renewable energy reducing electricity prices',[1] and his chosen policy instrument is the National Energy Guarantee (NEG) under discussion and negotiation with the states.[2] The electricity industry, as a whole, is in the throes of a major transition and transformation away from fossil fuels and it's the subject of great impact and disruption by innovative renewable energy technologies.

Australia has been engaged in a protracted three decades-long 'climate wars', and this has effectively stymied the development of a clear policy framework for climate policy, transition to renewables and investors in the energy sector.[3] For many years, that debate has been driven by and focused on the climate change issues and the target emissions, and has been politically a really fraught discussion. The government's preferred NEG approach is a horribly complex policy instrument that seeks simultaneously to tackle the three interrelated questions of the price of electricity, the reliability of electricity supply and the level of carbon emissions from the sector. All within one policy bundle. Understanding the likely impact of this policy instrument, turns particularly on how the industry itself will be transformed towards sustainability using renewable technologies.

Keywords: Base load; climate wars; electricity; electricity market; electricity price components; emissions commitments; energy; energy market; Energy Security Board (ESB); fossil fuels; least-cost emissions reduction; national energy guarantee (NEG); network reliability; network services; network stability; Paris Climate Agreement; renewable energy; renewable energy targets (RETs); renewable energy technologies; SDG7; SDG11; SDG12; SDG13; UNFCCC

Interviewee Profile

Dr. Chris Dunstan **(CD)** is Research Director, Institute for Sustainable Futures (ISF), University of Technology Sydney (UTS). Having completed a doctorate

DOI: 10.4324/9781003280316-13

study on the topic,[4] Chris is a specialist and prominent public commentator on issues of climate change, renewable energy and the electricity sector.

The Interview

ML: The NEG has three policy objectives: electricity price, reliability of power supply and carbon emissions targets. You have argued that the NEG is likely to achieve very little on all three counts in the foreseeable future.[5] According to government modelling,[6] savings are estimated up to $550 per year on the average for the average household over the next ten years. What sort of impact do you expect on prices as a result of the NEG?

CD: Electricity prices have gone up quite rapidly over the last couple of years and they are expected to fall over the next few years, regardless of whether the NEG is implemented or not. Of that $550 per annum figure, only $150 is attributed by the government and its modelling to the NEG. The remaining $400 is a reduction in price that is expected anyway, primarily due to more generation being built, and in particular more renewable energy being built, over the next few years, and the main driver for that is actually the current Renewable Energy Target (RET)[7] which runs through to 2020. So that, when I say the NEG impact on prices is likely to be relatively small, that is also what the government is saying; of the $550 saving, only $150 is coming from the NEG.

CD: Breaking the figures down, electricity prices comprise a number of elements. The first of two big ones is the cost of network services, paying for the poles, wires and substations that deliver electricity from the power stations to the customers. The NEG is not aiming to have any impact on network charges at all.

ML: Apparently in recent years, these networks have been termed as 'gold plated'.[8,9] Have their costs contributed to the big retail price increases we have experienced over the last couple of years?

CD: Certainly over the last seven or eight years, network investments had a big impact, but not over the last couple of years. We did have a massive boom in network infrastructure spending, particularly in Queensland and NSW, over the period of about 2010 to 2015. But that has passed and network investment is now falling. There was a recognition that we certainly overdid it, and in the most recent determinations by the Australian Energy Regulator (AER),[10] network investment has been wound back quite significantly, but that too has nothing to do with the NEG as a policy.

The NEG is focused on the other of the two big contributors to our electricity prices, and that is the cost of generation. Unlike networks, which is a regulated monopoly, where prices are essentially set by the regulator, generation operates in a competitive market and so it depends on the forces of supply and demand. What we saw over the last couple of years has been the closure of a number of power stations thereby reducing supply, particularly with the closure of Hazelwood Power station in Victoria.[11] That tightened supply and while demand remained much the same that led to a significant rise in electricity prices.

Now that supply is starting to increase again, most particularly because of investment in renewable energy, that's pushing prices down. What the NEG is proposed to do is give greater confidence for the market participants to invest in even more generation capacity over the next ten years. That increased supply will then have an impact on reducing prices even further than expected in the absence of the NEG.

ML: So in the generation space that we've been talking about, prices have been coming down because of renewables not because of any big investments. The closure of some coal-fired power stations brings us to the second target of the NEG, which is the reliability of the generation capacity. What and how is the NEG supposed to address the question of appropriate levels of investment and what is the need for investment in generation over the period that the NEG is to operate?

CD: This is one of the more complex parts of the NEG proposal. Essentially, it will look over a rolling ten year time horizon to estimate demand in the electricity market and the expected need for supply of generation. If there is an identified gap – that is, an expected shortfall in generation relative to demand – that will be announced to the market. That'll trigger the 'reliability' provisions of the NEG and the regulators will require that electricity retailers and other customers prove that they have adequate capacity to ensure that a shortfall of supply is not realised. That initial requirement is relatively light handed but if the expected shortfall persists to within a three-year period the requirements get a bit tougher.

The retailers who've purchased electricity to sell to customers will need to reveal their purchase contract details and if not regarded as satisfactory to close the expected gap in supply the regulator can impose upon them the costs of providing the required additional capacity. While this is certainly a more heavy-handed approach than in the past, it's probably also a good idea. In going through this transition away from coal to more renewable energy, it will provide an extra 'reliability' safety net, but the regulators aren't expected to have to trigger this reliability component because they expect the market to ensure that there's enough generation capacity anyway.

ML: I understand that modelling used for the NEG by the Energy Security Board (ESB) sees virtually no need for new generation capacity over the coming decade barring a nominal amount of 1000 MW, which could easily be satisfied by any form of energy.[12] Is that correct?

CD: That's the case at the moment but as we have seen over the last few years, for example, with the closure of the Hazelwood power station, there's only six-month notice between when the owners Engie announced and then actually closed it down. So, while neither the regulator (AEMC)[13] nor the market operator (AEMO)[14] anticipate such a shortfall at present, it's still possible. And from the point of view of prudence, there is an argument for putting these tougher 'reliability' provisions in place.

There's another dimension which people tend to overlook. On current projections, there is not a lot of closure of coal-fired power stations between now and 2030, but if we are going to be serious about addressing the climate problem and reducing Australia emissions, we probably need to close quite a few more coal-fired generation capacity by 2030. The NEG does not envisage that, but the nice thing about it and its reliability provisions is that if we do move more aggressively then we've got a mechanism to ensure as we move to lift coal and more renewables than there's a mechanism to ensure that that's done in a reliable way. So, it's a bit ironic because we're about to talk about the emissions component of NEG, that it actually provides quite a good mechanism to facilitate a much greater shift to renewables than the basis on which it is premised.

ML: On that question about reliability and investment in new generation, there was talk about last-minute changes to the NEG and reference to what was being called the NEG-Plus. There seemed to be suggestions that the government should underwrite private-sector investment in new coal-fired generation capacity. Is that correct, where did it come from and what's it all about given what you've just been saying?

CD: Yes, this was a strange eleventh-hour contribution coming, to my understanding, from outside the advice of the Energy Security Board (ESB).[15] It seems to be from the political realm, in particular from some government backbencher enthusiasts for coal-fired generation as a condition for their support for the NEG. As we have discussed, the 'reliability' provisions provide a 'safety net' and a mechanism to bring additional capacity to the market if it's required. I certainly don't see a need for this NEG. Plus additional underwriting. The idea is to get the private market to respond. It would be quite counterproductive if such government underwriting were to support technology that is neither environmentally sustainable nor economically competitive in the form of coal-fired generation.

ML: The third aspect of what the NEG is trying to achieve is carbon emissions reductions and the question of Australia's commitments to the Paris climate targets. What is the likely impact of the NEG on our emissions targets and commitments?

CD: The intent of the NEG is to apply Australia's Paris Agreement commitments,[16] of a 26% reduction in emissions to the electricity sector. There's been a lot of criticism of simply applying the same overall national target to the electricity sector when we know that the electricity sector is already reducing its emissions quite rapidly with the shift away from coal and towards renewables. There is recognition that there is a lot of very low-cost emission reduction that could be achieved in the electricity sector at a much lower cost than could be achieved in other sectors such as farming and transport. So, if we're going to take a least-cost approach to meeting our emission reductions targets, we should probably expect the electricity sector to contribute more than just that 26% emissions reduction.

ML: If there were in place a market mechanism as there was for a while, namely in the form of a carbon price, presumably those producers and emitters of carbon in the market who had relatively lower costs would be investing more in reduction and those with higher costs would be carrying less. As you say. That would deliver an overall lower, least cost of emissions reduction for the economy as a whole. Does the NEG imply some sort of *pro rata* idea that if the overall target we've got under Paris for Australia is 26%,[17] then each sector including electricity should carry 26%, which presumably will mean that the overall cost of meeting a national target is going to be much higher than it needs to be?

CD: That would be the consequence although it's not quite right to say that Australia is adopting the same target for every sector, because the only sector for which the government is actually proposing to have a firm target is the electricity sector. It remains to be seen what targets would apply to other sectors and whether they would be met at all, which might be also one of the issues that need to be considered. But if we were to meet our Paris obligations, and if we were to apply the 26% target to every sector, including sectors like transport and agriculture, then yes, that would likely be significantly more expensive than taking a least-cost approach, which allows for those sectors that can achieve reductions more cheaply to carry a larger share of burden.

ML: As you say, at the moment, the NEG certainly doesn't tackle the other sectors being focused as it is on the electricity energy sector, which is a major emitter of course, and being only one part of bigger energy policy questions. But aren't there suggestions that, even in the absence of the NEG, this sector anyway would be hitting Paris targets regardless?

CD: Yes, the modelling from the ESB suggests that in the absence of the NEG, emissions from electricity will fall by about 24% by 2030 as a result of the increased contribution from renewable energy. So the NEG is only providing a very small additional emission reduction by 2030. Indeed, if the market continues to grow for renewable energy the way it has, then there's every likelihood that we would meet that 26% emission reduction target within the electricity sector in the early years of the 2020 decade.

ML: I find all of this most perplexing. We've talked about electricity prices, which I think you've been saying are likely to come down to a large part anyway without the NEG. We've talked about the reliability and the need for additional investment in generation where according to the ESB's own modelling there isn't a foreseeable need, although there could possibly be in the future, but none foreseen or forecast. And now we're talking about emissions targets, which again in the absence of the NEG would be largely – if not completely – achieved. It seems that all three key policy objectives and targets are probably achievable without the NEG. But one last question on NEG emissions targets: being set so relatively low, including with reference to the ESB modelling, are they likely to even create an investment drought in renewables and likely discourage renewable investment and need later action?

CD: Well, there's two ways of looking at it. On the one hand, there's nothing in the NEG, and the way it's written, that puts a cap on the amount of renewables installed but on the other hand its whole rationale is that it creates greater certainty for investors. If we've got a policy like NEG that sets a target that is not binding in the sense that we meet the target by 2021–2022, then it seems to me that does not create an awful lot of certainty for investors.

As a consequence, from the investor's point of view, clearly this policy is not sustainable because it's not achieving anything. An investor might want to sit on their hands and wait and see what other policy gets put in place because this one is essentially ineffectual. So while the letter of the NEG doesn't put a cap on the growth in renewables, I think the practical impact could be that it creates more uncertainty or rather, it doesn't resolve the uncertainty that we have now. The consequence is that we don't get the greater investment in generation, and in particular, renewable generation that we need in order to drive electricity prices lower.

ML: If and when the NEG goes through, there are criticisms from a couple of the States and from the ACT,[18,19] that it is locking in weak emission targets for a decade by placing them in legislation and law rather than putting them in as regulations that can be readily changed administratively under the framework of the law. Is that a valid criticism?

CD: It's not a criticism with which I have a lot of sympathy. A few years ago, when the Coalition government came to power, it wanted to wind back the existing renewable energy target built into legislation, but it couldn't do that unless it changed the legislation. That meant they had to go through the Parliament to reduce the target which they did ultimately, but they needed to go through a long process of negotiation and as a consequence the renewable energy target was reduced but by nowhere near as much as the Coalition government had wanted.

As a consequence, we have now this very large investment happening in renewable energy, which is helping to drive electricity prices lower as we said earlier. So that having the target in legislation rather than in regulation provided greater stability. Now, the same people who are arguing for putting the renewable energy target in legislation are saying no, if you're going to have low emission targets you should put them in regulation.

I don't have a problem with it being in legislation but I do have a problem with the emissions targets being so low and very weak. If the government does want to change those targets, and it certainly should, it should make them much stronger. Whether there's a change of government or otherwise, that would mean going through legislation and it's not really locked in. Just because the proposed NEG legislation targets for the year 2030 doesn't mean that they can't be changed, it just means they need to be changed by legislation.

One of the nice things about the NEG is that because we would have the structure in legislation of those targets, it's much easier to change the number or level of the target than it is to create a whole new legislative structure so we would have to go through a legislative process. But I think whoever is in government will have to recognise the inadequacy of these proposed targets and they will need to change. I would rather have the NEG in place with weak targets and a solid legislative structure than to not have a structure at all. Certainly, it would also make it easier for future governments to put in regulations; but there's always the risk that the regulation goes downwards as well as upwards in terms of the level of ambition.

Conclusion

The complexities, trade-offs and politics involved in framing policy, legislation and regulation to achieve a transition in the electricity sector from fossil fuels to sustainable renewable energies are vividly demonstrated by Australia's experience with the National Energy Guarantee (NEG). The endeavour to integrate within the national electricity grid the three objectives of emissions targets, renewable energy technologies and affordable electricity prices not only became bogged down in political wrangling but ultimately came up with a framework that was 'ineffectual' on all three scores. Network stability was not advanced and sufficient investor certainty was not provided. While at the same time, the impact on holding prices down was marginal, and emissions targets and investment in renewable technologies would have been met anyway on the basis of previously set 'renewable energy targets'.

Seeking to meet Australia's Paris Climate commitments of 26% reduction in overall emissions by 2030 by focusing on the electricity sector puts a potentially higher load on reductions in other sectors such as transport and agriculture with more costly abatement profiles rather than minimising the overall cost to the economy by relying more heavily on available proven low-cost solutions in the electricity sector.

The debate was highly politicised and often 'toxic' in a framework of 'climate wars' that stymied long-term investment and least-cost restructuring of the sector for a sustainable future.[20] The Coalition government even entertained proposals from within its own ranks for massive government underwriting of additional investment in new coal-fired power stations in the name of network 'reliability' premised on 'base load' fossil energy-fired power stations.[21] The NEG proposal embedded emissions targets in the draft legislation which locked in specific weak targets. It did not offer the future flexibility to lift the targets by incorporating them as regulations under the legislation that would not require reference back to the legislature.

Notes

1 Stop These Things (2018) *Turnbull Trounced: Re Obsessed PM Ditched Over Ludicrous Plan to Double-Up on Subsidised Wind and Solar*, 25th August https://stopthesethings.com/2018/08/25/turnbull-trounced-re-obsessed-pm-ditched-over-ludicrous-plan-to-double-up-on-subsidised-wind-solar/

2 SMH Editorial (2018) Dropping NEG is Malcolm Turnbull's moral failure, *Sydney* sis-turnbull-s-moral-failure-20180820-p4zyjz.html

3 Crowley, K. (2021) Climate wars, carbon taxes and toppled leaders: The 30-year history of Australia's climate response, *The Conversation*, 15th October https://theconversation.com/climate-wars-carbon-taxes-and-toppled-leaders-the-30-year-history-of-australias-climate-response-in-brief-169545

4 Dunstan, C. (2018) *In the Balance: Electricity, Sustainability and Least Cost Competition*, PhD Thesis in Sustainable Futures, ISF UTS, November https://opus.lib.uts.edu.au/bitstream/10453/131582/1/01front.pdf

5 Dunstan, C. (2018) A pause in the climate wars is better than nothing, *Sydney Morning Herald*, 11th August www.smh.com.au/national/a-pause-in-the-climate-wars-is-better-than-nothing-20180809-p4zwl3.html

6 Energy Security Board (2018) National energy guarantee: Final detailed design, *COAG Energy Council*, 1st August www.apo.org.au

7 This paper describes the 2000 scheme and legislated target of an extra 20% renewables of electricity over 1997 by 2020 through creation and trading of renewable energy certificates, and assesses its impact. See St John, A. (2014) *The Renewable Energy Target: A Quick Guide, Parliamentary Research Paper*, Canberra: Parliament House, May www.aph.gov.au/About_Parliament/Parliamentary_departments/Parliamentary_Library/pubs/rp/rp1314/QG/RenewableEnergy

8 Vorrath, S. (2017) Electricity sector 'gold plating' behind sky-high prices – not renewables, *Renew Economy*, 27th July https://reneweconomy.com.au/electricity-sector-gold-plating-behind-sky-high-prices-not-renewables-14724/

9 This report from The Australia Institute revealed a 183% increase in cost of electricity over the previous twenty years, almost three times the rate of the national consumer price index (CPi): Richardson, D. (2017) Electricity costs, *The Australia Institute*, 27th July https://australiainstitute.org.au/report/electricity-costs/

10 Australian Energy Regulator (AER) *State of the Energy Market Annual Reports* www.aer.gov.au/publications/state-of-the-energy-market-reports

11 Ha, J. and Reeve, A. (2021) Coal plants are closing faster than expected: Governments can keep the exit orderly, *The Conversation*, 23rd November https://theconversation.com/coal-plants-are-closing-faster-than-expected-governments-can-keep-the-exit-orderly-172150
12 Parkinson, G. (2017) Schott: Modelling assumptions change, but result more or less the same, *Renew Economy*, 10th November https://reneweconomy.com.au/schott-modelling-assumptions-change-but-result-more-or-less-the-same-97327/
13 The Australian Energy Market Commission (AEMC) undertakes reviews and provides advice to governments on improvements to regulatory and energy market arrangements www.aemc.gov.au/
14 The Australian Energy Market Operator (AEMO) manages 'electricity and gas systems and markets across the country with the aim of ensuring access to affordable, secure and reliable energy' https://aemo.com.au/en
15 The Energy Security Board (ESB) was established after the Finkel Review which looked at energy security in the electricity market https://esb-post2025-market-design.aemc.gov.au/who-is-the-energy-security-board#about-the-energy-security-board-esb
16 Under the Paris Agreement, Australia must submit emissions reduction commitments known as Nationally Determined Contributions (NDC) including a national target which is its first commitment to the UNFCCC registry. The 2022 NDC committed Australia to '43% below 2005 levels by 2030, which is a 15 percentage point increase on Australia's previous 2030 target' from DCCEEW (2022) Australia submits new emissions target to UNFCCC, *Australian Department of Climate Change, Energy, the Environment and Water*, 16th June www.dcceew.gov.au/about/news/australia-submits-new-emissions-target-to-unfccc
17 DCCEEW (2015) *Australia's 2030 Emissions Reductions Target: Strong, Credible, Responsible, Fact Sheet, Commonwealth of Australia* www.dcceew.gov.au/sites/default/files/documents/summary-australias-2030-emissions-reduction-target.pdf
18 Gartrell, A. and Towell, N. (2017) State Labor premiers savage Malcolm Turnbull's energy policy, setting up a COAG brawl, *Sydney Morning Herald*, 17th October www.theage.com.au/politics/federal/state-labor-premiers-savage-malcolm-turnbulls-energy-policy-setting-up-a-coag-brawl-20171017-gz2alb.html
19 Chalmers, M. (2017) Labor states not happy with Turnbull's energy plan, *Crikey*, 18th October www.crikey.com.au/2017/10/18/crikey-worm-labor-states-not-happy-with-turnbulls-energy-plan/
20 In the spirit of Australia's continuing 'climate wars' the failure of the NEG was followed by repeated climate and energy policy failures including up to the COP26 in late 2021 where its policy was described as 'the weakest climate plan among the G20's developed nations'. See Dewan, A., Westcott, B. and Whiteman, H. (2021) Australia will be the rich world's weakest link at COP26 with hollow net-zero and emissions pledges, *CNN*, 26th October https://edition.cnn.com/2021/10/25/australia/australia-climate-net-zero-intl/index.html
21 Ha, J. (2021) More coal-fired power or 100% renewables? For the next few decades, both paths are wrong, *The Conversation*, 11th April https://theconversation.com/more-coal-fired-power-or-100-renewables-for-the-next-few-decades-both-paths-are-wrong-158529

12 Electric Vehicles (EV)

Infrastructure and Policy Barriers Lead to Laggardly Diffusion and Adoption

Interview With Peter Khoury

Introduction

This chapter discusses electric vehicles, their development and take-up in the Australian market, and the issues arising from the point of view of motorists confronted with the opportunities and challenges of adopting this new technology. Different segments of the population take-up new technologies at different rates, from early adopters through laggards.[1]

The individual motivations for technology adoption are complex; and are inherently social, developmental processes.[2] Broader policy, structural and infrastructure settings play an important role in influencing individual technology adoption choices. Electrical Vehicle (EV) technology and innovation, is a key component of carbon emissions strategy.

Keywords: Auto consumers; Charging infrastructure; Climate Wars; Connector standards; Electrical Vehicle/s (EV/s); Fast-charging; Federal Government; Hybrid vehicles; National Roads and Motor Association (NRMA); Paris Climate Agreement; Payback period; Policy vacuum; Range anxiety; SDG 9; SDG11; SDG12; Technology adoption; Technology diffusion

Interviewee Profile

Peter Khoury (**PK**) is Media Manager for the National Roads and Motorists Association (NRMA), part of a listed company, Insurance Australia Group (IAG). The NRMA, on behalf of its 2.6 million motoring members, is taking up and advocating on these issues.

The Interview

ML: Electric vehicles are having a reasonable initial rate of adoption in the Australian market of about 18 or 20,000 units to date (April 2020).[3] What are the opportunities and challenges of wider take-up?

PK: You are right that the penetration levels are going up, although they're coming off a very low base. We are seeing percentage year-on-year increases, and just last year (2019) alone, over 7,000 electric vehicles

DOI: 10.4324/9781003280316-14

were sold in Australia.[4] But when you consider that the number of petrol and diesel new car sales were well over a million, at 1.2 million, it puts it into some sort of context.

Australians are notoriously slow at adopting new technology and then once it does catch on, it moves ahead at breakneck speed and the best example of that is the smartphone. We weren't the first or the quickest to buy smartphones, but today their penetration per capita in Australia is the highest in the world.[5]

There is a sense of inevitability about the electric vehicle future in Australia if you look at what is happening globally.[6] The NRMA felt that we had an important role to play to get our community ready for that inevitability in the next decade or two. Australia is nowhere near ready for that future, both in terms of building the infrastructure that will be needed to keep people on the road and in terms of the sales uptake of electric vehicles.

A few things need to be done. First, is the building of a fast-charging network[7] – which the NRMA has been doing now for a couple of years. We've covered most of regional NSW. We've still got a way to go.

Second, we don't build cars in Australia;[8] and the countries that do and import them to Australia tell us that there will be a time where they will only be building electric cars. So that's why the NRMA is trying to get ahead of the curve.

ML: What for the individual motorist are the factors in their decisions to shift to electric vehicles financially, economically and technologically?[9,10]

PK: Off the top is the 'ticket price', which is way too high with the price of an electric vehicle compared to a similar conventional car, sometimes as much as $30,000 more expensive. That ticket price needs to come down considerably before it becomes more of a mainstream choice for motorists.[11] It will come down over time, but we're not there yet. While that challenge is not unique to Australia the price gap seems to be a lot higher here than in other countries.[12]

ML: What payback period for this relatively expensive investment are people seeing at the moment?

PK: Well, there're a few other factors you can think about before the payback period. The first is the 'range anxiety'. A lot of people who are buying EVs are only really driving them around city areas because they're concerned that once they leave Sydney, once they go away from the comfort of their own charging station at home, they confront 'range anxiety'. They don't know if there's going to be somewhere where you can top up your charge. That is a major factor in people's thoughts around buying electric vehicles.

Once you buy the EV, the cost savings are immediate and significant. Electric vehicles don't break down as much because there are fewer parts to worry about. Not being ripped off at the petrol browser is another factor with which a lot of families have to deal with periodic petrol price hikes. Also, because there are fewer parts to service you don't spend as much money and time in the auto mechanic shops. So over that extended period you start to see savings.

We're hoping to see initiatives introduced by governments to encourage the uptake of electric vehicles,[13] whereby insurance might be reduced, registration might be reduced. The government would also benefit from having more of these cars on the road.

So over time, once you buy your electric vehicle, there is no doubt about the cost savings to the driver. The cost of electric charge compared to the price of petrol is the significant saving; the plug as opposed to the bowser over that extended period of the lifetime. You start to see those running cost savings delivered to the owner of the vehicle, but unfortunately while the EV price is so high, there are a lot of people for whom it's not really a choice just now.

ML: Where do 'hybrid cars'[14] fit into this EV scenario both economically and technologically?

PK: Hybrids are playing a significant part in Australia particularly with most of the taxi fleet now using hybrid vehicles. Hybrids are a good stepping stone to electric vehicles. Our focus, as an organisation, went straight to electric vehicles purely from a strategic perspective; because that's where we believe they are the future. We believe that eventually the uptake here in electric vehicles will mirror what happens globally.

ML: The high-ticket price can be expected to fall significantly and quickly – given the substantial and rapidly increasing investment in R&D – and technology and manufacturing development by the global industry. I believe that Tesla, which is the leading market brand globally, also has a dominant market share in Australia, has reached a 1,000,000 sales figure only recently and is building new factories and extending into trucks.[15] What are the prospects from the global industry perspective of driving that ticket price down?

PK: That's where the drive will come from. It will come from overseas. It won't come from Australia because we import, we don't build. We don't have a car manufacturing industry. There's been argument and discussions around whether we should go back into the market since there is a new form of motor vehicle technology.

Australia will probably be a critical part of the global supply chain purely off the back of the amount of lithium that we have here in Australia. We are world leaders in that. What you will see is, well, the best comparison would be the smartphone. The first smartphones were way out of the price range for most people, and it wasn't until you started to see that mass move of people moving to the new technology as demand increased and as the range of what people were looking for increased, the price fell considerably and eventually kicked competitors out of the market.

We would expect nothing different from electric vehicles. Probably within the next five or ten years, we will start to get towards price parity. Once you get price parity, the future for petrol and diesel vehicles will be quite dead because the benefits are so extensive that most people will go straight to an electric vehicle. That shift will come globally, and it will happen quicker than people think. Given that we're not leading that shift because we're not building cars, we need to be ready for it because it's going to be here whether we like it or not.

ML: As you say, with no local car industry here there might still be opportunities in the supply chain, particularly the lithium required for the EV batteries in which we do have a global-scale resource. It's interesting that the UK in the post-Brexit environment with its motor vehicle industry problems was even considering trying to reinvest and redevelop their industry based on electric vehicle technology.[16] But I think that's beyond any aspirations that we might have as a country at this point.

You've mentioned that the NRMA is investing some of its membership money to develop an infrastructure of charging stations.[17] What are you doing there?

PK: Our initiative is particularly significant in light of the coronavirus where we're seeing a recognition around the world that our economies may have become too reliant on importing manufactured products from other parts of the world. We've become lazy and lackadaisical when it comes to using the ingenuity, extensive experience and expertise that we have in this country to do more of the things that we need for ourselves. Infrastructure is a good example of where Australia is leading the way.

We've partnered with an Australian company, Tritium, who build fast-charging stations and we have been building those stations across regional areas in New South Wales and the ACT. We specifically targeted regional areas because we want to open them up to tourism by encouraging people who live in Sydney to visit there on the holidays, to spend their money there to support regional communities. This is also a strategic focus for the NRMA because half of our membership lives outside Sydney.

Our Australian company partner builds new charging stations here using local employees. The technology is Australian. The lithium is Australian. We've built almost 40 of these charging stations across NSW and the ACT and we've done so strategically to open up regional areas.

We started in the Hunter Valley, then to the North Coast, followed by the South Coast, and then inland to Mudgee and down to the snow country. We've built these charging stations on these tourist routes so that people will be able to stop and charge as they go on their holidays.

Electric vehicles differ from petrol and diesel vehicles in that most of the charging will be done at home unlike conventional vehicles filling up at petrol stations. I think there's some confusion on this point. People have this view that we have to replace every service station in Australia with a charging station. But that's not actually how it's going to happen because in most cases people will drive their car with a full battery charged from home.

We are now also the majority shareholder of another Australian company, Charge Box, that is building a similar charging network across the country. So, we're now replicating what we're doing in New South Wales and the ACT in partnership together with other motoring clubs to build a national network. In Australia, we have the expertise and the innovation to do this without having to rely on other parts of the world. So while we rely on them for the car, at the very least, Australia will own the infrastructure and critically, this is really important when you think about the amount of work that NRMA does on petrol prices. The electricity that is going to be used to charge those cars will be Australian-made electricity, so we won't be relying on imports from overseas, which not only will help us to protect our members from volatile world prices but also it's a national security issue as well.

ML: That's impressive and sounds like a great opportunity. Are there any standards issues around building this infrastructure? Don't different makes and models of cars require different plugs at different charging stations?[18]

PK: You can pretty much charge most cars with our fast-charging network. I believe that we will start to see the standardisation of that issue as we move forward because it will become infeasible to need a different plug for every different car. Ease of use is going to be critical in making sure that this is a success. Also, as we move forward, other advances in technology will make the investment even more attractive, especially in terms of batteries and overcoming 'range anxiety'.

With batteries, we're already seeing some cars with ranges between 450 and 500 kilometres on a single charge which is getting closer to petrol and diesel vehicles. Battery storage will be critical. As I mentioned before, people will charge their cars at home and in order to protect the grid stability, it will be important that there is storage capacity at homes so that people are charging and storing their own energy. That's going to be vital, and again, that's an area where the NRMA is hoping that Australia can lead the way.

ML: You make the distinction between the fast-charging network that you're putting in and the charging at home. Am I right in assuming that charging at home will be a slow-charging operation (overnight) compared to the fast-charging (one hour or so) infrastructure you're putting in?

PK: Yes, for now that is the case. We should remember a lot of this technology is only being rolled out now and think about the sort of advances we have made over the past 100 years in the way cars look and perform. The charging capacity at home is slow but it doesn't necessarily have to be fast right now. You plug your car in overnight when no one is using the grid and charge it when you're asleep, in the same way that we do with our phones. Having said that, that's the off-peak period with the grid and we don't want a situation where the grid is at a permanent high-peak period; that's why battery storage technology is going to be so important moving forward.

ML: How will this new infrastructure of charging networks, supplemented by home charging, differ commercially from the existing huge number of commercial or oil company petrol stations that it will replace? Are oil companies or other private enterprises investing in fast-charging infrastructure, because presumably anyone who charges has to pay a commercial rate for the service?

PK: Yes, they are in America. I was in the United States last year and what really stood out is you would pull into these service stations and there are more Tesla charging plugs than there are petrol pumps. That's likely to be a path that most service stations will go down as an opportunity to transition their business, but the cost of charging the battery of an electric vehicle is nothing compared to filling up the tank of a car. In Australia, to fill up your car when petrol is around $1.50 per litre, you're not getting any change from $100 bucks while a full charge of an electric vehicle at the electricity rates that we're currently paying you'd be lucky to nudge $20 and that's with a decent size profit margin. Our NRMA charging network is currently free to members and it will always be free to members. We've built it not to make money but as a social investment and as a commitment to regional communities across Australia. Non-members will pay but they will be stunned at the difference between paying a fee at a plug and paying a significant fee at a browser.

An important role for the NRMA moving forward will be to ensure transparency and fairness of charging prices. There're a number of reasons why it will be a lot cheaper for motorists in Australia to charge their imported electric vehicles as opposed to filling up their imported internal combustion engine vehicle and the most critical of that is that we will be 100% energy self-reliant. It will be Australian electricity. Now, there is obviously a debate that is taking place in Australia right now about whether electricity should be generated from coal or from renewable energy or from nuclear or from whatever; and that debate rages, as it should, but one thing that will be certain is that the security of our transport future will rest solely in the hands of the Australian community. No longer will we be relying on importing oil from some of the most volatile parts of the world, and that will be a significant game changer for transport future in Australia and for every Australian family.

ML: What's the role for governments? What federal government policies and or regulations can influence this; and what, if anything, are they doing? Are they making investments? Are they looking at regulations and standards? Do they have a strategy?

PK: That's a very good question. They do have a strategy which we were expecting to be released in the next couple of months so we will wait and see.[19,20,21]

Leadership is probably the most important asset they can bring to the table right now. What you're going to see increasingly is that all the private-sector organisations like the NRMA are going to invest in the infrastructure because they see that as their role. To do that in partnership with the federal government will be crucial, whereby they can remove barriers to that industry growth and where they may also choose to invest themselves in encouraging the uptake of the technology in the rollout of the infrastructure.

When we started buying cars in Australia, it was the government that built the roads. Sure, the private sector built the service stations, and so we know that the government always has an important role to play when we're looking to shift such a significant part of our part of the country's DNA. They will have an important leadership role. There's work that they can do around removing tax barriers. The fact that most electric vehicles are captured in the luxury vehicle taxes is absurd. That immediately needs to be reversed and is something the government can do tomorrow.

We've been talking closely with the federal government. They are definitely on board in terms of understanding the need for Australia to get ready for electric vehicles because we're not ready for this future and they see benefits to us taking these steps, if for nothing else but that transport accounts for 20% of carbon emissions in Australia.

The Australian Government is looking to meet its Paris targets in terms of carbon emission reductions and knows that an easy way to do that would be through the transport sector. That can deliver immediate emission reductions even if you don't change the electricity grid.

I know there's been discussion around the idea that there's no difference, because instead of the emissions coming out of the tailpipe, they're coming out of the electricity grid, but in fact, electric vehicles with their more energy-efficient engines do produce lower carbon emissions than do internal combustion engines. They do reduce the carbon emission footprint of the transport sector, sometimes by upwards of 30% without doing anything to the grid. And if you look at the Tasmanian example where they have a broader mix in terms of their renewable energy sources energy, particularly with hydropower, then the savings can be upwards of 60%. So even doing nothing to the electricity grid, you deliver savings and there's a lot the federal government can do with its leadership. It can also support infrastructure, investment and technology investment. Obviously, no government would want to miss the opportunity of positioning Australia as leaders in lithium and the batteries because we have so much of that resource,[22] and using the tax system to encourage the take-up of these vehicles will help in many ways.

ML: State governments also have a role. NSW has announced quite an ambitious target of net-zero emissions by 2050,[23] along with a range of funded initiatives including for electric vehicles. What sort of things are state governments doing or capable of doing here, including with their own fleets?[24]

PK: What we're seeing at both the state and federal levels, especially now the state has released its policy, is some real leadership in this space and a shift in thinking, and that's the most important thing. The New South Wales government just released its energy plan to get to net-zero emissions.[25]

We need to encourage the transport sector to reform and that's what they're looking to do with their policy initiatives in terms of investing their own money, including partnering with the private sector to build infrastructure, looking at tax breaks for electric vehicle owners, and all the things that you would need to do to encourage a shift in policy.

Governments can't wait because you can't just leave it to the private sector alone. There is going to be this global shift whether we like it or not, and we don't want to get left behind because the economic and social benefits will not be delivered to families, and I don't think voters would be very happy about that either when that time comes.

Conclusion

The tortured path to adoption of Electric Vehicles (EV) by Australian motorists is a classic case study in the technical, social, economic and political complexity of diffusion of new technology. Australia is a global laggard in adoption of EVs.[26] Despite the technology's economic, national energy security and environmental benefits in contributing to meeting carbon emissions targets, its adoption by motorists has been plagued by a lack of a cohesive national strategy of government support entangled as it is politically in the inability of the country to confront climate change and sustainability and caught up in the ideological 'climate wars'.

While offering low operating costs to motorists, EVs are more expensive in Australia than elsewhere; in part, because many brands are caught up in a luxury car import duty payment,[27] despite the government policy decision that led to closure of the domestic vehicle industry.[28] There are considerable opportunities for Australian industry to participate in development of EV lithium batteries and charging infrastructure.

Consumers are also inhibited by 'range anxiety' that requires investment in a national charging infrastructure and provision of incentives and tax relief. Australia lacks EV charging standards and also needs to invest in modernisation of the national electricity grid to enable efficient input of renewable energy to the fossil fuel-powered generation system.

While the Federal Government has adopted a much criticised EV strategy with few incentives and investments to attract more buyers to EVs, State Governments have stepped forward into the policy vacuum; as well as private-sector actors, including the NRMA, a motorists' organisation, that is investing in a fast-charging infrastructure network.

Notes

1 The adoption segments are typically distributed on a normal curve with 17% early adopters to 18% laggards. See Roy Morgan Research, *Technology Adoption Segments* www.roymorgan.com/products-and-tools/technology-adoption-segments

2 Theories of technology diffusion and adoption include Roger's innovation diffusion theory, the Concerns-Based Adoption Model, and the Technology Acceptance Model. See Straub, E.T. (2017) Understanding technology adoption: Theory and future directions, *Review of Educational Research*, 79 (2): 625–649

3 Electric Vehicle Council (2021) *State of Electric Vehicles*, August https://electricvehiclecouncil.com.au/wp-content/uploads/2021/08/EVC-State-of-EVs-2021.pdf

4 Sales of electric vehicles in Australia tripled to 20,665 in 2021 (2% market share) from 6,900 in 2020 (0.78%) putting it on the precipice of an EV economic boom. See Sievewright, B. (2022) EV sales boom presents chance to capture serious electric benefits, if government acts now, *Electric Vehicle Council*, 31st January https://electricvehiclecouncil.com.au/news/ev-sales-boom-presents-chance-to-capture-sserious-electric-benefits-if-government-acts-now/

5 Smartphone penetration was 81% of the Australian population in 2017 and is estimated to reach 87% (23.6 million users) by 2026. See Hughes, C. (2023) Smartphone penetration as share of population in Australia 2017–2026, *Statista*, 3rd January www.statista.com/statistics/321477/smartphone-user-penetration-in-australia/

6 Global EV sales approached 17 million in 2022, triple the amount in 2018 and kept rising strongly in the first quarter of 2022 by 75% to 2 million units, despite emerging global supply chain disruptions due to COVID-19 and the Russian invasion of Ukraine. EVs are expected to represent some 30% of global vehicle sales in 2030 up from 10% in 2021 but still well short of the 60% share by 2030 needed to align with a net-zero CO2 emissions by 2050. See International Energy Agency (IEA) (2022) *Global EV Outlook 2022, Technology Annual Report*, May www.iea.org/reports/global-ev-outlook-2022

7 IEA, ibid: The global market value of electricity for the EV charging market is expected to grow 20-fold from 2021 reaching US$190 billion by 2030 which is equivalent to one-tenth of today's diesel and gasoline market value. There are substantial variations between countries but overall, the expected amount of public charging infrastructure might fall short of the size of the EV market being targeted. While most of the charging will be at home or workplace, it is nevertheless estimated that public charging units need to expand ninefold to over 15 million units in 2030 to meet target levels and provide users with adequate and convenient coverage

8 The Australian car manufacturing industry closed in 2017 as a consequence of government policies over 30 years and precipitated by global industry restructuring, bringing to an end 70 years of local car production. See Beer, A. (2018) The closure of the Australian car manufacturing industry: Redundancy, policy and community impacts, *Australian Geographer*, 49 (3): 419–438

9 Broadbent, G.H., Metternicht, G. and Drozdzewski, D. (2019) An analysis of consumer incentives in support of electric vehicle uptake: An Australian case study. *World Electric Vehicle Journal*, 10 (1): 11 https://doi.org/10.3390/wevj10010011

10 Secinaro, S., Calandra, D., Lanzalonga, F. and Ferraris, A. (2022) Electric vehicles' consumer behaviours: Mapping the field and providing a research agenda, *Journal of Business Research*, 150, November: 399–416

11 There are 31 EV models available in Australia, only 14 are priced under A$65,000, while the average cost of a petrol or diesel car is between A$20,000 and A$50,000, but prices are heading to parity. Half of Australians are hesitant to switch because of cost, and a third of drivers are not considering EV for next purchase. See Harris, R. (2021) High cost of electric vehicles make Australians hesitant to buy, *Sydney Morning Herald*, 30th October www.smh.com.au/politics/federal/high-cost-of-electric-vehicles-make-australians-hesitant-to-buy-20211029-p594e1.html

12 Chesterton, A. (2020) This is why your Tesla Model 3 is so expensive: Elon Musk concedes Australian pricing 'seems high', *Cars Guide*, 17th February www.carsguide.com.au/car-news/this-is-why-your-tesla-model-3-is-so-expensive-elon-musk-concedes-australian-pricing-seems

13 Parkinson, G. (2018) Senate inquiry to urge EV targets, range of incentives, *RenewEconomy*, 10th November https://reneweconomy.com.au/senate-inquiry-to-urge-ev-targets-range-of-incentives-17410/

14 Hybrid EV have both an internal combustion engine and electric motor which uses energy stored in batteries charged through regenerative braking rather than plugging into power plugs. See Momoh, O.D. and Omoigui, M.O. (2009) *An Overview of Hybrid Electric Vehicle Technology*, 2009 IEEE Vehicle Power and Propulsion Conference, September, pp. 1286–1292, IEEE

15 Incorporated in 2003, Tesla produced its one-millionth car in March 2020 while at the start of 2022, delivered 200,000 vehicles a quarter. See also Dean, B. (2023) Tesla revenue and production statistics for 2023, *Backlinko*, 27th March https://backlinko.com/tesla-stats

16 Investment in EV and battery R&D, and production, including the country's first mass-produced battery electric car, alongside production of electric vans, buses and trucks across ten vehicle manufacturers. See: Society of Motor Manufacturers and Traders (SMMT) (2022) *UK Automotive Invests 10.8 Billion Pounds in First Electric Decade*, 23rd March www.smmt.co.uk/2022/03/uk-automotive-invests-10-8-billion-in-first-electric-decade/#:~:text=The%20automotive%20industry%20has%20called,since%202011%2C%20with%20billions%20more

17 Schmidt, B. (2023) *The Evolution of NRMA's EV Charging Strategy, We've Got You Covered*, 14th August www.mynrma.com.au/electric-vehicles/charging/ev-charging-game-plan

18 The EV market lacks an Australian standard for charging connectors/plugs. See EVSE. *What is the Electric Vehicle Charging Standard in Australia?* https://evse.com.au/blog/evchargingaustralia/

19 Chanticleer (2021) Australia's electric vehicle strategy is a mess, *Australian Financial Review (AFR)*, 7th May www.afr.com/chanticleer/electric-vehicle-strategy-is-a-mess-20210506-p57pha

20 Australia lags behind in the adoption of electric vehicles. See Australian Government (2021) *Future Fuels and Vehicles Strategy*, Discussion Paper https://consult.dcceew.gov.au/future-fuels-strategy
21 A lack of new subsidies or tax incentives means EVs will remain too expensive for most Australians. See Stayner, T. (2021) Australia unveiled its new EV policy: Critics say we are still '10 years behind', *Special Broadcasting Service (SBS)*, 9th November www.sbs.com.au/news/article/australia-unveiled-its-new-ev-policy-critics-say-we-are-still-10-years-behind/v5ut828s0#
22 King, M. (2023) Australia's lithium powering the global energy transition, *Media Release, Minister for Resources*, 6th March www.minister.industry.gov.au/ministers/king/media-releases/australias-lithium-powering-global-energy-transition
23 Climate Council (2022) NSW makes gains in race to net zero with new targets, *Media Release*, 23rd December www.climatecouncil.org.au/resources/nsw-makes-gains-in-race-to-net-zero-with-new-targets/
24 Fisk, K. (2021) Australia's EV policies: What's happening in each state and territory in 2021-updated, *Which Car?* 9th August www.whichcar.com.au/news/australian-states-territories-ev-policies-september-2021
25 Ibid
26 Huynh, W. (2023) Why do Australians have less access to electric vehicles than their OECD counterparts? *Canberra Times*, 14th February www.canberratimes.com.au/story/8072136/why-is-australia-in-the-slow-lane-with-electric-vehicles/
27 Parkinson, G. (2020) Australia's luxury car tax threshold quietly lifted for electric vehicles, *The Driven*, 1st July https://thedriven.io/2020/07/01/australias-luxury-car-tax-threshold-quietly-lifted-for-electric-vehicles/
28 Valaadkhani, A. (2016) Collapse of Australian car manufacturing will harm R&D in other sectors, *The Conversation*, 21st October https://theconversation.com/collapse-of-australian-car-manufacturing-will-harm-randd-in-other-sectors-study-66984

13 Bitcoin, Cryptocurrency and Global Finance Industry Disruption

Dirty Little Energy Secret

Interview With Sean Foley

Introduction

Bitcoin[1] was launched as a 'digital currency' in 2009 referred to as a form of 'cryptocurrency'. Over the past decade, the price of Bitcoin investments rose from about $10,000 Australian to about $80,000 in that time.[2] However, it comes and goes and it's fallen back to about $50, so it's still a highly speculative and volatile asset class.[3] It has a lot of hype around it like a lot of new technologies.[4] Many people say that what we are now seeing with Bitcoin, Ethereum and other such offerings is just the front end of a 'first-generation' technological disruption of global financial, investment, savings and capital markets.[5]

Keywords: asset classes; banking; Big Four; Bitcoin; Bitcoin mining; Blockchain; BTC; CBDC; central banks; Coinbase; cryptocurrency; crypto exchanges; DarkNet; debanked; decentralised finance (DeFin); Diem; digital currency; digital yuan; digital tokens; distributed currency; distributed ledgers; e-CNY; e-RMB; energy supply; Ethereum; exchange-traded fund/s (ETF/s); fiat currency; finance; FTX; fungibility; gold standard; inflation; Libra; money laundering; money supply; NASDAQ; NFT; payments systems; proof-of-stake; proof-of-work; Reserve Bank of Australia (RBA); SDG 9; store of value; SWIFT; technology disruption; technology hype cycle

Interviewee Profile

Sean Foley **(SF)** is Professor of Applied Finance at Macquarie University in Sydney and was previously at Sydney University. He is the Head of Decentralised Assets within the Digital Finance Cooperative Research Centre, bridging industry, government and academia. He's published many articles including about market structure of cryptocurrencies, and with catchy titles like 'Sex, Drugs and Bitcoin'[6] and 'Bitcoin's Dirty Little Secret'.[7] Sean is currently actively researching the financial applications and utilisation of cryptocurrencies, including automated market makers, DeFi lending protocols and stable coins.

DOI: 10.4324/9781003280316-15

The Interview

ML: What is cryptocurrency?

SF: We can start by thinking about traditional currency that we've had for some 2000 or, at least, 1,000 years. This evolved from gold or silver coins, through paper money to more recent electronic-based card and transfer systems such as Visa and Mastercard, credit and debit plastic cards that can be used globally.

Cryptocurrency is supra-national. Unlike the Australian dollar, which is created by the Reserve Bank of Australia (RBA) and backed by the government, cryptocurrencies are 'trustless' in the sense that they are neither created by a national central bank nor guaranteed by them. Rather, they are based on a decentralised ledger system called 'Blockchain'[8], so that anybody can investigate or 'validate' any of the transactions made since the inception of the Bitcoin, Ethereum or any other cryptocurrency. They sit in a 'blockchain' so that you can see these transactions contracted through time and you can 'prove' that you 'own' them. Also, similar to the Visa network, Bitcoin in particular allows you to send your Bitcoins between each other and keep track of the balances and so on.

ML: So cryptocurrencies are rooted in Blockchain technology and referred to as a 'distributed ledger' that you can access yourself, and you emphasise 'trust'. It seems to imply that those who use it don't actually trust conventional money channels, governments and banks, is that right?

SF: Many users may not trust conventional monetary authorities but also you don't need to trust each other either using crypto. You're not trusting any centralised system but you're relying on a sort of 'codified currency' as if it were to be a 'store of value'. That's why you get high volatility in evaluations of the crypto asset because it has no 'gold standard', nor the financial system backing of any government. Its value at any moment is similar to that of your family house; it's really worth what anyone else is willing to pay for it, at any given moment.

ML: How have people come to trust it as 'store of value'? Typically, governments can print money at their discretion and stand behind its value as redeemable at a bank on demand. These are called 'fiat currencies'. What's the comparative story with Bitcoin that it is also referred to as 'deflationary'?[9]

SF: With Bitcoin in particular, there is an inbuilt restriction in its coding on how many Bitcoins will ever be in existence. This is why people often point to it as an anti-inflationary asset, unlike Aussie dollars. For instance, we saw the Australian government spend; let's say, a hundred billion dollars to pay JobKeeper allowances to avoid a COVID19-induced recession. This tends to devalue the existing stock of Aussie dollars. We're seeing really low interest rates as people try to push their money into property and other real assets.

Bitcoins, on the other hand, are inherently constrained in their total number. This is unlike the case with 'digital gold': gold-backed money where as the price increases, we start to dig gold mines further underground or search under the oceans in attempts to find ever more gold supplies. With Bitcoin, there is a total capped limited supply against the number 'mined' and in circulation at any given time, leaving the finite remainder yet to be mined.

ML: What is the total capped supply of Bitcoin, how many are in circulation, and how is its supply increased over time so as to reach its finite limited supply cap?[10]

SF: The number of Bitcoins that entered the 'digital economy' system started at about 50 new Bitcoins every ten minutes, and that entry rate halves and then halves again every few years indefinitely. It currently stands at a rate of 12.5 and will continue halving every four years until it effectively approaches 0, estimated to be by the year 2140.

The network functions in a similar way to Visa in that, if you buy coffee for $5, you will be paying a 1% fee to facilitate that transaction. The Bitcoin 'miners' not only receive some new Bitcoins when they solve a block, but they also receive some fees. They are volunteer participants in the network who have their transactions recorded on the blockchain and act as a 'record-keeping' service.[11]

ML: You've mentioned this word 'mining' in a couple of contexts. Originally when you were referring to traditional currencies and gold mining and gold supplies but also in referring to Bitcoin as proof-of-work (PoW) mining,[12] which seems to involve networks of computers? What's that mining process all about?

SF: What you're doing when you're mining a Bitcoin is you're trying to solve a cryptographic puzzle or '256 hash' for a 'block'; that in this case happens to be a 'chain' algorithm. You're taking a bunch of texts representing the transactions between individuals and you're adding a random number to generate a 256-character random string. You're looking for there to be 10 or 12 zeros at the front of that particular string.

Effectively, you're using computers to solve algorithms iteratively, like checking a long division calculation, until there are a sufficient number of zeros in the remainder. Once you have done so, it can be easily proved because the hash of these transactions is equal to a particular number. But it's very difficult to find one of those situations where you get a number of leading zeros at the start. So they're just cryptographic puzzles in which computers at different 'nodes' are competing against each other to solve. This is what drives the immense electricity consumption required by the Bitcoin mining network.[13]

ML: This sounds horribly complicated. But Bitcoin is only a particular application of that much broader technology isn't it, and cryptocurrency is only a subset of what blockchain technology can be used for. So who invented Bitcoin and who owns and operates it?

SF: Yes, that's right generally, but with Bitcoin we don't know the answers. There's this rather anonymous and elusive figure by the name of Satoshi Nakamoto, whose identity no one has been able to establish.[14] He wrote a 'white paper' which effectively describes the architecture of the blockchain system and it's run by widely dispersed 'miners' working at decentralised computer 'nodes'.

A lot of them are in China, or other countries that have an abundance of cheap power that is often fossil fuel driven. Many coal-fired power plants in China have Bitcoin miners sitting just outside them, conveniently consuming all this electricity. In effect, it's much easier to export a Bitcoin than it is to export electricity itself. No one really controls the Bitcoin network. It is the 'first generation' of cryptocurrencies and it's in theory pretty much like the decentralised Visa network. It allows you to move Bitcoins around between each other for a small fee.

Ethereum is what runs all of the other cryptocurrency architecture.[15] A lot of the cryptocurrencies don't have their own Blockchain. They reside on the Ethereum blockchain that provides a kind of platform, a bit like Amazon Web Services. It allows you to run code on the blockchain itself, and this has facilitated development of the various cryptocurrency offerings.

They can be thought of as 'decentralised finance' (DeFin) applications. There are even 'stock exchanges' that are running in this way on the Internet. I think Venezuela has put their entire Stock Exchange into a decentralised format on the Ethereum blockchain, but there's also lending that you can do there. Ethereum is effectively a 'second-generation' version. It's a lot more known and controlled by a high school dropout called Vitalik Buterin,[16] who recently became the second youngest billionaire after Bill Gates. The Ethereum Foundation retained the first 2,000,000 blocks of Ethereum, which is worth about $2.5 billion. They continually improve the working and architecture, just as with any start-up.

ML: Is your catchy article title 'Bitcoin's Dirty Little Secret'[17] a reference to its mining energy use? And how significant is this issue on a global scale?

SF: It's a really big issue and it is a reference to electricity consumption. The Bitcoin network currently uses significantly more power every year, than Ireland as a country. It's because there's so much wasteful computation going on; we're all guessing and checking, and we may all be guessing the same incorrect answers before somebody eventually solves the block. Also, as the price goes up so does the intensity of the competition.

If you're going to solve, say, twelve and a half (12.5) Bitcoins at once and you think that each of those Bitcoins is worth $50,000, that's a very quick way to make $600,000 in 10 minutes. There's a lot of competition for the mining of new Bitcoins and it ends up consuming a heck of a lot of electricity. This is one of the reasons that cryptocurrencies, such as Ethereum, are moving towards a 'proof-of-stake' network rather than 'proof-of-work'.[18]

In the new mode, you don't need to be working against each other simply to arrive at a consensus about which transactions should be included in the blockchain.

ML: You have written about the market structure of cryptocurrencies.[19] How would you characterise the current market structure globally, and what are the regulatory control systems bearing on it?

SF: The different cryptocurrencies trade 24 hours, seven days a week on centralised exchanges where there's a single point of balance.[20] In the same way, you might think about the Australian Stock Exchange (ASX) although there would be fewer household names that are trading on crypto exchanges.

The problem with centralised exchanges is that they can be hacked. If you have your shareholding certificates and if the ASX goes down no one really cares because your stocks are still there. The cryptocurrency network is a little bit different because there's the ability to move the assets around without anyone knowing who you are. There have been numerous hacks of exchanges where people's cryptocurrencies have been stolen and moved around. So, the crypto market structure from a trading perspective looks very similar to a typical stock exchange.

As far as regulation goes though, many regulators, particularly the Australian regulators, have been reluctant to help guide this nascent crypto industry along a path that would facilitate its innovation. There's not a lot of regulation at the moment in Australia. AUSTRAC, just as they monitor bank transactions, also monitor crypto transactions through these cryptocurrency exchanges.[21]

But it really hasn't given any development guidance. The UK, on the other hand, through the Financial Conduct Authority (FCA), has created 'regulatory sandboxes' to try to facilitate various cryptocurrency innovations.[22] If you think about the dotcom bubble in the 2000s, you didn't throw the baby out with the bathwater. There were a lot of good innovations, but there were also a lot of scams. It's the same potentially with crypto.[23]

ML: Sean, how much illegal activity is operating using cryptocurrencies like Bitcoin, such as money laundering and tax evasion? What sectors are we talking about – drugs, sex, and gambling? What's going on with the illegal dark side?

SF: Everything, and anything, is going on.[24] You can hire a 'hitman';[25] pay for 'live streams' of all sorts of services; buy credit card details; buy illicit or prescription drugs. You can request that someone be hacked. There's all sorts of stuff going on in the 'Dark Net'.[26] If purchasing drugs online,

I may be reluctant to use my credit card and also, sending large wads of cash in the mail is not advisable or provable. So just in the same way that eBay really hit its stride when it was partnered with PayPal, there was an explosion in the 'Dark Net' around 2013 when it became possible to send a unit of value that was difficult for regulatory authorities to track over the Internet. For the illicit drug networks, it removed banks as intermediaries in the transactions which was similar to the disruption that eBay posed to traditional bricks and mortar shops by removing them as intermediaries between suppliers and customers. Instead of going into a dark alley and negotiating with somebody you don't know about with a wad of cash in your pocket, what you saw instead was a marketplace where people could rate each other, for example, for provision of drugs and various services. They'd have a reputation and a rating. You'd know exactly what kind of thing you were getting.

You wouldn't have to worry about it being necessarily 'adulterated' with say, strychnine or rat poison or whatever. In this way, we saw this facilitation of illegal drug trade using crypto. I like to think about it as in 'waves of adoption'. Initially crypto, or Bitcoin, was just something for nerds and no one really had an application of why we would want this distributed Internet currency. Its first real application, the second wave, was the 'Dark Net' where it became used for money laundering, gambling and the avoidance of capital controls. For example, getting money out of countries like Korea, Brazil, Russia, China where it's not easy to move your money across borders.

The third wave was speculators. As the price of Bitcoin rose and people used it for whatever purposes, the speculators moved in to capitalise on the movement. Then and over the past two to three years, the hedge funds moved in. Now, we're seeing what I consider to be the 'last wave' of investment, which is Bitcoin 'exchange-traded funds' (ETF).[27] Canada has authorised four, or five, such funds. In some countries, they've got a few.

Australia is currently looking at regulating Bitcoin and Ethereum ETF on the Australian Stock Exchange (ASX).[28] This means that you don't have to handle the transactions yourself; you can buy just as you might an ASX200 ETF on the ASX.

ML: Some mainstream businesses are now getting behind cryptocurrencies, aren't they? For example, Elon Musk saying that he's going to accept Bitcoin as currency for his EVs and various other developments.[29] How is the world of commerce buying into this?

SF: More and more corporations are able to accept Bitcoin or Ethereum as a unit of currency. It's moving away from those illegal corners of the Internet to becoming more mainstream. As you say, Elon Musk has said that he'd accept Bitcoin. Microsoft accepts Bitcoin, and some credit cards will store your balance in Bitcoin or Ethereum.

Anytime you make a transaction, it'll just tell you how much crypto you need to make the purchase that you require. We're seeing a lot of integration with mainstream commercial players. I think people are starting to see the value in it. You're starting to see institutional adoption too.

Coinbase is one of the largest cryptocurrency exchanges and it recently listed on the NASDAQ in the US.[30] Regulation is coming full circle, and recognising that cryptocurrency is here to stay. We might have said that Bitcoin was a fad in 2015 and that it will blow over, but it is not a fad.

We're going to see a continued wave of innovation, particularly on the Ethereum blockchain. As we move to digitised finance, you get lending applications, decentralised marketplaces, non-fungible tokens (NFT) for art, all sorts of weird and wonderful ideas that can be facilitated by a blockchain; not just the movement in store of value.

ML: If you buy Bitcoin, can you cash out or are you stuck with Bitcoin?

SF: It's just like any other asset. If you buy BHP shares, you're not stuck with BHP. You can trade that BHP stock back for Aussie dollars and then go buy RioTinto, Telstra or any other stock. It's quite similar to Bitcoin. You can move it to an exchange, and from there you can sell it back for US$, AU$ or any of the other cryptocurrencies.

ML: You hear apocryphal stories about losing your password,[31] or the website reference; so how is that going to work out?

SF: Yes, it definitely is an issue and I think that's why a lot of people choose to leave their cryptocurrency on an exchange. We've got exchanges like BTC markets who facilitate the trading of Aussie dollars into cryptocurrencies. If you leave your Bitcoin with them, you'll be calling them then if you lose your password. It's fine.

Whereas, if you choose to withdraw that Bitcoin from the exchange and store it in your own home drive; then yes, if you lose the private keys for that Bitcoin address, you will have lost your money. There is no 1800 number to call for assistance!

ML: Didn't Facebook try to launch a crypto digital currency called Libra?[32]

SF: Yeah, the Facebook Libra was a project that was meant to be launched in 2020, and they'd started talking about it in 2019. It's subsequently turned into something called Diem,[33] with the idea that Facebook looked to create its own 'fiat currency' that would have some sort of stable value,[34] rather than with the price of Bitcoin which is entirely unregulated and oscillates wildly as we know.

At the other extreme is what we call central bank digital currencies.[35] China has just introduced one. Finland and Switzerland are looking at implementing their own, which is effectively just a tokenised Aussie dollar, which would have a pegged one-to-one value with a single national currency. Facebook Libra or now Diem was proposing to create a 'basket of currencies' using the British pound, the Euro and the US dollar. You would peg one Diem to the basket mix and it would always have a value related to the currencies of those large, developed economies.

About 20% of the world population, particularly in, say China, India and Africa; there are large numbers of unbanked individuals. So in countries like Ghana and Kenya, mobile phone companies step into the banking void and set up phone credit systems as a form of currency that people found very accessible and easy to transmit using their mobile phones.

I can send you $6 with Vodafone, and you could send $5 to your friend, and they use it as a mechanism of payment, particularly when they don't have banking infrastructure in place. Facebook realised that if they could make a stable store of value then they would be able to capture a large portion of this global unbanked population.[36] They would do that by joining with other companies who would act as validators of the transactions so it wouldn't be as electricity intensive, or wasteful as the 'proof-of-work' crypto network.

Companies like Uber and Visa would form the basis of this network and if the price of the currency went up, say because too many people bought them, then they would just print more. If the price of the Diem dropped too far away from the peg that they had committed to, then companies like Visa and Facebook would be tasked with buying back some of the Diem to maintain its value. That is the essential idea behind the Facebook cryptocurrency proposal.

ML: Another concept that comes in here is 'fungibility', meaning that any one dollar is much the same as another dollar; and one Bitcoin, as I understand, is much the same as another Bitcoin. In other words, they are 'fungible' or directly and mutually replaceable.[37] But now we have this category of rather intriguing, so-called 'non-fungible tokens' (NFT),[38] and we've just heard about a world record price of many tens of millions of dollars being paid for a piece of artwork in a JPEG, digital form which doesn't even belong to the person that buys it.[39] What's this all about?

SF: That's exactly right. One BHP share is much the same as another and I can trade them all independently in that they don't have individual serial numbers. They are fungible assets.

On the other hand, things like artwork or properties, are non-fungible, for example, my house is not the same as your house, even if they're on the same street. The Ethereum network has provided the ability for non-fungible tokens to be traded.

People are just starting to investigate the idea; it's almost like baseball cards in a sense, or comic books. You've got a certain asset that is not the same as another and we can create these different classes of almost collectible items. Artists like Banksy and others are trying to put onto a blockchain the ownership of this electronic artwork. I think it is quite strange, even bizarre because the only benefit you get is the ability to say: well, hey, that belongs to me; bragging rights maybe. Anyone else can still reproduce it, copy it and whatever.

ML: Is there some speculative or gambling element involved in these NFTs?

SF: There is definitely a speculative element but if you think about graffiti artists like Banksy, it is hard to sell your work on a piece of a wall so maybe this is a way to monetise a different art form. It does feel like a speculative bubble and who knows where it is going to go. While I own a whole bunch of Ethereum, I won't be rushing out to buy a whole bunch of digital art.

ML: How are mainstream banks, say the 'big four' in Australia, approaching cryptocurrency?[40]

SF: For many years they've approached it with a very long pole and with a lot of caution. The major currency exchanges in Australia have been very public with their experiences by which they were 'debanked' and the big four refused to deal with them. This was probably driven by a regulatory regime and the perception that Bitcoin is driven primarily by money laundering and that touching it is very risky.[41] But I think that is changing.

Recently, we've seen the launch of Coinbase on NASDAQ and that resulted in part in a significant windfall of over $200 million to Westpac from its seed investment it made in that fledgling exchange two or three years ago.[42] The major banks are starting to see this as a legitimate investment and with a slightly less cautious approach to cryptocurrencies. But it does pose an existential threat.

There are a number of emerging services, for example, you can borrow against your Ethereum by taking a spot contract and borrow dollars or AUS$ as you would against your house as an asset. If the asset price falls, they sell your Ethereum and you get the start. It's threatening to the governments' role as an economic entity and they have been wary of Libra and Diem by putting up barriers and regulatory hurdles to them. If all trade were to use, say, Diems instead AUS$; then the government can't print money, can't sell money, can't control money via interest rates, etc.

There are similar existential threats to banks. If you start moving payment networks and borrowing and lending away from the big four, it is a big threat not only to the banks but in part to the economy which is heavily tied to financial services.[43,44] But if we can harness the benefits that are already here, such as decentralised registries, decentralised exchanges and decentralised lending; then we can become an innovator and continue to remain a global leader in financial services.

ML: You mentioned countries such as China moving to and thinking about national currencies using a cryptocurrency base. Could this become significantly disruptive to countries' macroeconomic policies and currencies?

SF: Totally. I think that is why China has been so keen to adopt the digital yuan, e-CNY or e-RMB. They recognise the threat posed by a central bank digital currency (CBDC) to traditional payment system networks, such as SWIFT, who are quite worried about international money transfers.

It definitely has the potential, if the digital yuan is used as the 'rails' by which to move funds in and out of the crypto sphere. It may threaten, for example, the role of the US$ as the main reserve currency.[45]

We're starting to see central banks globally adopt cryptocurrency as a reserve asset alongside gold, the US$ backing that they tend to hold. It's an evolving space and it's threatening not just to regular enterprise but also the role of national currencies as a stronghold of values globally.

ML: You've mentioned some consideration by the Australian government of regulatory systems for cryptocurrency. Is the RBA playing in this space, pronouncing any views or doing anything?

SF: The RBA has been looking at creating a central bank digital currency for the Australian dollar, but they've been talking about this for the last five years, so I'm not holding my breath.[46] But they are definitely cognisant that this is something they need to at least be aware of and maybe start playing in.[47]

Conclusion

Cryptocurrency, most widely known through Bitcoin, is a potentially highly disruptive technological innovation impacting globally and domestically on banking, finance, investment and trading systems. It is developing rapidly and at the early stages of the innovation hype cycle that sees it moving through phases of high expectations, through disappointed expectations and eventually to widespread diffusion and adoption.

From a business model sustainability perspective, it is at too early a stage to make judgements. But as a frontier of often marginal economic activity, the technology has already been exposed as highly energy consuming, exploitative of labour, and speculative financially to the extent that it potentially threatens consumer confidence.

The key underlying technology is Blockchain which provides a platform for distributed ledger keeping, accounting and auditing not only of currencies but in many other sectors and supply chains of economic activity. The authentication and validation of crypto transactions involve a process known as 'mining' that consumes vast amounts of computing power and associated energy, on the scale of small country electricity consumption, to competitively solve complex 'blocks' of encrypted codes that is called 'proof of work'. These 'miners' tend to be located close to large power stations in developing countries where labour is cheap and energy is produced by fossil fuels.

As it moves through successive waves of innovation or disruption from marginal through to mainstream, it draws in a wider array of users and business models, including hedge funds, investment funds, exchanges, crypto platforms such as Ethereum, corporations, banks and governments, including central banks. A myriad of potentially highly disruptive, decentralised finance applications holds out the prospect of democratising access to finance, particularly in poorer countries with large, 'unbanked' populations.

Cryptocurrencies have been developed in lightly regulated, if not unregulated, environments which has been a spur to their innovation and diffusion. Increasingly, however, governments and international organisations have been moving to put in place-specific regulations, compliance and enforcement regimes. Inevitably, as digital currencies move through the early stages of their hype cycle and innovation waves; government regulators are prompted into action by high-profile failures, scandals and frauds such as FTX[48] that precipitates a sense of crisis.[49]

Notes

1 Frankenfield, J. (2023) What is Bitcoin? How to mine, buy, and use it, *Investopedia*, 13th October www.investopedia.com/terms/b/bitcoin.asp
2 Statista (2023) *Bitcoin (BTC) price per day from April 2013–9 October 2023* www.statista.com/statistics/326707/bitcoin-price-index/
3 Baur, D.G., & Dimpfl, T. (2021) The volatility of Bitcoin and its role as a medium of exchange and a store of value. *Empirical Economics,* 61 (5): 2663–2683
4 Dedehayir, O. and Steinert, M. (2016) The hype cycle model: A review and future directions, *Technological Forecasting and Social Change*, 108, July: 28–41
5 Wörner, D., Von Bomhard, T., Schreier, Y.P. and Bilgeri, D. (2016) *The Bitcoin Ecosystem: Disruption Beyond Financial Services?* ECIS 2016 Proceedings, Association for Information Systems at the AIS Electronic Library (AISeL), Research Paper 33 http://aisel.aisnet.org/ecis2016_rp/33
6 Foley, S., Karlsen, J.R. and Putniņš, T.J. (2019) Sex, drugs, and Bitcoin: How much illegal activity is financed through cryptocurrencies? *The Review of Financial Studies,* 32 (5): 1798–1853
7 O'Malley, N. and Zappone, C. (2021) Bitcoin's dirty little secret: It's not easy being green, *Sydney Morning Herald*, 8th May www.smh.com.au/environment/climate-change/bitcoin-s-dirty-little-secret-it-s-not-easy-being-green-20210506-p57pki.html
8 Yli-Huumo, J., Ko, D., Choi, S., Park, S. and Smolander, K. (2016) Where is current research on blockchain technology? – a systematic review. *PLoS One*, 11 (10): e0163477
9 Abid, I., Bouri, E., Galariotis, E., Guesmi, K., & Mzoughi, H. (2023) Bitcoin vs. fiat currencies: Insights from extreme dependence and risk spillover analysis with financial markets. *International Review of Financial Analysis,* 90, November: 102806
10 Abrol, A. (2023) How many Bitcoins are there and how many are left to mine? *Blockchain Council,* 28th September www.blockchain-council.org/cryptocurrency/how-many-bitcoins-are-left/

11 Lemieux, V.L. (2021) Blockchain and recordkeeping. *Computers*, 10 (11): 135
12 Nevil, S. (2023) What is proof of work (PoW) in blockchain? *Investopedia*, 27th May www.investopedia.com/terms/p/proof-work.asp
13 Huestis, S. (2023) Cryptocurrency's energy consumption problem, *Rocky Mountain Institute*, 30th January https://rmi.org/cryptocurrencys-energy-consumption-problem/
14 Percy, S. (2023) Leadership lessons from Bitcoin founder Satoshi Nakamoto, *Forbes*, 31st October www.forbes.com/sites/sallypercy/2023/10/31/leadership-lessons-from-bitcoin-founder-satoshi-nakamoto/?sh=6a3325943b2f
15 Samuel, C.N., Glock, S., Verdier, F. and Guitton-Ouhamou, P. (2021) Choice of ethereum clients for private blockchain: Assessment from proof of authority perspective, in *2021 IEEE International Conference on Blockchain and Cryptocurrency (ICBC)*, IEEE Sydney, Australia, pp. 1–5
16 Vitalik Buterin's website https://vitalik.ca/
17 O'Malley and Zappone (2021), op cit
18 Wendl, M., Doan, M.H., & Sassen, R. (2023) The environmental impact of cryptocurrencies using proof of work and proof of stake consensus algorithms: A systematic review. *Journal of Environmental Management*, 326, January: 116530
19 Svec, J., Aspris, A. and Foley, S. (2020) Market structure of cryptocurrencies, in Corbet, S., Urquhart, A. and Yarovaya, L. (eds) *Cryptocurrency and Blockchain Technology*, Chapter 6, pp. 97–112, Berlin: Walter de Gruyter
20 Aspris, A., Foley, S., Svec, J. and Wang, L. (2021) Decentralized exchanges: The "wild west" of cryptocurrency trading, *International Review of Financial Analysis*, 77, October: 101845
21 AUSTRAC and FinTel Alliance (2022) *Preventing the Criminal Abuse of Digital Currencies: Financial Crime Guide*, April www.austrac.gov.au/sites/default/files/2022-04/AUSTRAC_FCG_PreventingCriminalAbuseOfDigitalCurrencies_FINAL.pdf
22 Huang, S.S. (2021) Crypto assets regulation in the UK: An assessment of the regulatory effectiveness and consistency, *Journal of Financial Regulation and Compliance*, 29 (3): 336–351
23 Banks, D.A. (2022) Crypto was meant to solve financial corruption. The FTX scandal shows it's got worse, *The Guardian*, 16th December www.theguardian.com/commentisfree/2022/dec/15/crypto-financial-and-corruption-making-it-worse-ftx
24 Foley et al (2019), op cit
25 AP (2023) US woman who hired hitman using bitcoin to kill ex-husband gets five years in prison, *The Guardian*, 23rd July www.theguardian.com/technology/2023/jul/22/nevada-woman-hired-hitman-kill-ex-husband-sentenced
26 Kumar, A. and Rosenbach, E. (2019) The truth about the dark web, finance and development, *International Monetary Fund (IMF)*, September www.imf.org/en/Publications/fandd/issues/2019/09/the-truth-about-the-dark-web-kumar
27 Todorov, K. (2021) Launch of the first US bitcoin ETF: Mechanics, impact, and risks, *BIS Quarterly Review*, December www.bis.org/publ/qtrpdf/r_qt2112t.htm
28 ASX, *Investing in Crypto* www.asx.com.au/investors/learn-about-our-investment-solutions/etfs-and-other-etps/investing-in-crypto-assets
29 Partridge, J. (2021) Bitcoin price back above $40,000 after Elon Musk comments, *The Guardian*, 15th June www.theguardian.com/technology/2021/jun/14/tesla-will-resume-accepting-bitcoin-when-it-uses-more-clean-energy-says-musk
30 Toppa, S. (2023) Coinbase sees bitcoin ETF opportunity as 'much greater than just enabling new capital, *The Street*, 15th November www.thestreet.com/crypto/markets/coinbase-sees-bitcoin-etf-opportunity-much-greater-than-just-enabling-new-capital
31 Middleton, J. and Agencies (2022) Man who threw away £150m in bitcoin hopes AI and robot dogs will get it back, *The Guardian* www.theguardian.com/technol

ogy/2022/aug/02/man-hopes-ai-and-robot-dogs-will-help-recover-150m-in-bitcoin-from-landfill

32 Brühl, V. (2020) Libra – a differentiated view on Facebook's virtual currency project. *Intereconomics,* 55 (1): 54–61

33 Rrustemi, J., & Tuchschmid, N.S. (2020) Facebook's digital currency venture "Diem": The new Frontier . . . or a Galaxy far, far away? *Technology Innovation Management Review,* 10 (12): 19–30

34 Israel, K.F. (2021) The fiat money illusion: On the cost-efficiency of modern central banking, *The World Economy,* 44 (6): 1701–1719

35 Cheng, Y. (2023) The current status of central bank digital currencies and their development, in *SHS Web of Conferences,* Vol. 170, p. 01010, EDP Sciences. Kaifeng, China https://www.shs-conferences.org/articles/shsconf/abs/2023/19/contents/contents.html

36 Carmona, T. (2022) *Debunking the Narratives about Cryptocurrency and Financial Inclusion,* Brookings, Research Paper, 26th October www.brookings.edu/articles/debunking-the-narratives-about-cryptocurrency-and-financial-inclusion/

37 Berg, A. (2020) The identity, fungibility and anonymity of money, *Economic Papers,* 39 (2): 104–117

38 Kraizberg, E. (2023) Non-fungible tokens: A bubble or the end of an era of intellectual property rights, *Financial Innovation,* 9 (1): 1–20

39 Cascone, S. (2021) The 10 most expensive NFT artworks of 2021, from Beeple's \$69 million 'everydays' to XCOPY's \$3.8 million portrait of 'some asshole', *Artnet,* 27th December https://news.artnet.com/market/most-expensive-nft-art-yearend-2052822

40 Eyers, J. (2023) How crypto is forcing banks, funds towards new digital asset markets, *Australian Financial Review,* 13th October www.afr.com/companies/financial-services/how-crypto-is-forcing-banks-funds-towards-new-digital-asset-markets-20231013-p5ec0c

41 Belot, H. (2023) Crypto exchange Binance has Australian financial services licence cancelled by ASIC, *The Guardian,* 6th April www.theguardian.com/business/2023/apr/06/crypto-exchange-binances-australian-financial-services-licence-cancelled-by-asic

42 Yeates, C. (2021) Westpac set for windfall in US Coinbase float, *Sydney Morning Herald,* 7th April www.smh.com.au/business/banking-and-finance/westpac-set-for-windfall-in-us-coinbase-float-20210407-p57h8y.html

43 Partington, R. (2021a) Digital currencies pose threat to economy, warns Bank of England, *The Guardian,* 7th June www.theguardian.com/business/2021/jun/7/digital-currencies-pose-threat-to-economy-warns-bank-of-england

44 Partington, R. (2021b) Bitcoin could become 'worthless', Bank of England warns, *The Guardian,* 15th December www.theguardian.com/technology/2021/dec/14/bitcoin-could-become-worthless-bank-of-england-warns

45 Aysan, A.F. and Kayani, F.N. (2022) China's transition to a digital currency does it threaten dollarization? *Asia and the Global Economy,* 2 (1): 100023

46 Lowe, P. (2021) Payments: The future?, address, *Australian Payments Network Summit,* 9th December www.rba.gov.au/speeches/2021/sp-gov-2021-12-09.html

47 Alam, N. (2022) Australia is investigating a digital currency, or e-dollar, but its benefits seem slight and the risks to privacy large, *The Conversation,* 5th May https://theconversation.com/australia-is-investigating-a-digital-currency-or-e-dollar-but-its-benefits-seem-slight-and-the-risks-to-privacy-large-180099

48 White, S. (2023) The trial of 'crypto king' SBF is the Enron scandal for millennials, *USA Today,* 12th October www.usatoday.com/story/opinion/voices/2023/10/12/ftx-founder-sam-bankman-fried-trial-crypto/71141643007/

49 Clarke, T. (2022) *Corporate Governance: Cycles of Innovation, Crisis and Reform,* London: SAGE

14 Small Modular Nuclear Reactors (SMRs) Untried and Untested

Why All the Political Interest Now?

Interview With Jim Green

Introduction

There is a renewed political interest in nuclear energy issues at the national[1,2] and state government levels,[3] including in NSW in the context of decarbonisation, energy and climate policies.[4] A report from the NSW Legislative Council, Upper House, recommended lifting the ban on nuclear energy exploration and use in NSW.[5] There's also a draft bill to that effect before the NSW Parliament,[6] from upper house One Nation member Mark Latham. The then Deputy Premier, National Party member John Barilaro has been promoting the role of nuclear reactors and energy, including small, modular nuclear reactors (SMRs).[7]

The NSW Productivity Commission in a broad-ranging report aimed at lifting the productivity of the NSW economy commented, among other things, the opportunities emerging for SMRs for electricity generation and recommended removing the regulatory ban for SMRs.[8,9] These reports focus on 'innovative new nuclear power technologies' and especially on 'emerging new generation iii and iv reactors'[10] including SMRs.[11]

Keywords: AUKUS (Australia-UK-USA trilateral security pact), climate culture wars; cost overruns; decarbonisation; economics of nuclear power generation; electricity costs; energy; floating reactors; global nuclear industry; innovation learning curve; nuclear; nuclear fuel cycle; nuclear renaissance; SDG 7; reactor decommissioning; renewable energy cost; small modular nuclear reactors (SMRs); technology neutral

Interviewee Profile

Dr. Jim Green (JG) is the National Nuclear Campaign Director with Friends of the Earth (FOE). He holds an honours degree in Public Health (Wollongong) and a doctorate in science and technology studies (Wollongong), focused on the Lucas Heights research reactor debates. In addition to his activism, public advocacy and media commentary, he writes on nuclear power, including an extensive blog 'Nuclear Free Campaign'.[12]

DOI: 10.4324/9781003280316-16

The Interview

ML: Jim, what exactly are we talking about when we talk about small, modular nuclear reactors (SMRs)? What is the specific technology involved and why is it suddenly surfacing in political debate, particularly in the context of climate change policies?

JG: Those are very broad questions, so I'll take them in turn. What are we talking about? There's a history with SMRs, and it's a history of failure to date. The US Army was into the idea going way back 50 years or more. In fact, eight of these reactors were problematic and expensive and the programme was discontinued.[13]

The most interesting example is India, because that's the only country where there's been any serial continued rollout of a particular type of small reactor. It is the only real-world 'test case' we've got of whether the costs really come down and whether you can learn from your mistakes and improve the technology.[14] And it wasn't a great experiment, the best evidence being that the programme has been completely discontinued by the Indian government. Also, one of the ideas is that you can build these reactors quickly. But India built them very, very slowly, building one gigawatt of capacity, which is the equivalent of one large reactor, but over two decades. There was nothing exciting in that experiment which, as I've said, has been discontinued. To sum up, what we've got now, there's a few reactors that are under construction which have been described as SMRs, although they only loosely fit that definition.[15]

Argentina has been building one for decades, but the cost has escalated obscenely, with a 22-fold increase. They're looking at the best part of a billion dollars for a very small reactor at just 30 to 35 megawatts (MW). This is ridiculously expensive. Russia built a 'floating reactor', in other words, a twin reactor mounted on the back of a barge. The cost of that increased fourfold. The power it produces is estimated to cost $260 Australian per MW hour. To put that dollar figure in context, the Minerals Council of Australia says that you'd need to produce power at $60–80 Australian per MW hour to be competitive, which is far lower than the actual Russian reactor cost. Ghana is building some reactors, but they're not terribly serious about it, and there's concrete evidence that it is linked to their weapons programme and not to any interest in low-carbon electricity.

In summary, there's very few of these reactors under construction or operating. It's just an awful lot of hype and an awful lot of companies that are trying to attract government funding. That's really the main activity that's going on in the SMR sector.

ML: The nuclear power industry has been operating on a large scale globally for some time now since the Second World War. So why are small reactors now being talked about against the backdrop of what is happening with the global nuclear industry? Is it an industry that's growing with investment and production of electricity and with a place in the fuel and energy mix going forward on a global scale?

JG: One-word answer is definitely, 'no'. A short summary of the industry tells a fascinating story. The current number of nuclear reactors and power output is much the same as it was a decade ago. In fact, it is much the same as it was 30 years ago. There has really been no change.

You might remember all that talk about a 'nuclear renaissance' a decade ago and they did get up a head of steam.[16,17] The number of reactors under construction jumped very sharply in the late 2000s. So, there was some reality to this 'renaissance'; although there was nothing superhuman about it, had it continued, the industry would have been on a path for slow growth. But it didn't continue. The disaster that upturned the whole nuclear industry was, as everyone knows, Fukushima (2011).[18] There were multiple fires and chemical explosions that had a dramatic negative impact on the nuclear industry, not only in Japan but worldwide.[19,20]

That's the disaster that everyone knows about, but people are not so familiar with other nuclear 'economic disasters'. In the UK, there were six projects, only one of which has gone ahead and that is costing roughly A$25 billion per reactor for large reactors.[21] Even so, $25 billion is right out of the ballpark in terms of being cost competitive with non-nuclear alternatives.

I could give many other examples, but I'll just give one more. In the United States, the country with more reactors than any other country and more nuclear experience. Again, there were dozens of proposals, but only two of them got off the ground, one of them in South Carolina, and they abandoned that project in 2017 after the expenditure of A$13 billion. They ended up with $13 billion worth of concrete and scrap metal sitting at an unused nuclear plant. The other project in the United States is in Georgia and will likely reach completion sooner or later.[22] The original project cost estimate for two large reactors was A$20 billion. The current cost estimate is A$40 billion, so again, it's well out of the ballpark economically.

ML: Am I getting the impression that on a global scale, the rate of investment and production of nuclear-powered electricity is flattening out or falling? And that new nuclear plants are not being invested in around the world?

JG: Some are, but not a great number, and currently – and over the past decade or more – the number of new reactors coming online has matched the number of reactors that have been shut down. We're not going to see a repeat of this 30-plus year pattern of stagnation where the number of reactors now is much the same as it was 30 years ago. That's not going to happen because 30 years ago we had around 400 reactors that were new or young and had a long lifetime ahead of them. But currently, we've got a global fleet of power reactors that are ageing and are nearing their shutdown time.

Even organisations like the International Energy Agency (IEA) use terminology like a 'tsunami' of reactor closures and de-commissionings coming up. The industry would need to build about ten reactors every year worldwide just to stand still and to maintain the current pattern of stagnation, and there's no sign of that happening. If you look at the past few years, the number of reactor construction starts has been three or four. Well short of the ten that they would need just to stand still, let alone to have any growth.[23]

The reason I'm talking about large reactors is by way of 'segue' into this discussion about SMRs. The only reason there's all this hype about SMRs currently is because more and more people, companies, governments, and utilities are quite aware that the prospects for more large reactors are vanishing by the day. If the industry is going to survive, it will have to innovate. It's in that context that they're reinventing this idea of building fleets of small, modular reactors.

ML: It is against this background, that we might see this interest in small reactors as sort of response to the situation with the big ones; with the smaller ones offering presumably for the proponents the idea that they're safer because they're smaller scale, cheaper to build, and less risky, if they can be developed properly and implemented. I believe that there was a CSIRO report in the past year or so looking into the cost and technology of small modular reactors of the sort we're discussing.[24] What were its findings?[25]

JG: It didn't really cover itself in glory because the source of their cost estimates was unclear. With that qualification and accepting their estimate that power from SMRs, it would cost roughly A$300 per MW hour. If you look at wind and solar at a cost of $50–60 per MW hour, you see a massive difference. There's also been some work looking into comparing nuclear costs versus the costs of renewables plus storage. And again, without getting into the details but broadly speaking, it seems clear that renewables plus storage is a cheaper option than SMRs or large nuclear for that matter.[26]

ML: You mentioned in passing SMRs being cheaper and less risky and so on. Those claims are hotly contested and not something that everyone would accept. When you look at the cost of SMRs or any investment, you've got to distinguish between the construction and the long-term operating life. What is the situation with construction costs per unit of energy delivered with small modular reactors?

JG: Well, there's so few projects on which we can have a reality-based discussion of costs, but I mentioned the ones with which I'm familiar. The one in Argentina is interesting because it's a scaled-down conventional power reactor and its cost ought to be manageable, but it's not. It's the best part of a billion Australian dollars for a reactor which will have 32 megawatts of outputs, making it obscenely expensive.

The Russian one, from memory, was similar, maybe about a billion dollars with capacity of about 50 megawatts. The Russians are using that floating reactor to power oil and gas drilling for fossil fuel mining operations in the Arctic and not for any interest in low-carbon energy. In that case, what options do you have for power generation in the Arctic since you can't just connect to the Russian power grid in such a remote area? Maybe it's economically viable in such niche applications but it's certainly not for mainstream power supply, whether in Russia, Australia or anywhere else.

That also touches on an important point. There might be some niche applications for these small reactors, in our fossil fuel mining operations in the Arctic, the South China Sea or elsewhere, and in quasi-military or geopolitical operations. For example, Russia's attempts to attain control of the Arctic area and the Northern Sea route is a classic case. They are planning to build more floating power reactors for that purpose, but as I've just mentioned that has no relevance whatsoever to large-scale supply of electricity in any country, including Russia or Australia.[27]

ML: Because costs are such a major issue, I understand that the previously mentioned CSIRO report quoted something like A$16,000 a kilowatt for construction but that subsequently they revised that cost downwards by more than half. Does this reflect some huge innovation learning curve,[28] where the costs of these small reactors are falling steeply?

JG: Yes, that's the theory and you are right with those figures. CSIRO gives a range of possible figures, but the current construction cost figure they're sticking with is in that range of $16,000 per kilowatt and they do anticipate further learning and sharp drops in cost over some decades hence.

The problem I have with that is that there's no history of learning in the nuclear industry. It's often said to be the only industry with a 'negative learning' rate, even in countries which really ought to be able to improve their performance, such as the United States and France, the two countries with the most reactors. Costs have clearly increased, so there's a negative learning.

Why would you be assuming that the costs of new reactors, small or large, would be dropping more than half the current value when the experience has been that costs increase? It just doesn't make any sense. I think that CSIRO and our own Australian Energy Market Operator

(AEMO) were also getting bullied and harassed and they're just throwing the ball back into the nuclear lobby court.

If I may segue into another point; so much of this stuff just doesn't matter. There may be this minority nuclear push in NSW that you've mentioned; but for the government and its leaders – such as the Premier and the Energy Minister – it is a case of in one ear, and out the other. They understand that nuclear power is not viable economically. That it would be difficult politically. They are just not interested. They know that renewables are far cheaper. The federal parliament held an inquiry two years ago, and one of the fascinating features was the critical negative submissions about the prospects for nuclear power from the South Australian Liberal government, from the Tasmanian Liberal government, from the NSW Coalition government, though I'm not sure, but also definitely from the Queensland Liberal National Party.

Meanwhile, there's a push going on at the fringes which I would generally describe as being part of the 'climate wars' and the broader 'culture wars', hence the involvement of people like Mark Latham and John Barilaro. But governments have to deal with these issues seriously, whether Labor or Liberal, at state or federal level, and they're just not interested at all.[29]

ML: You mentioned that the innovation learning rates in nuclear generally and including small nuclear reactors are negative, that is, cost increases over time rather than falling. Why is that the case? Nuclear reactors have been around a long while, even the small ones, and have also been operating in small niches like submarines. Is there a technology problem with nuclear *per se*? Why are the costs so out of hand and unpredictable?[30]

JG: A lot of people who are much more familiar than I am with the details of these issues still throw their hands up in the air and I can't really work it out. My best answer is that safety requirements have increased over the years and that simply means more costs: technology costs, buffer zones, regulatory costs, and insurance costs, although the latter are usually covered by the state, but all these sorts of costs have been going up year on year and decade on decade. I would say that's the main reason why you get a negative learning rate with nuclear.

The industry's main response to that has been to increase the size of reactors. The ones that have been built in the UK are gigantic; two reactors at 1,600 MW each, whereas a typical large reactor is 1000 MW. But the reason I mention that is that it's just so counterintuitive and arguably so ridiculous to imagine that small reactors will solve the economic problems when they will almost certainly worsen them because you get dis-economies of scale. If you're building say, a 250 MW reactor, you will get one-quarter of the power of a 1000 MW large reactor, but all your other costs are not going to scale down by a factor of four. There are big economies of scale in nuclear reactors, in materials, staffing, security: those sorts of things don't simply scale down with smaller reactors which just don't make any economic sense

For all the hype around SMRs, the level of private-sector funding is laughably low and not nearly enough to get projects off the ground. Governments are also very sceptical. Typically, if you're looking at the US or Canada or the UK, they're throwing tens of millions of dollars at some of these projects, but you need hundreds of millions, indeed billions of dollars to get these reactors off the ground and it's not at all clear where that money is going to come from. A few of these small reactors will be built because there's such desperation in the industry that they'll throw in some dollars and lobby furiously for government subsidies but most of it's just hot air. It's going nowhere.[31]

ML: Some of the argument that's been made for SMRs, including here in NSW, suggests that there is a place in the response to climate change; because they're obviously, a non-greenhouse gas emitting energy source and therefore good for the environment, but can the project timelines involved, deliver an impact on the time frames needed to meet the climate target commitments?

JG: Again, there's just so few real-world, completed projects on which to base an answer to that question.[32] I have done calculations for those three or four projects where some figures were available, and construction time frames have been 8 to 12 years, and in some cases those reactors have been completed.

In Argentina, they've been talking about building SMRs since the 1980s, and they still haven't built their first reactor. When we're talking about learning rates, you know, the industry in their imagination thinks that you might build these small reactors over a period of three or four years, and you'll learn from your mistakes and improve the technology and it's going to work like that. But in Argentina, they've been talking about this endlessly for 40 years and still haven't built their first reactor.

ML: Government regulations have possibly been a factor in the slowing of these learning rates from a safety and other points of view. The reports in NSW, particularly the Productivity Commission report, seem generally to place strong emphasis on improving productivity in many sectors by deregulating what it calls 'outdated' regulations. The NSW Legislative Council committee recommended that the government should deregulate nuclear small modular reactors so that the private sector can get ahead with it at a faster rate.

JG: Yes, it's interesting. I mean, it's a defensible position to be critical and sceptical of nuclear power, but still to want the bans at state and federal levels to be repealed. As you'd know, Friends of the Earth (FOE) and other like-minded groups have some predictable responses to that, whether it's waste management, safety, public acceptance and so on.

Another important point is that nuclear energy politics is tied up with the political ideology of the 'culture wars'. That's why people like Clive Palmer, John Barilaro and Mark Latham are involved; they are the 'culture warriors'. If you turn on Sky News and watch for a couple of months, I'll bet you they'll be promoting nuclear power as part of the 'culture wars'.

The risk and one of the reasons why we should maintain the nuclear bans is to protect taxpayers from 'nutjob' 'culture warrior' politicians who would gladly bet billions of dollars of our money on extremely high-risk projects. To give just one example of how high risk these projects can be and how much taxpayers can lose, take the United Kingdom twin reactor project. The cost, as I mentioned, is about A$25 billion per reactor while the Chinese and French investors are being guaranteed a very healthy sum for every unit of energy produced by their reactors for 35 years.

That subsidy is already roughly twice the going rate for wholesale supply of electricity in the UK. The total subsidies for that project, the European Union estimates at £30 billion or EUR 58 billion.[33]

A A$50 billion subsidy is just unbelievable. Those are the sorts of costs that I don't want to be imposed on me or you or any other Australian taxpayer by crackpot 'nutjobs'. The current legal bans protect us from those economic risks and that's one of the strong reasons I think the bans should be maintained.

ML: The government report that I mentioned is calling for a 'technology neutral' approach to climate change responses.[34] Yet, as we can see, nuclear power seems only able to survive with supporting regulatory systems and vast public subsidies.

JG: All technologies are not 'neutral'. There's only one energy source that can and has been used to produce material for weapons of mass destruction, and that's nuclear power and the nuclear fuel cycle, generating highly enriched uranium or plutonium for nuclear weapons, or also tritium, which is used to initiate and boost nuclear explosions and other materials as well. There is a real history here with half of the ten countries that have produced nuclear weapons to have done so under the cover of civil nuclear programmes. Australia makes a fascinating case study.[35]

There's only been one serious push for nuclear power in Australia and that was under Prime Minister John Gorton in the late 1960s, and he later admitted that one of the reasons they wanted to build a nuclear reactor was to give them the plutonium. That would have given them the option of building nuclear weapons if they wanted to go down that path. That's one of the many issues on which the Productivity Report simply failed to consider in its superficial analysis.

Conclusion

In Australia, there has been a latter-day push for the adoption of SMRs as a carbon-free path to tackling climate change and meeting carbon emission commitments and targets. This has been promoted largely by fringe politicians associated with the broader political 'climate wars' and 'culture wars',[36,37] including within the NSW Parliament by committee reports and draft legislation calling for a lifting of the legal and regulatory ban on nuclear power. The NSW Productivity Commission advocated a broad programme of sector-wide deregulation to boost productivity including for a 'technology' neutral response to climate change that would embrace nuclear power. But no technology is 'neutral' and not least nuclear technology with its track record of 'mass destruction' military use and global arms proliferation.

On a global scale, the civil nuclear power industry has hit a 30-year plateau from which it is unlikely to recover, driven not only by the impact of the Fukushima disaster but primarily by the soaring costs of nuclear power in defiance of any apparent cost reductions through the innovation 'learning curve'. Private investors will not commit without enormous public subsidies since nuclear generation cannot approach the cost-effectiveness of alternate sources, including the growth of renewable energy technologies. SMRs have been touted as a cost-effective innovation but despite a long history of very high cost, niche applications, including on nuclear submarines,[38] and for remote area fossil fuel development in the Arctic, only a handful of attempts have been made over a couple of decades to build them, with projects and programmes abandoned at much cost and over lengthy periods of development.

Even if SMRs are able to be built and operated cost-effectively, the lead times involved in development make them unable to deliver carbon-free electricity on the time scale required to meet carbon emissions reductions to fulfil climate change commitments and targets.

Notes

1 Hurst, D. (2023) Peter Dutton ramps up nuclear power push and claims Labor down 'renewable rabbit hole, *The Guardian*, 2nd July www.theguardian.com/australia-news/2023/jul/07/peter-dutton-ramps-up-nuclear-power-push-and-claims-labor-down-renewable-rabbit-hole

2 This article looks at Australia's commitment to the AUKUS agreement for nuclear submarines and associated technologies: Borger, J. (2023) AUKUS nuclear submarine deal loophole prompts proliferation fears, *The Guardian*, 14th March www.theguardian.com/world/2023/mar/13/aukus-australian-submarine-nuclear-loophole-proliferation-fears

3 This *inter alia* reviews the existing regulatory and policy framework: Thomas, N., Macgregor, S., Gardiner, D., Wylynko, B., Slocombe, C., Tsacalos, A. and Packham,

A. (2020) Parliamentary inquiries open the dialogue on nuclear energy and uranium mining, *Clayton Utz*, 2nd April www.claytonutz.com/knowledge/2020/april/parliamentary-inquiries-open-the-dialogue-on-nuclear-energy-and-uranium-mining

4 This report addresses the prerequisites for nuclear energy in Australia: Australian House of Representatives Standing Committee on Environment and Energy (2019) *Not Without Your Approval: A Way Forward for Nuclear Technology in Australia*, Canberra: Commonwealth Parliament https://parlinfo.aph.gov.au/parlInfo/search/display/display.w3p;query=Id%3A%22publications%2Ftabledpapers%2F58833ce7-8b03-4b63-aa2b-d5403b659ae8%22

5 NSW Standing Committee on State Development (2020) *Uranium Mining and Nuclear Facilities (Prohibitions) Repeal Bill 2019*, Sydney: NSW Parliament www.parliament.nsw.gov.au/committees/inquiries/Pages/inquiry-details.aspx?pk=2525#tab-termsofreference

6 Latham, M. (2019) *The Uranium Mining and Nuclear Facilities (Prohibitions) Repeal Bill 2019* www.parliament.nsw.gov.au/bill/files/3612/First%20Print.pdf

7 Smith, A. (2020) Barilaro's nuclear push bitterly dividing coalition, *Sydney Morning Herald*, 9th March www.smh.com.au/politics/nsw/barilaro-s-nuclear-push-bitterly-dividing-coalition-20200308-p547zm.html

8 See Bloch, M. (2021) NSW productivity commission has 'lost the plot' on nuclear power, *Solar Quotes Blog*, 3rd June www.solarquotes.com.au/blog/productivity-commission-nuclear-mb2021/

9 NSW Productivity Commission (2021) *Rebooting the Economy*, White Paper www.productivity.nsw.gov.au/sites/default/files/2022-04/Productivity-Commission-White-Paper-2021.pdf

10 Generation iii and iv reactors are 'advanced reactors' with gen iii in operation in Japan and others under construction in other countries, while gen iv designs are still on the drawing board. See World Nuclear Association (2021) *Advanced Nuclear Power Reactors,* April https://world-nuclear.org/information-library/nuclear-fuel-cycle/nuclear-power-reactors/advanced-nuclear-power-reactors.aspx

11 ANSTO (2019) *A Way Forward for Nuclear Technology in Australia with Public Approval,* 13th December www.ansto.gov.au/news/a-way-forward-for-nuclear-technology-australia-public-approval

12 Green, J. *Nuclear Power Myth-Busting Q&A* https://nuclear.foe.org.au/author/jim-green/

13 Bierman, P. (2021) The US Army tried portable nuclear power at remote bases 60 years ago – it didn't go well, *The Conversation*, 20th July https://theconversation.com/the-us-army-tried-portable-nuclear-power-at-remote-bases-60-years-ago-it-didnt-go-well-164138

14 Ramana, M.V. (2015) The forgotten history of small nuclear reactors, *IEEE Spectrum,* 52 (5): 44–58

15 See *World Nuclear Organisation on "Small Nuclear Power Reactors"* www.world-nuclear.org/information-library/nuclear-fuel-cycle/nuclear-power-reactors/small-nuclear-power-reactors.aspx

It defines and explains the technology that the IAEA refers to as 'small and medium reactors' (SMRs) rated between 300 and 700 Mwe (Megawatt electric), but that the acronym more commonly refers to 'small modular reactor'. The latter are designed for serial construction and collectively comprise a large nuclear power plant, using diverse prefabricated modules to expedite construction.

16 'For two decades since 1990 the nuclear industry has hoped for a worldwide 'nuclear renaissance' spurred by growing need for non-fossil fuels . . . most of the world is still waiting' from Hibbs, M. (2016) The nuclear renaissance? *Carnegie Endowment for World Peace*, 20th November https://carnegieendowment.org/2016/11/30/nuclear-renaissance-pub-66325

17 The 'Renaissance' is still hoped for in the 2020s. See Nuttall, W.J. (2022) *Nuclear Renaissance: Technologies and Policies for the Future of Nuclear Power*, London: Routledge
18 Kadota, R. (2019) *On the Brink: The Inside Story of Fukushima Daiichi*, Kumamoto: Kurudahan Press
19 Paillere, H. and Donovan, J. (2021) Nuclear power 10 years after Fukushima: The long road back, *IAEA*, 11th March www.iaea.org/newscenter/news/nuclear-power-10-years-after-fukushima-the-long-road-back
20 Kurokawa, K. and Mehkati, N. (2021) 10 years after Fukushima, safety is still nuclear power's greatest challenge, *The Conversation*, 6th March https://theconversation.com/10-years-after-fukushima-safety-is-still-nuclear-powers-greatest-challenge-155541
21 Moore, C. (2022) Hinkley Point C schedule 'remains unchanged' despite fears of 11 year delay, *New Civil Engineer*, 1st December www.newcivilengineer.com/latest/hinkley-schedule-remains-unchanged-despite-fears-of-11-year-delay-01–12–2022/
22 Clifford, C. (2023) A new nuclear reactor in the US starts up: The first in nearly seven years, *CNBC*, 7th March www.cnbc.com/2023/03/07/a-new-nuclear-reactor-in-the-us-starts-up-for-first-time-in-seven-years.html
23 IEA (2019) *Nuclear Power in a Clean Energy System*, May www.iea.org/reports/nuclear-power-in-a-clean-energy-system
24 Graham, P., Hayward, J., Foster J. and Havas, L. (2021) GenCost 2020–21: Final report, *CSIRO* https://publications.csiro.au/rpr/pub?pid=csiro:EP2021-0160
25 Ludlow, M. (2022) Nuclear Energy too expensive to replace fossil fuels: CSIRO, *Financial Review*, 11th July www.afr.com/companies/energy/nuclear-energy-too-expensive-to-replace-fossil-fuels-20220711-p5b0pd
26 McMahon, J. (2019) New solar + battery price crushes fossil fuels, buries nuclear, *Forbes*, 1st July www.forbes.com/sites/jeffmcmahon/2019/07/01/new-solar–battery-price-crushes-fossil-fuels-buries-nuclear/?sh=7c00124c5971
27 Sovacool, B.K. and Ramana, M.V. (2015) Back to the future: Small modular reactors, nuclear fantasies, and symbolic convergence. *Science, Technology, and Human Values*, 40 (1): 96–125
28 Jamasb, T. and Kohler, J. (2007) Learning curves for energy technology: A critical assessment, in Grubb, M., Jamasb, T. and Pollit, M. (eds) *Delivering a Low Carbon Electricity System: Technology, Economics and Policy*, Cambridge University Press www.eprg.group.cam.ac.uk/wp-content/uploads/2014/01/eprg0723.pdf
29 The NSW government subsequently ruled out support for One Nation Mark Latham's bill to remove state bans on uranium mining and nuclear facilities. See Sanda, D. (2020) NSW premier rejects Latham's uranium bill, *Canberra Times*, 25th August www.canberratimes.com.au/story/6895432/nsw-premier-rejects-lathams-uranium-bill/
30 This study which reviewed costs over 50 years. See Eash-Gates, P., Klemun, M.M., Kavlak, G., McNerney, J., Buongiorno, J. and Trancik, J.E. (2020) Sources of cost overrun in nuclear power plant construction call for a new approach to engineering design, *Joule*, 4 (11): P2348–P2373
31 This article states SMR cost as much as $16,000 per KWh, 50 to 100% more than large-scale nuclear, with wind and solar at under $2,000 per KWh. See Ludlow, M. (2022) Nuclear energy too expensive to replace fossil fuels, *Australian Financial Review*, 11th July www.afr.com/companies/energy/nuclear-energy-too-expensive-to-replace-fossil-fuels-20220711-p5b0pd
32 Parshley, L. (2020) The countries building miniature nuclear reactors, *BBC News: Future Planet*, 10th March www.bbc.com/future/article/20200309-are-small-nuclear-power-plants-safe-and-efficient
33 Greenpeace European Unit (2018) *Exposed: Euro 58 Billion in Hidden Subsidies for Coal, Gas and Nuclear*, 13th September www.greenpeace.org/eu-unit/issues/

climate-energy/1519/exposed-e58-billion-in-hidden-subsidies-for-coal-gas-and-nuclear/
34 Aisbett, E., Cheng, W. and Beck, F. (2021) *Green Industrial Policy and Technology Neutrality: Odd Couple or Unholy Marriage? Zero Carbon Energy for the Asia Pacific (ZCEAP) Working Paper*, Canberra: ANU, 3rd March www.anu.edu.au/files/document-collection/ZCWP01-21%20Green%20Industrial%20Policy%20and%20Technology%20Neutrality_2.pdf
35 Lowe, I. (2021) *Long Half-Life: The Nuclear Industry in Australia*, Melbourne: Monash University Press
36 Corrigan, S. (2021) Is a ceasefire near in the climate culture wars – or – is it about to go nuclear? *Corporate Affairs Australia*, 25th October https://corporateaffairs.com.au/climate-culture-war/
37 Krugman, P. (2023) Climate is now a culture war issue, *New York Times*, 7th August www.nytimes.com/2023/08/07/opinion/climate-is-now-a-culture-war-issue.html
38 Kapetas, A. (2021) *Limiting the Nuclear Proliferation Blowback from AUKUS Submarine Deal, The ASPI Strategist*, Canberra: Australian Strategic Policy Institute, 21st September www.aspistrategist.org.au/limiting-the-nuclear-proliferation-blowback-from-the-aukus-submarine-deal/

15 Hydrogen-Based Economy

Shipping Sunshine to the World

Interview With Tony Wood

Introduction

The former Chief Scientist of Australia, Alan Finkel, developed a National Hydrogen Strategy which was subsequently endorsed by governments, in which he argued –among other things – that we have an opportunity to ship sunshine to the world. (2019: v).[1] That was the vision for transforming Australia into a hydrogen-based economy.

Hydrogen is probably the most abundant element on earth. It's very light as a gas, but the problem is that it doesn't occur freely. It occurs in combination with other elements and to access it as a potentially low-carbon energy source and to help us with decarbonisation in response to climate change, we have to apply energy to it, whether it's in the form of water or hydrocarbons.

Keywords: aluminium; ammonia; Australian Renewable Energy Agency (ARENA); batteries; brown hydrogen; carbon capture and sequestration (CCS); climate change; COP26; electric vehicles (EV); electrolysis; explosives; fertiliser; gasification; green hydrogen; green steel; heavy-duty transport; hydrogen; hydrogen economy; Hydrogen Energy Supply Chain (HESC); hydrogen fuel cells; iron ore; liquid hydrogen; maritime; natural gas; net-zero emissions; renewable energy; road transport; SDG 7; SDG 9; SDG 12; SDG 13; shipping; solar energy; steel; supply chain; water; technology roadmap; wind energy

Interviewee Profile

Tony Wood **(TW)** AM has been the Director of the Energy and Climate Change Program at the Grattan Institute,[2] based at the University of Melbourne since 2011. He previously had a long career in energy, including 14 years with Origin Energy. He was with the Clinton Foundation as an energy and climate adviser (2009–2014); and also worked (2008) with Professor Ross Garnaut on the first, landmark Australian report on climate change commissioned by Prime Minister Kevin Rudd.[3] Tony is a Fellow of the Australian Academy of Technology and Engineering (AATE).

DOI: 10.4324/9781003280316-17

The Interview

ML: To what extent was the National Hydrogen Strategy (2019) taken up and funded? How does that fit in with the overall national approach based on a 'Technology Roadmap'?[4]

TW: The government has identified that to move towards a 'net-zero-emissions' economy over the coming decades[5] – as everyone basically agrees – there is a need to debate how quickly we can get there. A range of technology development is required. There are known technologies that will contribute to an accelerated reduction in emissions, for example, solar is a low-cost renewable energy that can replace fossil fuels. However, in other sectors, that's not so easy. The technologies are either expensive or not so clear, and that means technology development is required.

Accordingly, the government commissioned its Chief Scientist, Alan Finkel, to develop a 'technology investment roadmap'.[6] I would disagree with the government though, when they say it's all about technology and not taxes.[7] I would argue that it's technology and taxes, because it's all very well to get new technologies in place but still need to have some way in which people, the community and energy consumers in the market would actually pay for these new 'green technologies'. That's the fundamental reason for having a technology investment roadmap. It is now, however, in its present form, one of the key planks of the government's climate, long-term emissions reduction strategy. It's also part of what the government will take to the big international climate conference, COP26, which was delayed from last year, but will now be held in Glasgow probably later this year.[8] The role of hydrogen technology features as one of a number of new technology opportunities in the roadmap, the government's zero-emissions strategy, as well as in the national hydrogen strategy.

ML: What role can hydrogen technology play and what is the opportunity it offers for Australia as a source of very large-scale, low-cost, renewable energy?[9] The roadmap generally doesn't set targets or much of a timetable, but in respect of hydrogen it flags green hydrogen, green steel and green aluminium as areas of opportunity. The investment envisaged is in the order of $300–400 million but is this on the scale and timeframe needed to meet emissions targets? What is the idea anyway of 'green hydrogen'?[10]

TW: Hydrogen doesn't naturally occur by itself but in combination with other elements. There are two common and widespread forms of hydrogen compounds. First, as hydrocarbons, which are manifold combinations of hydrogen and carbon in various proportions, for example, as natural gas or even LPG. The challenge with hydrocarbons is that when burnt as a fuel, they produce greenhouse gases.

The second most common form of hydrogen is the water molecule, combining hydrogen and oxygen in a ratio of 2:1 molecules, respectively. The way we mostly use hydrogen in Australia today is in the middle of chemical processes. For example, in making fertilisers, petrochemicals or explosives, we usually start with natural gas which is referred to as the 'feedstock'. The hydrogen is not being used as a source of fuel or energy but rather as a chemical feedstock and we run a process which separates the carbon from the hydrogen.

The carbon we get rid of, which is where the greenhouse gas emissions come from; the hydrogen we retain and marry it up with other things to produce, in particular, fertilisers in the case of urea in Queensland or elsewhere in Australia, or explosives in the form of ammonium nitrate. They are very important inputs to those industries. The hydrogen never leaves the chemical plant and is always held internally as an intermediate product between the input of natural gas and the output of fertilisers, petrochemicals or explosives. That's where hydrogen currently sits.

The interesting thing about hydrogen is that in respect of both those feedstock processes and hydrogen itself, instead of producing hydrogen from natural gas, we could produce it from something else, most excitingly, from water. We need to use renewable electricity to split the water molecule into its two constituent parts, namely, hydrogen and oxygen. We can then keep the hydrogen for use in the production of fertilisers and explosives. Alternatively, it can be used as an 'energy carrier' which is an exciting future role of hydrogen.

ML: If taking the water resource route to green hydrogen rather than the fossil fuel natural gas route, what happens to the oxygen that is split out? Is oxygen a valuable commodity in itself; didn't we find sadly and tragically during COVID-19, that there was a desperate lack of supply?

TW: Oxygen, being itself a major constituent of our atmosphere, will be mostly vented to the atmosphere. The process is somewhat circular. If we start with renewable electricity from the sun to split water to make hydrogen, then, if we burn that hydrogen, for example in a power station, the product of that combustion is water.

ML: So basically, the process of electrolysis used to split water into hydrogen and oxygen using electrolysis is a form of artificial photosynthesis.[11] We start with water, we finish with water and the oxygen ends up being combined with hydrogen again. That's a pretty benign by-product and process, isn't it?

TW: Absolutely, and so isn't that a great outcome, right? So that's the big plus side of green hydrogen from water. It is somewhat intriguing that people talk about green hydrogen; hydrogen gas itself is not green. It is a colourless gas, but what is meant is that it is 'green' when it is produced from renewable energy and that is possible when using natural gas to start with. If you do that, you can do one of two things with the carbon dioxide emission today. What we do is basically vent that CO_2 directly to the atmosphere and broadly speaking that's called 'grey hydrogen'.[12]

If you capture that carbon dioxide, so it doesn't enter the atmosphere, you need basically to bury it underground or under the sea using a process called 'carbon capture and sequestration' (CCS).[13] That's called 'blue' hydrogen, with very low emissions, possibly close to zero as with renewable 'green' hydrogen, but coming from a fossil fuel and requiring the extra process of capturing the CO_2 which you don't require if you're producing it from water.

The problem with the water process at the moment is that it's still relatively expensive.[14] The focus of the technology investment roadmap is to drive down the cost of producing hydrogen from electrolysis of water so that eventually it becomes far more competitive with alternative sources of hydrogen. The government has set what they call 'stretch targets' for this cost reduction, as have many organisations around the world.

ML: You have mentioned ammonia, which we import for fertilisers and explosives production. Is there potential and do we have commercialised technology at scale to produce 'green ammonia' using our hydrogen?[15]

TW: While not globally significant, Australia is an important producer of our own fertiliser and a lot of that is produced from our own natural gas. We do make hydrogen in plants such as Orica's explosive plant in Newcastle,[16] or Incitec Pivot's fertiliser plant in Brisbane.[17]

We know how to do that but the trick is when we're going to replace that process using Australian natural gas with Australian renewable energy. That's where not just Australia, but the world, has relatively little experience. For example, the government has said, we'd like to see hydrogen at $2.00 a kilogram. I won't even try to describe exactly how much a kilogram of gas would be because hydrogen is the lightest element in the world. Handling and transporting, it is also a fairly tricky process because of the very small molecules.

Cost is important because at the moment to produce hydrogen from renewable energy with the very low-cost renewable energy, which we have seen happen dramatically in Australia and around the world in the last ten or 15 years, would still be costly at around $5–6 a kilogram. By way of comparison, it is the equivalent of about $15–16 a gigajoule of gas. That's probably about two to three times what we've been paying for natural gas in this country for the last 20 or 30 years. So it's not a very cheap source of energy, but as a feedstock it might be interesting.

Splitting water requires a lot of renewable energy and to do this at scale requires very large wind and solar farms. Also, for the electrolysis process, you need large amounts of water. This is effectively performing as a reversible battery that takes water and electricity and converts them into hydrogen and oxygen. The process is well understood but a lot of work is being done in China, Germany and elsewhere to find ways of driving down the cost of the electrolysis process. The government is also funding the Australian Renewable Energy Agency (ARENA) to undertake such projects here so that green hydrogen can be used economically to produce green steel or green ammonia.[18] That technology focus is very important.[19]

ML: Australia is the world's largest exporter of iron ore and it's important to our economy, but basically we ship it out as an unprocessed commodity. What would be involved in our using cheaply produced green hydrogen to process the ore and export high-value-added green steel?[20]

TW: At the risk of turning this into a chemistry course, let me just take you through that process at a very high level. Iron ore is basically iron oxide and it looks like rust when you dig it out of the ground, which it is basically, being a combination of iron and oxygen.

The iron ore is mined in places like the Pilbara in Western Australia and shipped out to export markets from there. To turn iron ore into iron requires processing it in a blast furnace using metallurgical coal. Metallurgical coal also comes from Australia, mostly from the east coast of Queensland.

So we are sending iron ore from the west coast and metallurgical coal from Queensland to Asia where they process them into steel, a much higher valued product. The metallurgical coal in the blast furnace strips out the oxygen from the iron oxide, leaving the iron behind and forming carbon dioxide as a by-product. We've been doing this for decades and making money out of it while contributing indirectly to global climate change. Steel manufacturing around the world contributes about 7% of emissions, so this is a big climate change challenge.[21]

ML: So green hydrogen offers an alternative technology path for reducing the iron oxide into iron and steel, and thereby reducing carbon emissions?

TW: Yeah, what happens is that you have a different technology, but basically you use the hydrogen to strip off the oxygen from the iron, leaving the iron behind again. But in addition, when you combine the hydrogen with oxygen, you produce water which means a very attractive alternative because you've now got effectively zero emission iron.

To turn that iron into steel requires a small amount of carbon, because steel is basically a mixture of carbon and iron. But that's the end part of the process. The big deal is how you reduce the iron oxide to iron, and that's where this is a really exciting possibility particularly if we could do it in Australia using Australian renewable energy and renewable hydrogen. Not only would we be able to replace our carbon-intensive commodity exports which eventually the world will not want anyway, but we'd also be able to replace jobs which are currently pretty significant with more than 50,000 jobs in the carbon-intensive manufacturing sectors. We could replace those jobs with new export opportunities and add new economic value for Australia which would be a great outcome.

There's a lot of work to be done to achieve this transformation, but the work is proceeding. For example, Twiggy Forrest, head of Fortescue Metals, was recently talking excitedly about the possibilities of doing this in Australia.[22] It would be a big change for the Australian economy. But as we've said, it would also require development of significant, dedicated solar electric energy capacities in those locations; perhaps in the form of individual, dedicated but distributed grids rather than drawing on the national distribution system.

ML: We've been discussing the opportunity that a transition to a hydrogen-based economy might afford Australia not only to move to a low-carbon economy but to generate new wealth and opportunities in sectors such as ammonia, fertilisers, iron and steel. We could have a similar discussion perhaps about aluminium,[23] but what's happening in the world of transport and hydrogen?[24]

TW: Transport contributes significantly to greenhouse gas emissions but the technologies to get us towards zero emissions are still relatively new.[25] Electric vehicles are becoming more available in Australia.[26] Their driving range on a full battery is improving all the time, and it won't be long before their purchase cost is cheaper than that of an internal combustion engine for personal vehicles. EV batteries need regular charging at a charging station but the infrastructure is limited and it takes longer than filling your car with petrol.

An interesting alternative way of fuelling a car instead of with petrol or diesel is to use hydrogen. You could burn hydrogen in the engine, but the more interesting technology now being developed is hydrogen fuel cells,[27] which are basically the reverse of a battery. You put the hydrogen through a fuel cell and produce electricity, which then is used to drive your vehicle.

This has two significant advantages. One is that fuel cells weigh much less than EV batteries but are currently significantly more expensive than the batteries used in the Tesla and Nissan Leaf EVs. The weight penalty you pay is much less so for long-distance heavy transport, tow trucks and even trains. Hydrogen fuel cells may be a much more interesting alternative than battery EV technology.[28]

The second advantage of hydrogen fuel cells is that you'd have a tank on board the vehicle and fill it with hydrogen in the same way that people fill their car with LPG today. It is the same with hydrogen but then you have a fuel cell on board rather than a gas tank. At this stage, it is expected that we're likely to use batteries for personal and small commercial vehicles, and hydrogen and fuel cells for large transport. On the other hand, Hyundai and others are looking to make fuel cell personal cars, so we'll see how that technology battle plays out.[29]

ML: I believe there are some currently on trial by the ACT Government.[30] The other good thing from a climate change and pollution point of view, if you go down the hydrogen fuel cell track for cars, is that the exhaust is steam and water, right?

TW: Absolutely. Hydrogen fuel has benefits beyond climate change, because a lot of the products of combustion in the vehicle are not particularly great from a general health perspective. If we will have our vehicles driving around without producing any emissions, either as battery cars or as hydrogen cars, that would have an enormous beneficial impact on health quality in our cities and suburbs.

The other thing about hydrogen is that it is potentially a way of fuelling ships in the marine sector which currently run on a very dirty and polluting form of diesel fuel called bunker oil. There's a whole range of potential applications emerging in the maritime sector.[31]

ML: Apparently the Japanese are now building ships to transport hydrogen, aren't they?[32]

TW: There's a very interesting project related to this underway in the LaTrobe Valley in Victoria that is making hydrogen from coal, which still ends up with carbon dioxide, as part of the large-scale Hydrogen Energy Supply Chain (HESC) project.[33]

A number of major Japanese companies, together with the Victorian government, are developing the project to produce hydrogen from brown coal for export in a dedicated hydrogen ship to Japan.[34] One of the reasons the Japanese were very interested in this is because they had intended to make the Tokyo Olympics, which as we know was supposed to have been held last year, a Hydrogen Olympics.[35] They wanted all the vehicles driving around in the Games to be hydrogen powered.

Although the Olympics didn't go ahead as originally planned due to COVID-19 they did subsequently take place. Second, the shipping project was a lot longer in being developed but the first shipment did eventually happen.[36]

In any event, it's questionable whether that's the best long-term way of producing hydrogen, but it's certainly a way of testing the entire supply chain.[37] In the long term, you still have to deal with the carbon dioxide that's produced when you manufacture hydrogen from coal. Interestingly, this particular 'gasification' process of producing hydrogen using brown coal is often referred to as 'brown hydrogen'.[38] So we've got all these different colour labels for hydrogen production.[39]

ML: How well are we positioned with our policies, technology roadmap, funding and incentives to navigate the pathways and scale up these hydrogen technology pathways? In what time frame is it realistic to develop these opportunities, and capitalise on the substantial international trade opportunities for higher value added?

TW: Australia is extraordinarily well positioned to take advantage of this opportunity. We have, unusually but not uniquely in the world, a very large renewable energy resource of wind and solar. Often we have situations where the wind and solar isn't being generated at the same time, which is not a bad thing because sometimes the sun is shining when the wind isn't blowing, and vice versa.

We also have a relatively small population so we don't have that many domestic applications and demand for using green hydrogen. Using green hydrogen for exports is a very big opportunity and where the challenges emerge. For example, there is the project being proposed by Mike Cannon-Brookes and others in Northern Australia to either export renewable energy to Asia along undersea cables,[40] or possibly as hydrogen from the North West shelf.[41]

These are exciting possibilities, but the challenge is to drive down the cost of the technology. It is going to be at least a decade or more before we start seeing these things becoming practical. Even today, the company Energy Australia announced that they will build a dual fuel, hydrogen and natural gas, power station in the Illawarra by 2023–2024,[42] which is when the Liddell coal-fired power station is due to close.

So it may not be that far away when those sorts of things start to be realised. Fuel cell cars are already being built and commercially available in the US. Ultimately, there's a lot to be done to drive down the cost because some of the hydrogen technologies are very expensive and I think we're very well positioned. The challenge, of course, is for governments – federal, state, federal and local – to work closely together and with industry if we are to capitalise on what could be an extraordinarily positive thing for Australia. As Ross Garnaut said, to make Australia once again into a serious global energy superpower.[43]

ML: They certainly do sound like very exciting opportunities for Australia to transform our industry and our economy developing and exploiting renewable hydrogen while at the same time meeting the climate change challenges by 'shipping sunshine'[44] to the world. I guess, this is a matter of commitment, focus and support.

Conclusion

Hydrogen as the most common element on earth and a fuel that on combustion, unlike carbon-based fossil fuels carries zero-carbon emission energy, offers a seductive promise in an age needing to transition to a sustainable, net-zero energy future. That promise embraces its use both as a renewable source of energy replacing fossil fuels in most sectors of the economy including the manufacture of steel or aluminium, and as a replacement carbon-free feedstock for a range of important industrial processes and products such as ammonia, fertiliser and explosives.

The neologism 'hydrogen economy' has in Australia contributed to grand visions of our becoming a low-carbon superpower that can 'ship sunshine' to the world. There are many potential technological pathways and choices and 'all clean hydrogen is not equally clean'.[45] There is a rainbow spectrum of 'clean' hydrogen varying from green through to black, with stops at blue, brown and pink along the way each reflecting a different degree of net carbon content according to the production process and supply chain involved.

These variations arise according to whether the source of hydrogen is from water where it associates with oxygen, or from various hydrocarbons where it associates in many and complex variations with carbon. Using renewable energy sources such as solar and wind, keep the hydrogen supply chain carbon-free, while using fossil fuels such as coal or natural gas do not. Green hydrogen, which is totally carbon free, comes from splitting water using renewable energy in a process called electrolysis. At the other extreme, black or brown hydrogen splits either water or a hydrocarbon by the application of energy from a fossil fuel. From a sustainability perspective, emissions-free sources of hydrogen are unlikely to be practical and affordable for decades.[46] The options for development and diffusion are highly path-dependent and require finance as well as a variety of government policy targets, funding, incentives and regulations.

Notes

1 COAG Energy Council (2019) *Australia's National Hydrogen Strategy*, Commonwealth of Australia www.dcceew.gov.au/sites/default/files/documents/australias-national-hydrogen-strategy.pdf
2 Grattan Institute https://grattan.edu.au/
3 Garnaut, R. (2008) *The Garnaut Climate Change Review: Final Report*, Port Melbourne, VIC: Cambridge University Press
4 Climate Council (2020) *Unpacking the 'Tech Roadmap'*, 22nd September www.climatecouncil.org.au/resources/unpacking-tech-roadmap/
5 Reuters (2022) *Australia Passes a Law for Net Zero Emissions by 2050*, 8th September www.reuters.com/world/asia-pacific/australia-passes-law-net-zero-emissions-by-2050-2022-09–08/
6 Australian Department of Industry, Science, Energy and Resources (DISER) (2020) *Technology Investment Roadmap Discussion Paper, A Framework to Accelerate Low Emissions Technologies*, Canberra: Department of Climate Change, Energy, the Environment and Water, Australian Government, May https://consult.dcceew.gov.au/australias-technology-investment-roadmap-discussion-paper
7 Holmes a Court, S. (2021) Scott Morrison is hiding behind future technologies, when we should just deploy what already exists, *The Conversation*, 8th November https://theconversation.com/scott-morrison-is-hiding-behind-future-technologies-when-we-should-just-deploy-what-already-exists-169016
8 Eckersley, R. (2021) 'The Australian way': How Morrison trashed brand Australia at COP26, *The Conversation*, 12th November https://theconversation.com/the-australian-way-how-morrison-trashed-brand-australia-at-cop26–171670

9 Bloomberg NEF (2023) *2H 2023 Hydrogen Market Outlook: The Demand Question,* 19th October https://about.bnef.com/blog/2h-2023-hydrogen-market-outlook-the-demand-question/
10 Hassan, Q., Abdulateef, A.M., Hafedh, S.A., Al-samari, A., Abdulateef, J., Sameen, A.Z., Salman, H.M., Al-Jiboory, A.K., Wieteska, S. and Jaszczur, M. (2023) Renewable energy-to-green hydrogen: A review of main resources routes, processes and evaluation, *International Journal of Hydrogen Energy*, 48 (46): 17383–17408
11 Bessarabov, D. and Millet, P. (2018) Brief historical background of water electrolysis, in *PEM Water Electrolysis; Solar Driven Green Hydrogen Generation and Storage*, Chapter 2, pp. 17–42, Cambridge, MA, USA: Academic Press
12 Hermesmann, M. and Müller, T.E. (2022) Green, turquoise, blue, or grey? Environmentally friendly hydrogen production in transforming energy systems, *Progress in Energy and Combustion Science*, 90, May: 100996
13 Zhao, Y. and Itakura, K.-I. (2023) A state-of-the-art review on technology for carbon utilization and storage, *Energies,* 16 (10): 3992
14 International Renewable Energy Agency (IRENA) (2020) *Green Hydrogen Cost Reduction: Scaling up Electrolysers to Meet the 1.5 degree C Climate Goal* www.irena.org/-/media/Files/IRENA/Agency/Publication/2020/Dec/IRENA_Green_hydrogen_cost_2020.pdf
15 BP (2021) *Study Confirms Feasibility of Large-Scale Production of Green Hydrogen and Green Ammonia Using Renewable Energy in Australia*, Press Release, 11th August www.bp.com/en/global/corporate/news-and-insights/press-releases/bp-study-confirms-feasibility-of-large-scale-production-of-green-hydrogen-and-green-ammonia-using-renewable-energy-in-australia.html
16 Johnson, K. (2023) Federal Government to spend $70 million on Newcastle 'hydrogen hub' that will power Orica, *ABC News,* 13th July www.abc.net.au/news/2023-07-13/newcastle-hydrogen-hub-70-million-orica-origin-energy-government/102596112
17 Brann, M. (2021) Fertiliser prices boom as Incitec Pivot plans closure of Gibson Island plant, *ABC News*, 13th November www.abc.net.au/news/rural/2021-11-13/incitec-pivot-shut-brisbane-plant-amidst-fertiliser-price-boom/100610750
18 ARENA (2023) *Success for ARENA Hydrogen R&D Funding*, 11th May https://arena.gov.au/blog/success-for-arena-hydrogen-rd-funding/
19 Patonia, A. and Poudineh, R. (2022) *Cost-Competitive Green Hydrogen: How to Lower the Cost of Electrolysers?* The Oxford Institute for Energy Studies, Paper 47 www.oxfordenergy.org/publications/cost-competitive-green-hydrogen-how-to-lower-the-cost-of-electrolysers/
20 Allen, J. and Honeyands, T. (2021) Green steel' is hailed as the next big thing in Australian industry, *The Conversation*, 2nd June https://theconversation.com/sis-all-about-160282
21 Ibid
22 Regan, J. (2022) Fortescue signs deal to produce hydrogen-fuelled green steel, *Renew Economy*, 20th December https://reneweconomy.com.au/fortescue-signs-deal-to-produce-hydrogen-fuelled-green-steel/
23 Hunt, P. (2021) Australia takes first step towards green aluminium, *Mining Magazine*, 21st May www.miningmagazine.com/power-remote-power/news/1410614/australia-takes-first-step-towards-green-aluminum
24 United States Environmental Protection Agency (EPA) (2023) Hydrogen in transportation, *EPA*, 10th October www.epa.gov/greenvehicles/hydrogen-transportation
25 Henriques-Gomes, L. (2018) Transport emissions continue to rise as Australia lags behind other nations, *The Guardian*, 12th September www.theguardian.com/environment/2018/sep/13/transport-emissions-continue-to-rise-as-australia-lags-behind-other-nations
26 Nazifi, M. and Chenu, M. (2022) What's stopping Australians from buying electric cars?, *Macquarie University: The Lighthouse Magazine*, 21st April https://light

house.mq.edu.au/article/april-2022/whats-stopping-australians-from-buying-electric-cars
27 Hassan, Q., Azzawi, I.D., Sameen, A.Z. and Salman, H.M. (2023) Hydrogen fuel cell vehicles: Opportunities and challenges, *Sustainability*, 15 (15): 11501
28 Oak Ridge National Laboratory (2021) *Heavy-Duty Vehicles an Ideal Entry Into Hydrogen Fuel Cell Use*, 23rd April www.ornl.gov/news/heavy-duty-vehicles-ideal-entry-hydrogen-fuel-cell-use
29 Martin, P. (2023) Hyundai unveils the 2024 version of its hydrogen-powered Nexo fuel-cell car, *Hydrogen Insight*, 12th June www.hydrogeninsight.com/transport/hyundai-unveils-the-2024-version-of-its-hydrogen-powered-nexo-fuel-cell-car/2–1–1465779
30 MacLean, A. (2016) ACT government orders hydrogen-powered Hyundais, *Drive*, 30th August www.drive.com.au/news/act-government-orders-hydrogen-powered-hyundais-gr4938/
31 Reinsch, W.A. and O'Neil, W. (2021) Hydrogen: The key to decarbonising the global shipping industry? *Center for Strategic and International Studies (CSIS)*, 13th April www.csis.org/analysis/hydrogen-key-decarbonizing-global-shipping-industry
32 Paul, S. (2023) World's first hydrogen tanker to ship test cargo to Japan from Australia, *Reuters*, 21st January www.reuters.com/business/environment/worlds-first-hydrogen-tanker-ship-test-cargo-australia-japan-2022-01–20/
33 Kurmelovs, R. (2022) 'Just a new fossil fuel industry': Australia to send first shipment of liquified hydrogen to Japan, *The Guardian*, 20th January www.theguardian.com/australia-news/2022/jan/21/just-a-new-fossil-fuel-industry-australia-to-send-first-shipment-of-liquefied-hydrogen-to-japan
34 Readfearn, G. (2023) Japan to spend $2.35bn on turning Victorian Latrobe Valley coal into 'clean hydrogen', *The Guardian*, 7th March www.theguardian.com/environment/2023/mar/07/japan-to-spend-235bn-on-turning-victorian-latrobe-valley-coal-into-clean-hydrogen
35 Joosse, T. (2021) The 'hydrogen Olympics' lit a torch for the clean fuel's future, *Scientific American*, 30th July www.scientificamerican.com/article/the-hydrogen-olympics-lit-a-torch-for-the-clean-fuels-future1/
36 Australian Trade and Investment Commission, *Australia Exports World's First Shipment of Liquified Hydrogen to Japan*, Austrade www.globalaustralia.gov.au/news-and-resources/news-items/australia-exports-worlds-first-shipment-liquified-hydrogen-japan
37 Kurmelovs (2022), op cit
38 National Grid (2023) *The Hydrogen Colour Spectrum* www.nationalgrid.com/stories/energy-explained/hydrogen-colour-spectrum
39 Weiss, T., Gamage, C., Blank, T.K., Lillis, G. and Wall, A.J. (2022) Hydrogen reality check: All 'clean hydrogen' is not equally clean, *Rocky Mountain Institute*, 4th October https://rmi.org/all-clean-hydrogen-is-not-equally-clean/
40 Hannam, P. (2023) Sun cable: Mike Cannon-Brookes takes charge of 'world-changing' solar project, *The Guardian*, 7th September www.theguardian.com/environment/2023/sep/07/sun-cable-mike-cannon-brookes-takes-charge-of-world-changing-solar-project
41 Ker, P., Macdonald-Smith, A. and Fuary-Wagner, I. (2023) Australia's export dilemma: Solar via cable or hydrogen by ship? *Financial Review*, 23rd January www.afr.com/companies/energy/how-should-we-export-australia-s-renewable-energy-if-at-all-20230116-p5ccrl
42 Macdonald-Smith, A. (2021) Energy Australia commits to carbon-neutral gas plant, *Financial Review*, 4th May www.afr.com/companies/energy/energyaustralia-commits-to-carbon-neutral-gas-plant-20210504-p57omo

43 Garnaut, R. (2019) *Super-Power: Australia's Low-Carbon Opportunity*, Melbourne: Latrobe University Press
44 Finkel, A. (2023) *Powering Up: Unleashing the Clean Energy Supply Chain*, Collingwood, VIC: Black Inc. Books
45 Weiss, T., Gamage, C., Koch Blank, T., Lillis, G. and Jardine Wall, A. (2022) Hydrogen reality check: All 'clean hydrogen' is not equally clean, *Rocky Mountain Institute*, 4th October https://rmi.org/all-clean-hydrogen-is-not-equally-clean/
46 Romm, J.J. (2004) The hype about hydrogen, *Issues in Science and Technology*, XX (3) Spring https://issues.org/romm-hydrogen-clean-energy/

Section III

Agriculture, Land and Water Resources

16 Agricultural Productivity Improvement

The Role of Digital Technologies

Interview With Richard Heath

Introduction

Agriculture is an important sector in the Australian economy.[1] It has become significantly transformed over the last 40 or 50 years and indeed in the 200 or more years since Australia was colonised.[2]

In 1965, its percentage contribution to GDP was 12%; but GDP value these days is down around 2.4%,[3] which is a big change in its role and significance to the economy. People employed directly in agriculture in the mid-1960s were around nearly half a million. These days it's around 300,000.[4]

This sector also makes a large economic contribution to export income. Some 75% of agricultural production is exported and that accounts for a large proportion of Australia's total exports. However, with structural change in the Australian economy, that's fallen from levels of over 20% to down around half that these days. There are about 140,000 farmers and graziers, and they occupy about 60% of the land area of the country and use a significant proportion of about 25%, including with irrigation, of the nation's water resources in what is the world's driest continent.[5]

Productivity performance, that is, use of technology and innovation to do things more efficiently, has been at the heart of the success of the sector, which is arguably the most trade-exposed and internationally competitive sector in Australia.[6,7] The reduction over the decades in its level of protection and subsidy assistance has provided the incentive and forced restructuring to become more productive and competitive.[8]

What's the future for the agricultural sector and what role is technology and innovation going to play as we go forward, particularly from a productivity point of view? What role will digital technology play and what of the role of funding of R&D; and by extension, the levels of investment and further restructuring?

There are big challenges facing the sector, not least, for example, in water use in times of drought, floods, storms and climate change; what might be their impact on the sustainability of use of land and water resources by the sector?[9]

DOI: 10.4324/9781003280316-19

There have been many reports about agriculture and its future, and particularly its technology,[10,11] with two further major reports forthcoming.[12,13]

Keywords: agribusiness; agriculture; AgTech; carbon markets; ecosystem services (ESS); ecosystem services payments; environmental water flows; incubators; innovation; Internet of Things (IOT); knowledge-based economy; natural accounting systems; productivity; Rural Research and Development Corporations (RRDCs); SDG9; SDG 11; SDG 12; SDG 15

Interviewee Profile

Richard Heath **(RH)** is Executive Director of the Australian Farm Institute (AFI), an independent institute that conducts research on policy issues affecting Australian agriculture.[14] Richard has considerable background in research and development in the agricultural sector and in the university sector. His background is in farming, and for most of his life he has been a farmer up near Gunnedah in northern NSW. Since his farm was sold a few years ago, he has worked in the R&D space and is now with the Australian Farm Institute.

The Interview

ML: What are, broadly, the technology challenges and opportunities for productivity improvements in Australian agriculture and its competitiveness; and what are the main drivers?[15,16,17]

RH: Australian Prime Minister Morrison commissioned a report to examine the potential boost to the economy if all existing digital technologies were suddenly adopted in Australian agriculture, and if the barriers that exist today suddenly disappeared.[18] The review came up with a figure of about $20 billion. Given that the current output of agriculture is about $60 billion that is a significant gain and provides a 'boundary' of sorts for the opportunity with new digital technologies.

ML: What kind of digital technology applications are we talking about?

RH: There are so many examples and I'd start by saying that as you outlined in your introduction, Australian agriculture has been particularly good at taking up technology when there's a proven benefit. The story of productivity growth in Australian agriculture has very much been a story of technology uptake to help with things like labour efficiency and that incremental growth from technology update will continue as automation becomes more widespread through agriculture, such as say, technologies to selectively spray weeds rather than spraying entire paddocks and so on, then that's going to continue the story of incremental productivity growth through available technologies.

What's particularly interesting now though, and what is potentially going to offer step changes in productivity rather than continuing incremental growth is where data come into the picture, and where insights from the use of data and data analysis deliver entirely new production methods or ways of producing crops and animals that lead to big increases in productivity.

ML: As in so many areas of digital transformation in the economy, the underlying opportunities in the processing of big data involve sophisticated skills as well as an efficient telecommunications infrastructure. How well placed and capable is our farming sector in the take-up of digital technology? For example, I've heard it suggested that we have a 'digital divide' in the country in terms of limited access to infrastructure for communications and accessibility of big data systems; and what's the attitude of farmers and graziers to these new digital technologies and the skills they need?

RH: There is certainly a 'digital divide', and it is a big issue in terms of realising digital technology opportunities. Connectivity in rural areas is getting better, and there is a range of commercial providers offering new solutions for productivity going beyond existing telco offerings.

The demand is strong because farmers are realising the opportunity that can be gained through Internet of Things (IOT) connectivity and by compiling data for new insights. They're looking for solutions and so there's innovative technology developing around local area networks and even small packets of data; it's not suitable for broadband being small packets of data communicating directly with satellites and edge computing. This technology is starting to help with the data situation in Australia.

The question about attitudes towards data is much more interesting and one that does have cultural barriers around it at currently. This is a global issue and not just to do with Australian agriculture.

On the question of hesitancy, it takes infrastructure, skills and expertise to do this sort of data analysis. It's not something that individuals can take on themselves; even if they could, the data power will be realised in combination from lots of farms and even among regions. It's that power of looking at data over big areas in terms of patterns of production that will deliver the insights. That's going to require individuals being comfortable with contributing or sharing their data with others, and that 'best practice' standards and procedures will be adopted to ensure confidence that the data are not going to be sold; and that you are going to obtain 'fair value' from the data that you contributed to the data pool. A lot of thought and development is on hand with a view to providing that data-sharing security to farmers.

ML: Traditionally in Australia, the public sector has largely both funded and performed agricultural research and development; including through CSIRO, through a unique and successful model of statutory rural research and development corporations (RRDCs) which are collaborative with the industry and government and funding research.[19] Also, historically, through primarily states-based, agricultural extension services, the fruits of the publicly funded research have been made available to farmers generally, rather than having them locked away under patent systems.[20]

This government-funded approach is premised on significant 'positive externalities' so that all farmers can benefit and on limited 'product differentiation' and direct competition between farmers. Do we need to change our way of thinking about the funding of research, development and extension in the digital era?

RH: It's going to continue to be important, but it's not going to be the sole way that digital technologies are introduced, or their benefits realised. The public sector is still going to be critically important in delivering datasets and probably for good research for which there will be limited business models for the private sector to deliver. Things like much better weather and soil datasets across Australia; those fundamental 'public good' datasets that are critical for inclusion as part of the overall data pool to deliver insights are going to remain in the public domain.

The reality is though that the analysis of that data is increasingly happening in the private sector, in the start-up world, and in venture-funded operations because of the speed with which these organisations can move and because of the skill sets that increasingly reside there. It's going to have to be more of a partnership than it has been between the private and public sectors.

To be honest, this is where we are falling behind a little bit in Australia compared to some other countries, particularly the Netherlands, Israel and to a large extent the US. They have 'innovation ecosystems' involving public and private sectors that work well together to deliver outcomes; their structures for doing that are much more advanced than we have here in Australia.

ML: That does sound potentially challenging and is consistent with the broader story about digital innovation throughout the economy and in particular, the role of start-ups. Australia appears to be falling behind internationally on that score though there does seem to be significant potential for us to build that sort of business, across the agricultural 'value chain', which is referred to as 'AgTech'.[21]

But as you say, we seem to be attracting relatively small levels of investment relatively; this has always been a problem, hasn't it, getting early stages of venture capital funding into later stages that can take companies into substantial growth? Government does its thing and funds 'accelerators', 'incubators' and such like support for start-ups, but it seems hard to get past those early stages.[22] This is going to be important, isn't it, in the agricultural sector?

RH: It's going to be very important, and I think that a mentality change can really help with that. In your introduction, you talked about the importance of agriculture as an export sector. We need to think about the 'knowledge economy' more generally, as an export sector.[23,24]

We're never going to be a big market for the application of technology, because of our small population and the limited number of farm businesses; we're small compared to where a lot of the leading technology is developing. But there is nothing preventing Australian AgTech businesses and their intellectual property (IP), and our knowledge economy sector more generally, competing in those global markets. We just need to understand and embrace that opportunity.

If the government focused on AgTech as a component of the knowledge economy, as important an export sector as say, beef, then the likelihood would be higher of realising the public–private partnerships required to move into global markets.

ML: The point you make about needing to think of agricultural technology in a broader 'knowledge economy' context, raises another interesting issue. The agriculture sector is not only large but also diverse, and in many senses quite fragmented between the very different arms; from farming and grazing, from dryland through irrigation, from intensive feedlots to broadacre operations, from market gardens through horticulture, from small family farms through large-scale agri-businesses, and from forestry through agri-forestry, and food production to processing. Is there a need in the context of digital innovation, for the sector itself to rethink how it thinks of itself, its business models and its value added and its sustainability; as it moves forward with these new technology challenges?

RH: In your introduction, you mentioned 300,000 people employed in agriculture. That's directly in agriculture; in the food supply chain more generally, and the inputs into agriculture, it's well over 1,000,000 Australians that are employed. It's a very diverse sector.[25,26] That is something that we've always talked about at the Farm Institute, and that the sector itself, more generally, has tried to get across.

There is a perception of the sector, rooted in a 'nostalgic' understanding of what agriculture used to be but that is nothing like reality these days. It is an incredibly diverse sector with many and various opportunities. Increasingly, people are coming into agriculture from outside, from other industries looking at the opportunities. Yes, we do need to get better at capturing and embracing that interest, and particularly the technology coming in from other sectors, and working out how it can be incorporated into agriculture in Australia.

ML: As you observe, Richard, there is a tendency, culturally and politically in Australia, to look with a certain nostalgic understanding, maybe even sometimes with a 'romanticised' view of agriculture as yeoman farmers on family farms.[27] Of course, there are still many of those, albeit far fewer now than in the past due to structural changes in the sector. But as you pointed out, the industry is now very big and diverse in composition and activities, and at the same time becoming more integrated, particularly as it moves forward.

Perhaps, the government too needs to rethink the way that agriculture fits into the economy, and how it supports its further development and competitiveness, particularly for the well-being of regional and rural communities. A couple of the big challenges for the sector are water management and climate change.

What perspective do you have as AFI on these issues? The politics is just dreadful, what with the burning of water plans, water buybacks, water theft and Royal Commissions of Inquiry in the Murray–Darling Basin,[28,29] it all seems a bit of a mess and yet so important to the future of agriculture.

RH: Water policy and issues are undoubtedly and will continue to be one of the biggest issues that we have in agriculture in Australia. Water is the biggest limit to production, obviously, in the driest continent. Technology has a massive role to play in delivering better outcomes in water policy.

It astounds us at the AFI constantly that the policy debates go on in the absence of actual data. It's one of the things that continually frustrates us across the board, not just in water policy, that so many aspects of agriculture have such terrible data available to make good decisions. Accurately knowing how water is being used, where it's going, to better inform and understand what we have available and how it should be used, you would think would be an absolute.

The fundamental thing that we should have is a properly informed policy discussion, but we don't have the granular data that we need and that technology can increasingly provide; better monitoring and real-time information in an ongoing way should help us make better decisions on water management.

ML: Data limitations could indeed be addressed with new technology but there are also issues of political economy in all this. Literally, billions of dollars have been spent chasing so-called irrigation water efficiencies and 'water buybacks' on behalf of the environment and paid for by taxpayers; but in part because we perhaps don't have good data, it's not immediately clear what has been achieved, is it?[30,31]

RH: You referred to 'so-called' irrigation efficiencies but they are real irrigation efficiencies. There is no question that amazing technology is being used to apply water where and when it's needed. Plants get exactly what they need and no more, no less; and that has delivered water saving outcomes across the board. The problem is it's very difficult to get good data around that because of the lack, as I said before, of a centralised or standardised way of reporting it and of measuring it in the first place.[32] These good and important gains that are being made are being discounted, and instead what happens is that the bad example gets reported and there's no ability to counter that with data about the good outcomes.

ML: No doubt technologies have delivered improved efficiency of water used in production but given that the savings are paid for using public money with a view to returning water to the environment, the question is where those savings are going. As you say, if we haven't got good data and monitoring systems, we don't know the environmental benefit in terms of tackling climate change, for example. How do you see that broader challenge, to farmers and farming business models, as we confront the increasing uncertainties and risks of running farming enterprises in an age of climate change variability and intensification?

RH: Where new technology and data analysis have another important real role to play is that complex farming systems are invariably better at building climate resilience and yet they are difficult to research and to understand historically with traditional science. There is quite a change now in our ability through very sophisticated machine learning to understand complex farming systems in terms of the benefits that they deliver and the increased resilience that they can build into farming systems. That's one of the strongest areas where the value, the 'public good', can be delivered out of data analysis and understanding farming systems.

ML: Yes, it is about building resilience and adaptability in the face of climate change but isn't it also a matter of farming business models, and particularly in the management of risk in these uncertain times?[33] Are risk management systems in Australia in farming as well developed as in other countries in terms of, say, for example, the discussions and issues we're having around drought responses?[34]

RH: There are far fewer commercial risk mitigation products like income insurance, available for farming businesses in Australia than in other countries.[35] However, in every other country where there are mature markets for those products, they've been subsidised by the government to get them up and running. There is no market where they emerged without some government assistance, while historically our government has been unwilling to provide subsidies.

Australian agriculture has been proud of the fact that we have competed on the global stage without high levels of government assistance compared to our export competitors. How long we can keep doing that particularly in relation to building more resilient farming systems where we're basically talking about protecting 'natural capital' at the expense of productivity, in some cases? Where does the revenue stream come from for that?

AFI is looking at the rest of the world where payments for 'ecosystem services' (ESS) which build and protect natural capital as a 'public good' are being delivered to farmers.[36] There's a recognition that this 'public good' should be paid for and thereby provide alternative revenue streams to farms, including during drought, while protecting' natural capital' on behalf of the public.

It would be great if we could develop such ESS schemes in Australia and tie new technology into that. Technology will be important in developing these market mechanisms. Being able to monitor, measure and know that the outputs are being delivered is increasingly being enabled by technology, including satellite imagery and monitoring.

ML: While the ESS payments approach is more widely used overseas,[37] a sceptic might suggest that by using the 'green box' mechanism this is one way in which countries can avoid breaching their commitments to minimising agricultural subsidies under various trade agreements.[38,39] For whatever reasons, Australia has not to date chosen to tread that path.[40] Nevertheless, technology and research are important to moving in directions like carbon farming and sequestration through changing land management practices. As you say, you've got to be able to know what you're getting for your money and how you're managing it, don't you?

RH: Yes, that's where research and technology come in because to have a market you've got to be able to define and quantify what you're selling. Carbon markets are promoted as an opportunity for agriculture,[41] but currently we don't know how to make them work across the farming landscape, in terms of say, how much carbon there is in soils, how much potential there is, and how you'd go about monitoring that in an ongoing way to enable carbon market operation.[42,43]

Conclusion

The Australian agricultural sector is large, significant economically and socially, and is a world-class competitive exporter of the greater part of its production.[44] It occupies a vast land area and is the major user of water resources on the driest continent.

Technology and innovation have been a vital component in maintaining the sector's international competitiveness through increased productivity and consequent substantial structural changes, as protection was reduced and as it became the most trade-exposed sector of the economy. The increasing frequency and severity of droughts, bushfires, storms and floods, as a manifestation of climate change have strained the resilience, adaptability and sustainability of the sector which has responded with new business models, agribusiness integration of value chains, and adoption of new digital technologies. Adoption of digital technology will require enhanced skills, changed behaviour and practices, including attitudes towards the sharing of farm data, and access to more venture capital to drive development of cutting-edge AgTech innovation.

Not only is agriculture moving away from thinking of agriculture in the traditional ways, but importantly it is moving into a knowledge-based economy, requiring a more integrated view of agriculture and hopefully taking its place in what some have labelled as a 'biologically derived economy' where the different aspects of farm practice, land and water management, and finance and risk management are highly integrated.

Emerging 'market mechanisms' relying on new technologies, for example, in ecosystem services payments, carbon and water markets have embarked on a complex and difficult path to more sustainable agriculture based on 'natural accounting systems' and methodologies that will need to establish trust in their integrity and positive environmental impact. Public policy is working in increasingly close and new modes of collaboration and partnership with the private sector, including farmers.

Notes

1 ABARES Insights (2023) Snapshot of Australian Agriculture 2023, *Department of Agriculture, Fisheries and Forestry (DAFF)* www.agriculture.gov.au/abares/products/insights/snapshot-of-australian-agriculture
2 Henzell, T. (2007) *Australian Agriculture: Its History and Challenges*, Clayton, VIC: CSIRO Publishing
3 ABARES (2023), op cit
4 Ibid
5 Ibid
6 Mullen, J. (2007) *The Importance of Productivity Growth in Australian Agriculture*, 51st Annual Conference of the Australian Agricultural and Resource Economics Society, Presented Paper, 13–16th February, Queenstown, NZ https://citeseerx.ist.psu.edu/document?repid=rep1&type=pdf&doi=d631a8b0264c30f6feb346f48ab79e2ba5f87393
7 Pratley, J. and Rowell, L. (2017) Evolution of Australian agriculture, in Pratley, J. (ed) *Principles of Field Crop Production*, Graham Centre for Agricultural Innovation, Wagga Wagga: Charles Sturt University www.csu.edu.au/research/grahamcentre/publications/e-books/principles-of-field-crop-production
8 This article notes that support of Australian agriculture at two percent of revenue is among the least subsidised in the world and has resulted in its flourishing and high export orientation: Jasper, C. (2020) ABARES report finds that step up in global agricultural protection will cost Australian farmers, *ABC News*, 29th May www.abc.net.au/news/2020-05-29/australian-farmers-least-subsidised-but-global-protection-rising/12299074
9 Howlett, B. and Henry, R. (2021) Australian agriculture and climate change: A two-way street, *Australian Academy of Science*, www.science.org.au/curious/policy-features/australian-agriculture-and-climate-change-two-way-street

10 Australian Council of Learned Academies (ACOLA) (2020) *The Future of Agricultural Technologies*, Horizon Scanning Series, Report by Expert Working Group, Melbourne https://acola.org/hs6-future-agricultural-technologies/
11 Dufty, N. and Jackson, T. (2018) Information and communication technology use in Australian agriculture: A survey of broadacre, dairy and vegetable farms, *ABARES* www.agriculture.gov.au/abares/research-topics/productivity/productivity-publications/ict-use-summary
12 Dufty, N. and Jackson, T. (2018) Information and communication technology (ICT) use in Australian agriculture: A survey of broadacre, dairy and vegetable farms, *ABARES*, Research Report 18.15, November, Canberra www.agriculture.gov.au/sites/default/files/sitecollectiondocuments/abares/ict-use-australian-agriculture.pdf
13 Hughes, N., Galeano, D. and Hatfield-Dodds, S. (2019) *The Effects of Drought and Climate Variability on Australian Farms*, Canberra: ABARES
14 Australian Farm Institute (AFI) www.farminstitute.org.au
15 AFI (2013) *Australian Agriculture Losing Competitiveness*, 2nd February www.farminstitute.org.au/australian-agriculture-losing-competitiveness/#:~:text=The%20conclusions%20of%20the%20ABARES,has%20decreased%20over%20recent%20years and ABARES report on agricultural productivity rates in Australia, Canada and USA over the last 40 years
16 See AFI report on long-term decline: AFI (2007) *Productivity Growth in Australian Agriculture* www.farminstitute.org.au/product/productivity-growth-in-australian-agriculture-trends-sources-performance/
17 National Farmers' Federation (NFF) (2013) *Australia's First Blueprint for the Future of Food and Fibre*, Media Release, 14th February https://nff.org.au/media-release/australias-first-blueprint-for-the-future-of-food-and-fibre/
18 Keogh, M. and Henry, M. (2016) *The Implications of Digital Agriculture and Big Data for Australian Agriculture*, Research Report, Sydney, Australia: Australian Farm Institute www.crdc.com.au/sites/default/files/pdf/Big_Data_Report_web.pdf
19 Productivity Commission (2011) *Rural Research and Development Corporations*, Report No 52, Canberra www.pc.gov.au/inquiries/completed/rural-research/report
20 Hunt, W., Birch, C., Coutts, J. and Vanclay, F. (2012) The many turnings of agricultural extension in Australia, *The Journal of Agricultural Education and Extension*, 18 (1): 9–26
21 AgTech or Agricultural Technology. Campbell, C. (2022) Analysis: The state of AgTech in Australia, *Terem.Tech*, 22nd February https://terem.tech/the-state-of-agtech-in-australia/
22 In respect of incubators and accelerators studied, this paper finds that their economic impact is inconclusive: Bliemel, M.J., Flores, R.G., de Klerk, S., Miles, M.P., Costa, B. and Monteiro, P. (2016) *The Role and Performance of Accelerators in the Australian Start-Up Ecosystem*, Commonwealth Department of Industry, Innovation & Science (Made public 25th May), UNSW Business School Research Paper, 2016MGMT03 https://papers.ssrn.com/sol3/papers.cfm?abstract_id=2826317
23 Wood, J. (2003) Australia: An under-performing knowledge nation? *Journal of Intellectual Capital*, 4 (20): 144–164
24 This Productivity Commission Report (2015) *Barriers to Growth in Services Exports*, examined a number of knowledge-based sectors but did not include agriculture-related services www.pc.gov.au/inquiries/completed/service-exports/report
25 IBISWorld (2023) *Agribusiness in Australia – Market Size, Industry Analysis, Trends and Forecasts (2023–2028)*, March www.ibisworld.com/au/industry/agribusiness/1904/#IndustryStatisticsAndTrends

26 IBIS (2023) *Agribusiness in Australia – Market Size 2008–2029*, 17th March www.ibisworld.com/au/market-size/agribusiness/
27 There is the cultural view of agriculture as going 'into the very soul of the nation' and 'it is as much a religion as an industry', with a resulting 'blindness' among other things to its impact on the environment. See this essay by Hughes-d'Aeth, T. (2018) Dark Emu and the blindness of Australian agriculture, *The Conversation*, 15th June https://theconversation.com/friday-essay-dark-emu-and-the-blindness-of-australian-agriculture-97444
28 Beasley, R. (2021) *Dead in the Water*, Sydney: Allen and Unwin
29 This book review looks at *Dead in the Water* by Richard Beasley that recounts how Australia's Murray–Darling Basin, the largest in the country and accounting for 60% of Australian agricultural production, is an epic failure of poor water governance. See: Salt, D. (2021) Dead in the water – an 'angry book' on our greatest environmental catastrophe, *Global Water Forum,* 23rd April, www.globalwaterforum.org/2021/04/23/dead-in-the-water-an-angry-book-on-our-greatest-environmental-catastrophe/
30 This article documents the failure of the $13 billion plan to restore sustainability to the major Australian river system: Kingsford, R. (2022) It's official: The Murray-Darling Basin Plan hasn't met its promise to our precious rivers. So where to now? *The Conversation*, 4th August https://theconversation.com/its-official-the-murray-darling-basin-plan-hasnt-met-its-promise-to-our-precious-rivers-so-where-to-now-188074
31 This article is on irrigation water efficiency and buyback projects: Foley, M. (2022) $1.8 billion plan to help save Murray-Darling river system set to fail, *Sydney Morning Herald*, 2nd August www.smh.com.au/politics/federal/1-8-billion-plan-to-help-save-murray-darling-river-system-set-to-fail-20220802-p5b6ld.html
32 Pereira, H. and Marques, R.C. (2017) An analytical review of irrigation efficiency measured using deterministic and stochastic models, *Agricultural Water Management*, 184, April: 28–35
33 Elders Insurance (2015) *The Importance of Risk Management for Farmers*, 18th December www.eldersinsurance.com.au/resources/the-importance-of-risk-management-for-farmers
34 Kimura, S. and Antón, J. (2011) *Risk Management in Agriculture in Australia*, OECD Food, Agriculture and Fisheries Papers, No 39, Paris: OECD Publishing https://doi.org/10.1787/5kgj0d8bj3d1-en
35 This report examines a range of risk management strategies, options, and tools, and concludes that the range of mitigation products in Australia is 'immature': Laurie, A., Curtis, M., Heath, R., Darragh, L. and McRobert, K. (2019) Australian agriculture: An increasingly risky business, *Australian Farm Institute*, www.mla.com.au/contentassets/82fb9bbbad4a4c679e8b2ac44e2df6c9/f.eva.1803_final_report.pdf
36 AFI (2019) *Valuing Agriculture's Natural Capital*, Canberra: Roundtable, 15th October www.farminstitute.org.au/valuing-agricultures-natural-capital/
37 This research notes over 550 ESS active programs with US$36–42 billion in estimated annual transactions but finds that comprehensive and reliable data about them has proved difficult to find: Salzman, J., Bennett, G., Carroll, N., Goldstein, A. and Jenkins, M. (2018) The global status and trends of payments for ecosystem services, *Nature Sustainability*, 1 (3): 136–144
38 This infographic explains how 'green box' subsidies for environmental protection are acceptable if they do not provide product price support or distort prices or trade: World Trade Organisation (WTO) *Domestic Support in Agriculture: The Boxes* www.wto.org/english/tratop_e/agric_e/agboxes_e.htm
39 This article looks at how to replace EU agricultural subsidies to the UK with a UK-specific set of payments referred to as the new 'environmental land management scheme' to help UK farmers become more productive and sustainable: Casalicchio,

E. (2020) UK unveils post-Brexit plan to phase out current farm subsidies, *Politico*, 30th November www.politico.eu/article/uk-farm-subsidies-post-brexit-plan/

40 Australian Department of Agriculture, Fisheries and Forestry (DAFF) (2012) *Ecosystem Services Report*, Discussion Paper, July www.agriculture.gov.au/agriculture-land/farm-food-drought/natural-resources/ecosystem-services/ecosystem-services-report

41 This roadmap elaborates a vision and targets for 2030 including carbon abatement of up to 480 MtCO2, and revenue of up to $24 billion: Carbon Market Institute (CMI) (2017) *Australian Carbon Farming Industry Roadmap*, 2nd Edition https://carbonmarketinstitute.org/app/uploads/2017/06/CMI-Carbon-Farming-Industry-Roadmap-Second-Edition.pdf

42 Wentworth Group of Concerned Scientists (2016) *Accounting for Nature: A Scientific Method for Constructing Environmental Asset Condition Accounts* https://wentworthgroup.org/wp-content/uploads/2017/07/Wentworth-Group-2016-Accounting-for-Nature.pdf

43 This article discusses the practical difficulties in operating carbon markets that have been highlighted by revelations of fraud: ANU College of Law (2022) *Australia's Carbon Market a Fraud on the Environment*, 24th March https://law.anu.edu.au/news-and-events/news/australia's-carbon-market-fraud-environment

44 This graph estimates that between 60 million and 130 million people (including Australia's domestic population of 25 million) can be fed by the agricultural sector of the country: Deloitte (2015) People fed per hectare 'food bowl' rhetoric or reality: How many people can Australia feed? *Agribusiness Bulletin* www.deloitte.com/content/dam/Deloitte/au/Documents/consumer-business/deloitte-au-cb-agri-people-fed-per-hectare-300915.pdf

17 The Second Domestication of Dairy and Beef

Food 2.0 Proteins Without the Animals

Interview With Lesley Hughes

Introduction

What is the future of food production as we enter the era that is being called Food 2.0?[1] The development of animal-free milk is likely to decimate the traditional dairy industry within a decade, and plant-based meat is set to up-end the beef market. On one set of projections, this new biotechnology puts us on the cusp of the deepest, fastest, most consequential disruption in food and agricultural production since the first domestication of plants and animals 10,000 years ago.[2] This biotech revolution or the 'second domestication' refers to microorganisms and technologies of 'precision fermentation'[3] which seem to presage the 2020s as the decade of the 'peak cow'.[4]

Keywords: agriculture; animal protection; animal welfare; beef; bioengineers; biotechnology; cellular agriculture; cheese; designer food; dairy; (UN) Food and Agricultural Organisation (FAO); Food 2.0; food revolution; genetically modified yeast; lactose intolerance; livestock-based agriculture; meat substitute; milk; peak cow; plant-based food; precision fermentation; protein; second domestication; synthetic food products; SDG 9; SDG 11; SDG 12; SDG 15; UNEP

Interviewee Profile

Professor Lesley Hughes (**LH**), Emeritus, an ecologist, is Distinguished Professor of Biology, and Interim Executive Dean, Faculty of Science and Engineering at Macquarie University, and formerly the Deputy Vice Chancellor (Research).[5] Her principal research interests are in the implications of climate change on species, ecosystems and conservation. A former lead author of the IPCC 4th and 5th Assessment Reports, federal Climate Commissioner, and current Councillor and Director with the Climate Council of Australia, she is also a member of the Wentworth Group of Concerned Scientists.

DOI: 10.4324/9781003280316-20

The Interview

ML: Welcome Lesley. Could you give us an idea of how milk is being re-engineered with new biotechnology? What's happening and how?

LH: The technology is a fermentation technology, which is quite an old technology because yeast is the 'superstar' microorganism that will be used for this; has been used for centuries, probably for thousands of years, to brew beer and to make bread. Essentially, what some biomedical technologists are doing now is genetically modifying yeast, so that they can produce animal protein and eventually, animal lipid as well. Once you can produce animal protein in a big stainless steel fermentation vat, it opens up all sorts of possibilities for creating 'synthetic products' without the use of the animal at all.

ML: What's involved in the process of a typical dairy cow, 'the factory on legs',[6] which is quite a process and perhaps not as efficient as many of us might like to believe. What production levels do they achieve over a lifetime, what is the impact on the environment, on the usage of water and on the animals' welfare?

LH: The dairy industry is a huge user of water[7] and land.[8] It produces enormous quantities of greenhouse gas emissions,[9] and many people are very concerned about the animal welfare aspects of it too.[10] Cows produce milk for their calves. For a cow to produce milk for most of its life, it needs to be kept in a constant cycle of pregnancy. It wasn't until I started my research on this topic that I fully realised just how exploitative the dairy industry is.[11]

When a calf is born, it generally only spends about a day with its mother before it's taken away. Female calves are then bottle-fed and eventually themselves are put back into the dairy herd. Male calves, however, that can't ever produce milk are excess to requirements and there's only two fates possible for them. Some of them are fattened up for a few months for veal, and the rest are usually slaughtered within five days, so they're known as 'bobby calves',[12,13] and their fate is an open, rather nasty 'little secret' in the dairy industry.

A cow gives birth to a calf when it's about two years old and they are generally artificially inseminated. The calf is taken away and will produce milk for about ten months when the milk production tapers off. It'll get a few weeks rest before giving birth again, and so on, in a constant cycle of being milked and being pregnant.

Cows in Australia are milked twice a day, and can live for about 20 years, but most of them go to the abattoir after about six or seven years because by that stage their milk production has tapered off to the point that they're no longer economical to feed. Dairy cows have quite short, rather exploited lives, and end up usually as pet food or mincemeat, because their meat is considered of lesser quality than that of cows bred for beef production.

Over that lifetime, for each of the about 30,000 litres of milk that a cow will produce, it will use some 500 litres of water as a minimum. Over the 'productive' lifetime of six or seven years, the cow will belch forth about 800 kilograms of methane, which is a very potent greenhouse gas.[14]

All in all, it is far from being a sustainable industry, and I think some would regard it as quite a cruel industry. In fact, milk straight from a cow is generally 87.7% water,[15] and that means that producing milk from artificial technologies – synthetic milk – is far easier and more efficient than producing meat, which of course requires hundreds of millions of cells to be produced in a laboratory. Milk being mostly water, there are far fewer cells to create.

ML: Most of the world's population is lactose intolerant.[16] Plant-based dairy alternatives are growing rapidly in the market and the dairy industry is fighting back. However, what we're talking about here is, I understand, something completely different. This technology of synthetic genes, fermentation tanks and biotechnology fermentation; apparently, opens up the prospect of programming microorganisms. What is involved and what does it hold for the future?

LH: If we take milk as the example and focus on the proteins, which is what most people have been focusing on so far, there are six different proteins in milk: four casein proteins and two whey proteins. These are quite simple compared to the average protein, so they're relatively easy to replicate since we know the amino acid sequence that codes for those proteins because it's published in readily available databases.

Clever geneticists have figured out how to programme yeast, effectively using a 'new' gene that is inserted to produce those milk proteins. Those proteins can then be harvested from the fermentation tank and added to the water to produce something quite like milk. What they're working on now is to also produce fats that are similar or indeed chemically identical to the fats in milk. They hope, once they've cracked the code, that by adding all of that together, you can produce milk, indeed, a sort of 'designer milk' that is virtually chemically identical to milk from a cow. It would then be possible to leave out the 'bad' bits such as the lactose, the bacteria, which would increase the shelf life of the milk, the hormones that we all take in when we drink milk, or the antibiotics used to promote animal growth. In this way, you can basically design milk that is essentially an animal protein and lipid product, but without all the undesirable elements that milk might contain.

ML: Isn't that absolutely astounding! Designer milk and designer food out of all this new technology. The World Economic Forum report sees these developments as a part of the wider 'fourth industrial revolution'.[17] It strikes me that it's almost as if designing food is like designing software. It uses 'open-source', publicly accessible technology, but are we still pretty much at the 'start-up' stage with this synthetic gene milk?

LH: Yes, we are at the start-up stage, but it's changing very rapidly.[18] The first milk start-up began in 2014. It was created by two young biomedical engineers who had independently become vegan because of ethical and environmental concerns about the livestock industry, but they both really liked cheese and were disappointed with the vegan cheese offerings. Frankly, having tried vegan cheese lately myself, I agree with them. It's not a great product yet, so they figured that they could fiddle around and try first to make the synthetic milk protein by using yeast which they did.

They started a company, originally called Move Free, which later rebranded as Perfect Day. They started with $30,000 in a small lab. They won a couple of competitions and since then, they've attracted investment. The last I read was that they've now got $200 million investment from some of the world's largest food processing companies.[19] They produced a 'teaser' which was ice cream that they sold online and it sold out in a few hours. They're now looking to not only produce actual milk that you'd be able to buy in a bottle in the supermarket but also sell into the lucrative ingredient market. Not all milk produced is drunk as milk or eaten as cheese or yoghurt; much of it goes into things like sports formulas, biscuits and other processed foods and manufactured goods.

ML: I understand that they're already moving into various cheeses, mozzarella, and that a New Zealand company is into seafoods and leather, egg whites and mayonnaise.[20] Sounds like a vast ingredient market opportunity for the new technology?

LH: There are many companies now starting up in this space because of tremendous worldwide interest in moving away from livestock agriculture for environmental, health and welfare issues. The Economist dubbed 2019 'The Year of the Vegan'.[21] There is exponential growth in interest in plant-based foods, at least in richer Western countries, and this sort of fermentation technology is tapping into that growing market.

ML: Perhaps we could segue from animal-free milk to the new world of animal-free products generally, and plant-based meat. This poses more of a challenge I understand than milk per se. What's going on with 'meat alternatives'?[22]

LH: There are two kinds of meat alternatives. Most people will have seen in their supermarket products from companies called Alternative Meat, Beyond Burger or Impossible Burger. Those are 'meat substitutes' made of plants of one sort or another. That's one kind, and it's becoming successful.

A second type will be available in a few years called 'cell-based' meat where an animal cell is cloned and the product is somewhat analogous to synthetic milk. It is an animal product but made in a laboratory rather than by killing a cow, sheep or pig. That technology is still very expensive but it's developing with big investment by some heavy-hitting investors.

In a few years, you might be seeing cell-based meats and burgers readily available competitively priced. Producing something that has the texture and taste of a steak is rather more challenging than producing something that's minced up. So, I think we're still quite a way from a perfectly cultured laboratory-produced steak, but we are closer to laboratory-produced mincemeat.

ML: Are we indeed in the 2020s poised on the threshold of the decade of the 'peak cow'? You cite economic predictions about what's happening with this. What challenge is this posing to the conventional industrial food production systems that we've grown up with and rely upon, particularly in Australia?

LH: The analogous situation is the challenge posed to fossil fuel production by renewable energy. I think this new food technology will have similar or possibly even greater disruptive capacity to traditional livestock agriculture.

My interest was spurred by a report from the American think tank RethinkX that analysed the US dairy and beef market in the light of this developing technology.[23] They make some provocative and bold predictions such as about the number of cows in the US. They project to fall by 50% by 2030 and 75% by 2035, with widespread bankruptcies of not only farming operations but the supply chains that are involved. They point out that on average a dairy cow is about 4% 'efficient', that is, only about 4% of the input into a dairy cow comes out the other end as a product that you can sell. On the other hand, with precision fermentation technology you don't have to feed a cow so the process is far more 'efficient' in use of inputs. Once they've cracked the formula, they will be able to produce these protein-based products far more cheaply with, of course, less emissions, less water, less land, etc., than we do today using rather 'inefficient' livestock.

ML: This disruption is also going to have a huge impact on existing jobs and implications for the new jobs that will be created and the skills required?

LH: Yes. Just as coal mining jobs will become vanishingly small over the next ten or 20 years and renewable energy jobs are building, it's an analogous situation here. Existing jobs will be lost in farming and traditional agricultural supply chains. These will potentially be replaced by new jobs, with probably different people with different skills. It'll still be industrial-scale food production, but it'll be using fermentation vats rather than animals.

ML: I think you've referred to 'bioengineers' and raise the question of whether existing workers in the food industry can be retrained to become 'bio-engineers' or whether a new breed will need to be developed. You also suggest that these fermentation food production facilities will typically be located closer to urban area markets than have been traditional farming and production activities in rural and regional areas.

LH: The geographic implications of this new technology are enormous. If you can produce, say, milk in a vat, you can do that anywhere and so might as well do it close to your main market to save money on transport. Also, once food production is separated from the geography of farming, it also becomes separated from the vagaries of climate, weather and seasonality. This 'new wave' industrial food production will be much more stable, but it will take place in different places, so that the tyranny of distance and weather will no longer apply.

ML: How is Australia positioned in reacting to these huge agricultural and food production challenges and opportunities? Dairy along with beef are a very significant agricultural industry sectors for us in terms of jobs, exports and associated services, and an Australian Dairy Plan is about to be released.[24]

LH: The challenge is enormous. Dairy is Australia's third largest agricultural industry. It's worth about $4 billion a year, and it employs more than 100,000 people. It's a big industry, so there's a lot potentially at stake. The industry has been going through a very tough time over the last two or three decades. The number of farms has fallen. Milk production is actually at almost its lowest level in the last couple of decades. A lot of that is due to the profits in the dairy industry for farmers being small to non-existent because the costs of labour, water and feed are greater than the farm-gate prices at which they sell their bulk milk.

There is a move by the government to try to address this issue, and as you said, there's been a group and it's chaired by the former Victorian premier, John Brumby, who have put together a draft plan for the dairy industry.[25] It's a very upbeat document and makes a lot of recommendations about the internal workings of the industry. Most of the recommendations are aimed at things like marketing, better contracts between processes and farmers, and those sorts of things. It does mention the problem of what they call 'climate volatility', though there seems to be a reluctance to use the phrase 'climate change'. They do acknowledge that increased climate volatility is affecting profits, but they make no mention, for example, of any need for climate adaptation, which I found extraordinary; there's a sort of single-sentence reference in the whole report. The report is about 40 pages long, but there's also only a single sentence that acknowledges that there may be some sort of technological disruption in the future, so it's a very internally facing document. It's all about the price 'wars' between the processors and the farmers. It doesn't acknowledge at all the growing external storm that's coming down the pipeline in terms of disruptive technology or climate change, which I actually found quite extraordinary.

ML: It is indeed remarkable that as a country and as an agricultural industry we do not seem to at least be squaring up to these disruptions and thinking them through. I recently on this programme interviewed the Australian Farm Institute (AFI) about the future impact of technology on agriculture and I do not believe that a single mention was made of these challenges. I heard a lot about digital technology and agriculture which is good stuff, but I don't think I heard mention in that interview of the issues we are discussing here. By way of contrast, the New Zealand dairy people seem to be in the usual New Zealandish way, fronting up to the issues in a more proactive manner. I think they've got a much bigger industry, possibly three times the size of Australia's?

LH: Yes, little New Zealand actually supplies nearly 40% of the world's dairy commodities, which is really extraordinary when you think about it. It's worth about $14 billion a year to the New Zealand economy, and it's their most valuable export.[26] Their chief scientists a couple of years ago made a speech where he warned about the implications of this new technology. Whether the average dairy farmer is paying much attention. I don't know. Dairy farmers work very hard, and they've got a lot of problems, but at least the New Zealanders do seem to be acknowledging that it's an issue. I think for the Australian dairy industry, while there may be some individuals that are aware of this, there doesn't seem to be much public discussion, and that was one of the reasons why I wrote the article.

ML: It's a global challenge as you pointed out, the FAO estimates of needing to feed a world population of up to 10 billion people,[27] and I think you quote some estimates that say there's 70 billion animals slaughtered a year for human consumption and rising global meat consumption trends.[28] As places get richer, they want to eat more meat, but none of these things as you point out meet sustainable development goals, let alone the Paris climate change agreement. I think you say that 'livestock-based agriculture' is not only an ecological disaster but a highly inefficient way to feed the world.

LH: That's right, and all new technologies have pluses and minuses. The minuses of course in this case are the disruption to existing livelihoods and to those regional towns and economies that rely on traditional agriculture; there are these minuses for individuals, but the pluses are enormous, I think. I'm an ecologist, environmentalist and climate change researcher, and I think that the opportunity to feed the world using these new technologies in a nutritious way in an efficient way with far less animal welfare, land, water and emissions problems has got to be a good thing. Also by reducing the amount of arable land used for farming, we have the opportunity to revegetate, to reforest, to support habitats for biodiversity and to sequester more carbon in the landscape. For me as an environmentalist, the pluses are enormous, but I absolutely acknowledge the pain and dislocation that these changes will bring to many communities.

ML: Yes, ultimately technology change and transformation confronts and presents great political and social challenges, as well as opportunities. You end your article by quoting Michael Pollan's 'Eating is a political act',[29,30,31] and ask the question of whether politicians and consumers will buy into these news technologies and possible solutions. That is the big question we're left with.

Conclusion

Emerging new synthetic food technologies of precision fermentation and cellular agriculture are opening up transformational opportunities for more sustainable agriculture on a global scale, taking us into the 'second domestication' of animals. Beyond existing plant-based alternatives to dairy and indeed meat products predictions are that the emerging range of dairy fermentation-based technologies for milk, cheese, ice cream, yoghurt, etc. will find us during the 2020s in the decade of 'peak cow'. New cell-based meats and products beyond plant-based products such as 'impossible burgers' are still in early stages of laboratory development and very expensive but with every prospect of rapid evolution and commercialisation in the coming decade. We are seeing the emergence of 'Food 2.0' delivering 'Proteins without Animals'.

The potential environmental benefits of synthetic 'designer' food production as a replacement for existing factory livestock-based agriculture are on a monumental scale given the huge areas of land and vast quantities of water currently required globally. Reclaiming these natural resources will not only reduce major sources of pollution and degradation but potentially open up new opportunities for revegetation, reforestation and improved plant and animal biodiversity. The methane emissions from livestock are a significant source of global carbon emissions with global climate impacts at least an order of magnitude greater on a per unit basis than from carbon dioxide emissions; reducing methane emissions from agriculture is critical to meeting global climate and emissions reductions targets. There are also significant animal health and welfare benefits.

As with any significantly disruptive and even transformational technological change, there are negative transitional impacts to be managed socially and economically. Existing old technology and practices jobs and skills are lost and made redundant, and existing agricultural and pastoral communities, towns and regions are displaced. Appropriately managed, these are replaced over time with new skills and practices, in this case in bioengineering jobs and facilities most likely more closely located to major centres of population. Global population growth scenarios make sustainable global food security highly implausible; the new synthetic, cellular and fermentation food production technologies hold out an opportunity to deliver. 'Eating is a political act' and it will take political will, courage and practical measures alongside significant social and cultural adaptation to make the technology transition to sustainable global livestock agriculture and food security.

Notes

1 Bradshaw, T. (2014) Food 2,0: The future of what we eat, *Financial Times*, 31st October www.ft.com/content/bfa6fca0-5fbb-11e4-8c27-00144feabdc0
2 Hughes, L. (2020) The milk of human genius, *The Monthly*, 1st March www.themonthly.com.au/issue/2020/march/1582981200/lesley-hughes/milk-human-genius#mtr
3 Vanhercke, T. and Colgrave, M. (2022) What's brewing? Precision food proteins from fermentation, *CSIRO*, 25th January www.csiro.au/en/news/all/articles/2022/january/whats-brewing-precision-fermentation
4 Goldstone, H. and Partan, E. (2019) We've reached 'peak cow', report says, *WGBH*, 11th December www.wgbh.org/news/national/2019-12-11/weve-reached-peak-cow-report-says
5 Hughes (2020), op cit
6 World Animal Protection (2021) *Cows, Calves and Ending Factory Farming*, 9th December www.worldanimalprotection.org/blogs/cows-calves-and-ending-factory-farming
7 Khan, S., Abbas, A., Rana, T. and Carroll, J. (2010) *Dairy Water Use in Australian Dairy Farms: Past Trends and Future Prospects*, *CSIRO*, Water for a Healthy Country Flagship Report Series https://publications.csiro.au/rpr/download?pid=changeme:1189&dsid=DS1 This report describes the dairy industry as Australia's largest water consuming industry, accounting for one-third of land under irrigation
8 This article quotes that livestock provides just 18% of food calories, 37% of protein but takes up 83% of farmland: Carrington, D. (2018) Avoiding meat and dairy is 'single biggest way' to reduce your impact on Earth, *The Guardian*, 1st June www.theguardian.com/environment/2018/may/31/avoiding-meat-and-dairy-is-single-biggest-way-to-reduce-your-impact-on-earth
9 Moate, P.J., Deighton, M.H., Williams, S.R.O., Pryce, J.E., Hayes, B.J., Jacobs, J.L., Eckard, R.J., Hannah, M.C. and Wales, W.J. (2015) Reducing the carbon footprint of Australian milk production by mitigation of enteric methane emissions, *Animal Production Science*, 56 (7): 1017–1034
10 Beaver, A., Proudfoot, K.L. and von Keyserlingk, M.A. (2020) Symposium review: Considerations for the future of dairy cattle housing: An animal welfare perspective. *Journal of Dairy Science*, 103 (6): 5746–5758
11 Animals Australia (2020) *The Reality of Dairy: Killing Calves*, 20th December https://animalsaustralia.org/our-work/farmed-animals/what-happens-to-dairy-calves
12 Moran, J., Hopkins, A. and Warner, R. (1991) The production of pink veal from dairy calves in Australia, *Outlook on Agriculture*, 20 (3): 183–190
13 Cave, J.G., Callinan, A.P.L. and Woonton, W.K. (2005) Mortalities in bobby calves associated with long distance transport, *Australian Veterinary Journal*, 83 (1–2): 82–84

14 UN Environment Programme (UNEP) (2021) *Methane Emissions Are Driving Climate Change: Here's How to Reduce Them*, 20th August www.unep.org/news-and-stories/story/methane-emissions-are-driving-climate-change-heres-how-reduce-them This blog post cites a UNEP and Climate and Clean Air Coalition assessment report of farming-related methane emissions
15 Harvard School of Public Health (2023) *The Nutrition Source: Milk* www.hsph.harvard.edu/nutritionsource/milk/#:~:text=Whole%20cow%27s%20milk%20contains%20about,skim"%20has%20virtually%20no%20milkfat
16 This research estimates 68% globally have lactose intolerance: Storhaug, C.L., Fosse, S.K. and Fadnes, L.T. (2017) Country, regional, and global estimates for lactose malabsorption in adults: A systematic review and meta-analysis, *The Lancet Gastroenterology & Hepatology*, 2 (10): 738–746
17 Schwab, K. (2016) The fourth industrial revolution: What it means, how to respond, *World Economic Forum*, 14th January 2016 www.weforum.org/agenda/2016/01/the-fourth-industrial-revolution-what-it-means-and-how-to-respond/
18 Wilson, A. (2019) Got milk? This $40m startup is creating cow-free dairy products that actually taste like the real thing, *Forbes*, 9th January www.forbes.com/sites/alexandrawilson1/2019/01/09/got-milk-this-40m-startup-is-creating-cow-free-dairy-products-that-actually-taste-like-the-real-thing/?sh=4e99b35340dc
19 Coyne, A. (2022) Nestlé joins forces with perfect day on animal-free dairy project, *Just Food*, 13th September www.just-food.com/news/nestle-joins-forces-with-perfect-day-on-animal-free-dairy-project/?cf-view
20 Bojovic, M. (2022) Synthetic milk is coming, and it could radically shake up dairy, *Science Alert*, 29th August www.sciencealert.com/synthetic-milk-is-coming-and-it-could-radically-shake-up-dairy
21 The Economist (2020) Interest in veganism is surging, *The Economist*, 29th January www.economist.com/graphic-detail/2020/01/29/interest-in-veganism-is-surging [Can't access the 2019 magazine]
22 Lee, H.J., Yong, H.I., Kim, M., Choi, Y.S. and Jo, C. (2020) Status of meat alternatives and their potential role in the future meat market – a review, *Asian-Australasian Journal of Animal Sciences*, 33 (10): 1533–1543 www.ncbi.nlm.nih.gov/pmc/articles/PMC7463075/
23 Seba, T. and Tubb, C. (2020) *Rethinking Food and Agriculture 2020–2030 – The Second Domestication of Plants and Animals, the Disruption of the Cow, and the Collapse of Industrial Livestock Farming*, RethinkX www.rethinkx.com/
24 Dairy Australia (2020) *Australian Dairy Plan* (The Brumby Plan), September www.dairyaustralia.com.au/about/collaboration-partners/australian-dairy-plan
25 Ibid
26 Dairy Australia (2021) *Why Isn't Australia Exporting the Same Amount of Milk Products as New Zealand?* 30th April www.dairy.com.au/dairy-matters/you-ask-we-answer/why-isnt-australia-exporting-the-same-amount-of-milk-products-as-new-zealand
27 UN Food and Agricultural Organisation (FAO) (2009) *Global Agriculture Towards 2050: The Challenge. High Level Expert Forum-How to Feed the World 2050* www.fao.org/fileadmin/templates/wsfs/docs/Issues_papers/HLEF2050_Global_Agriculture.pdf
28 Block, K. (2023) More animals than ever before – 92-2 billion – are used and killed each year for food, *The Humane Society of the United States*, Blog, 5th June https://blog.humanesociety.org/2023/06/more-animals-than-ever-before-92–2-billion-are-used-and-killed-each-year-for-food.html
29 Eisen, M. (2009) Michael Pollan: Eating is a political act, *The Cornucopia Institute*, 20th July www.cornucopia.org/2008/11/michael-pollan-eating-is-a-political-act/
30 Pollan, M. (2007) *The Omnivore's dilemma: The search for a perfect meal in a fast-food world*, New York: Bloomsbury
31 Pollan, M. (2008) *In Defence of Food: The Myth of Nutrition and the Pleasures of Eating*, New York: Penguin

18 The Murray–Darling Basin Environmental Catastrophe

Federalism Politics and Best Available Science

Interview With Richard Beasley

Introduction

The Murray–Darling Basin (MDB) is home to Australia's most precious and scarce resource: water. It provides water for over three million people and contributes to a significant proportion of Australia's agricultural production. From its early colonial days, the river has a sorry story to tell; it has been grossly mismanaged and depleted, and is in a very sad condition.[1]

This is, arguably, one of the biggest stories of public policy mismanagement in Australia. Not least, to tell, that some $13 billion of taxpayer money is being spent on the Murray–Darling Basin Plan (MDBP), to revitalise and rehabilitate the healthy ecology of the river to a sustainable condition. This is a very ambitious and, not to say, visionary plan that appears in the face of evidence-based data, analysis and recommendations to have not delivered very much at all at the end of the day because of politics.[2] While the river's condition continues to deteriorate, not least in the face of increased climate change stress, its management continues to be politically fractious.[3]

Keywords: agriculture; Basin Plan; biodiversity; catchment management; climate adaptation; climate change; double counting water savings; environmental flows; federalism; fish kills; food production; infrastructure efficiency; irrigation efficiency; lost water; migratory birds; Millennium Drought; Murray–Darling Basin (MDB); Murray–Darling Basin Authority (MDBA); Murray–Darling Basin Plan (MDBP); National Water Initiative (NWI); overallocation; Ramsar Treaties; peer review; return flows; river ecology; Royal Commission South Australia; SDG 6; SDG 11; SDG 12; SDG 13; SDG 14; SDG 15; sulphite soils; Water Act 2007; water buybacks; water governance; water recovery; water resources modelling; wetlands

Interviewee Profile

Richard Beasley SC **(RB)** has written the book 'Dead in the Water'[4]. Its subtitle is 'A very angry book about our greatest environmental catastrophe, the death of the Murray–Darling Basin'. Beasley is a barrister, educated at the universities of Adelaide and Sydney, and was made a silk in 2011. The book is

DOI: 10.4324/9781003280316-21

an advisedly 'forensic' analysis of the illegality and mismanagement of public money of one of our greatest natural resource assets. Richard was the senior legal counsel assisting the South Australian Royal Commission into the Murray–Darling Basin.[5]

The Interview

ML: Richard, what was the rationale for the groundbreaking National Water Initiative (NWI) and its associated reforms in 2004,[6] and how did it establish a national blueprint for sustainable use of water – including to try to resolve the problems on the River Murray?

RB: The impetus for it was that we were in the middle of one of the worst droughts recorded since white people turned up in Australia in 1788. It was the 'millennium drought' which went on for about ten years.[7]

Unfortunately, that warming and drying trend experienced in the Murray–Darling Basin brought on by that millennium drought is likely to become the norm rather than a terrible aberration. In any event, things got so bad that there was very little water going into the Murray–Darling system, which is where as you implied in your introduction, 60% of Australia's farms are located, as well as at least 16 really precious internationally listed wetlands.

There are both economic and environmental factors at work. So little water was available to the system that the riverbanks were exposed to that extent for the first time in about 10,000 years since the last Ice Age. In that epoch, the sea at Bondi Beach was 130 metres further out than it is now.

Once the riverbanks were exposed to air to this unprecedented extent, some of the contacting water turned into sulphuric acid causing a terrible environmental catastrophe.[8] So, Prime Minister Howard in the last days of his government managed to get the National Water Act reform legislation through parliament.[9] He had to use the Commonwealth Government's foreign affairs powers over international treaty obligations to override constitutional powers of the states because not all of them, particularly Victoria, would agree to give the Commonwealth government their power over water.

The resulting Water Act is a complex piece of legislation and, arguably, our most important environmental law. In relation to the Murray–Darling Basin, it provides that a Basin Plan be developed by a new federal government authority to be called the Murray–Darling Basin Authority (MDBA).

Whilst the Basin Plan is very complex, with many objectives and elements, at its core is this: we're still going to use water for irrigation in the Murray–Darling Basin, we're still going to grow food and fibre, but we're going to stop at the point where we're destroying the environment. What we're recognising explicitly through the Water Act is that we've overallocated water to irrigated agriculture; it's killing our environment and it's only going to get worse with climate change. So we've got to take some of that water back and give it to the environment and the way we'll do that is not leaving the decision with the Liberal Party or the National Party or the Labor Party or with the Greens, but we'll do this only on the basis of what the law says is quote: 'best available scientific knowledge'.

ML: The Water Act is a remarkable piece of Commonwealth legislation based not on its powers to control the environment directly because that power under the Constitution lies with the states. The legislation was accordingly framed on the basis that the federal government had signed up to a number of international environment treaties.[10,11,12,13,14] That is the constitutional linchpin and validity of this legislation, is it?

RB: That's right. Prime Minister Howard said to all the states involved in the basin: Queensland, NSW, Victoria, SA and the ACT, we can't keep going the way we are. He even gave a speech basically accepting that climate change was happening, and that the science was sufficiently convincing that there's a drying and warming trend in the basin with overallocated water to big irrigation.

We have to stop that, so he asked the states to give the Commonwealth government power over the waters. All the states said yes, except Victoria.[15] They held out so Howard had to go back to the drawing board and said, OK we've signed up to the Ramsar convention over wetlands,[16] the biodiversity convention, the climate change agreement and several treaty obligations over migratory birds. I'll draft a Water Act that does what I want it to do in terms of returning water to the environment and the way I'll make it constitutional is by returning water to the system, and in this way Australia will be fulfilling its international environmental treaty obligations. That's how it was made legal.

ML: The mismanagement of the Murray–Darling Basin over decades has arguably been characterised by overallocation of water. Water licences have been given by state governments to users who own the land, or consumptive users as they're called, which far exceed the flows available. Is the basic idea of the plan to somehow take back these overallocated water licences,[17] which can then be reallocated to sustain the environment and thereby meet the treaty commitments?

RB: That's right, but not in a compulsory way and so that Plan could maintain irrigation that has been developed in the basin for a hundred years but now on a sustainable basis. We've overallocated water licences to people to grow food and fibre in the basin without having any regard to the environment.

We've literally pumped the Murray dry, as was the slogan, and we've certainly achieved that and often with the Darling River too. Instead, the Commonwealth has acquired water for the environment. It is not by compulsory acquisition of water licences but in significant part by purchase from licensees on a voluntary sale basis, paid for as part of the $13 billion budget you've mentioned.

Often, what farmers or irrigators have done is not to sell their entire water entitlement but sell some of their water rights back to the government so that most of them stayed in farming. Some didn't, some sold their entire entitlements but that's how it worked. That was the main way through which the Commonwealth acquired water to sustain the river's environmental health.

ML: You mentioned that the legislation says that the way in which the river is to be managed is on the basis of 'the best scientific evidence'. What is the sense and importance of that very explicit provision within the Act?

RB: The Act says that we have to reach, what's called, an environmentally sustainable level of take; that is, we'll allow as much water to be taken out of the river system for economic purposes provided we stop at the point where we start killing the environment or at least its key parts. In developing the basic plan under the Water Act, a whole raft of scientists were put to work, including hydrologists, aquatics people, all sorts of flora and fauna experts, and ultimately computer modellers.

They worked out how much water needed to be acquired by the Commonwealth government to return as environmental flows in the Murray–Darling system to get the flow rates at the right times of the year, every certain number of years in terms of small floods and larger floodings, how much is needed on a yearly average to make sure that we protect and restore the 2,442 key environmental assets,[18] including the 16 Ramsar listed wetlands,[19] that we've got in the Murray–Darling Basin. That was a decision and a judgement left entirely to scientists, not as a policy decision, but as the law. Unfortunately, it hasn't been followed

ML: This is central to your reasoning and argument in the book, namely, that the management decisions have been undertaken illegally; that is, not in accord with the core of the legal obligations, that the best available science be deployed by the Murray–Darling Basin Authority in drawing up the plan and identifying how much water has to be returned to the environment.

The exercise was undertaken diligently. A lot of scientists were consulted, a big report called *The Guide* was written,[20] and then it was burnt in the streets of country towns and occasioned much angst and anger in the Murray–Darling Basin among other places.[21] What were the findings in terms of the range of flows, and why were they exciting people so much?

RB: What you just described as the reaction to what was called 'The Guide' to the basin plan was what the Murray–Darling Basin Authority (MDBA) put out before drafting the actual 'Basin Plan', which is formally required under the Commonwealth legislation. They said: Look, the scientists are telling us, having done about four years' work, that to save our environment and to get the proper flow rates in this system we're going to need to recover and return from consumptive users and irrigated agriculture, mining, etcetera to the system, to the environment, somewhere between about 4,000 and 7,000 gigalitres a year of water; that's billions of litres of water a year on average.

To give some idea of scale, Sydney Harbour is often used as a measuring stick and has a capacity of about 500 gigalitres of water. So somewhere between 8 and 14 Sydney Harbours a year have to be returned in terms of water to the environment to save it. The reaction to that, as you say, was that *The Guide* document was burnt in many country towns; and irrigation lobbyists certainly were pressuring the government and bureaucrats to say this is ridiculous, that's too much water for the environment.

ML: To be clear, this is to be done on a voluntary basis in the main part from users that have licences to be paid for and returned to the river.[22] Why did it occasion such an incredible and unprecedented reaction? You write of the 'great legal error' involved. What was that legal error in this process?

RB: The great legal error was a misinterpretation by the Murray–Darling Basin Authority (MDBA) as to whether the Water Act[23] is an environment-first law; or whether the basin plan is to be drafted in a way that somehow miraculously balances environmental, economic and social outcomes and maximises them all at the one time.

I actually don't think, at the end of the day, that this misinterpretation is that important. Even though they screwed up the legal analysis, as a matter of fact, the amount of water that ultimately was decided as required by the environment doesn't get within a bull's roar of being based on 'best available science'. That is just as a matter of fact even if there hadn't been this legal misconstruction.

ML: So they had these water return targets in a pretty big range of 4,000–7,000 gigalitres. Presumably, at the bottom end, there might at least be some little chance of saving the river in a sustainable way; at the top end, a much better chance. Subsequent to the burning of *The Guide* books, there were changes in the political situation and agency leadership with a new process undertaken. This ended up with a target in the 2000s gigalitres range; what you call a 'postcode fix'. What was this new process and politics, and the implications for the handling of the science advice?

RB: Clearly, the instructions from the changed government were that the Water Act is not an 'environment-first' law. We're going to interpret it as one under which economic and social outcomes get the same weight as the environment. The chairman of the Murray–Darling Basin Authority (MDBA) resigned.[24]

His press release effectively said: We've been working on the understanding and the legal advice for years that this is an environment – first law, so I'm out of here. And suddenly without any proper explanation given either in 2011 or to this day, the figure that the environment needed dropped somehow from the science-advised range of 4,000–7,000 billion litres a year on average, down to 2,750 billion (giga) litres.

In one paragraph in one report, the Basin Authority said: We've changed our modelling. No scientist that gave sworn evidence that the Royal Commission, or any scientist I've ever spoken to that's in this field, has ever been able to explain how 2,750 billion litres of water returned to the environment will possibly – is possibly – can possibly be a lawful figure. They say it's not a scientific figure; it's a political fix. There was a running joke within the MDBA that the figure was not decided on science but politics . . . and also on postcodes. That is, that the lobbyists and the irrigation people were only ever aware of a figure that started with 2 or 2,000: it was a NSW postcode (2,000), not Victoria (3,000), not Queensland (4,000), not South Australia (5,000), etc.

ML: Richard, apparently this process of reduction in the return flows needed and based on best scientific advice involved attacks on scientists; moves to censor them and an all-round lack of transparency.

RB: The Murray–Darling Basin Authority (MDBA) says it's a scientific organisation.

It's not, because it's never released all of its work and all of its modelling as to how they say 2,700–2,750 billion litres of water returned to the environment each year represents the equivalent of an environmentally sustainable level of take.

They've never exposed that and, of course, that means it's not science; because science is something that's open, completely transparent, where someone, whoever it is, puts out all their work and results to enable other scientists to check that work. It's called 'peer review'. They've never done that.[25]

Therefore, it's not a scientific organisation. In saying that it's not a scientific figure, I'll be careful; I'm a lawyer, not a scientist. I'm basing that on reports and evidence from the CSIRO that told the Murray–Darling Basin Authority (MDBA) very clearly that a return to the environment of 2,800 billion litres of water a year, will not achieve the flow rates that are needed in the long term to protect and restore the environment of the Murray–Darling Basin.[26]

MDBA had that from our leading scientific organisation. They were also told that unless you also factor in climate change projections over the next 20 or 30 years, you might as well not do this at all because it's going to get hotter and drier. For each 1 degree C that the temperature goes up in the basin, we're going to lose 15% of runoff and water. MDBA said: Thanks very much for that advice but we're not going to put climate change projections in our figures for water, because the water needs for the environment would need to go up too much.

CSIRO writes back and says that it is scientifically indefensible to do that. MDBA and other Commonwealth authorities having received that advice, despite the fact that they're spending our taxpayer money, just says, nah, we're not doing that.[27]

So the Basin Plan as it stands has no projections in its modelling for climate change impacts in the future which seems pretty nuts given that it's meant to be a plan for the future and it's not going to be altered again to take account of climate change.[28]

ML: Presumably, whatever figures they have modelled are based on the past 100 years or so of records; as distinct from what science might inform us about the expectations going forward. Can we move on to the $13 billion being spent to implement the Plan, and maybe even more in the future?[29]

I understand that it is being spent in two main ways: to take back or recover environmental water from existing licensees. One, as you mentioned, is to buy back the water voluntarily from those who own the licenses; and the other is from so-called infrastructure efficiency works in the form of resulting use efficiencies. First, what is the story with the buybacks? What actually happened and how much water was bought back at what cost?[30]

RB: The buy back has been capped at 1,500 gigalitres a year on average and that has been acquired and paid for by the Commonwealth. That's now a legislated cap and the government can't buy anymore than 1,500 gigalitres. This has been in response to complaints from people in the Bush and through the National Party arguing that buying backwater from irrigators and farmers is decimating rural communities and the economies of the regions and rural towns.[31]

There is very little evidence of that. Good economists would tell you that while some very water-dependent small towns were impacted by some water purchases; in the main, downturns in rural and regional economies are almost unaffected by the purchase of water. They are, on the other hand, much more greatly impacted by things like mechanisation, changes in soil, commodity price fluctuations, and all these things. So that argument seemed to be nonsense.

The other way the Commonwealth says it has recovered and acquired water is through what's called efficiency measures. For example, a farmer typically sprays their crop and some of the water went to grow the plant, some into the ground, some back into the groundwater, and some evaporated. To make them more efficient, the government paid people – for example – to install drip irrigation that is a far more efficient way to water and grow crops. In exchange for that public investment in the farmer's irrigation infrastructure, that farmer would give some of their water efficiency savings back to the government, at least notionally on paper rather than necessarily in the form of real return flows to the river.

There's been at least 60 years' research on such efficiency schemes and the scientific consensus is that they don't work; they cost the government a lot and become a handout for increased production from irrigation retaining the water savings on the farm.[32] So I'm not sure they've been a success at all, and that scheme has now been scrapped by the Commonwealth government and in the budget that was passed yesterday.

ML: So at the end of the day with these two approaches and this big budget of $13 billion nominally, they capped the buybacks at 1,500 gigalitres and now they've stopped these infrastructure efficiency works. All this money is being spent, but what has been achieved in terms of buyback and efficiency returns to meeting the river flow target level?[33]

RB: The Commonwealth says that it has now acquired about 2,100 gigalitres of the 2,750 it has targeted,[34] and it's not going to make the states recover the other 600 or so gigalitres to get up to that recovery target. They say they're going to put in place new schemes under the Basin Plan that are called engineering 'supply measures'. These are some 'miraculous' as yet not fully defined ways of building infrastructure or operating waters that will yield the recovery target shortfall required.[35]

To give you one example, that incidentally doesn't look like it's going to go ahead anyway, a change to the way that the Menindee Lakes were operated so that water was taken out of those lakes much more quickly than done historically. There's not always water in those lakes; and by moving it more quickly downstream and out of the lakes, it is claimed that you can save a lot of evaporation in future that previously would have occurred.[36]

ML: Returning for a moment to the infrastructure efficiency mechanism, for example, earth channel irrigation is not as water efficient as lined channels; spray irrigation is not as efficient in water use as trickle irrigation, etc. Yet the science and research revealed the efficiencies achieved were rarely recovered for the river.[37] We could have ended up paying people to use more water for more development, is that right?

RB: Absolutely. One of the other scientific findings that were forgotten in funding these efficiency measures is that when crops are spray-irrigated, not all that water is lost to the environment. The evaporated bit is lost, while the bit that goes on the plant for its growth is obviously not lost. However, the water that's otherwise said to be lost as excess that goes on the ground either runs back to the river system if the farm is near a river, or it gets into the groundwater and gets back to the environment that way.

ML: In other words, the so-called 'lost water' as a measure of inefficiency in water use was actually being returned to the environment as a, quite substantial, previously unrecognised 'return flow'?[38]

RB: Exactly. The MDBA was 'double counting' how much water they were saving through efficiency measures; which is what several scientists have been complaining about for ten years or so to the Authority.

You're not saving the water you think you are because you've got to take into account the water that may not have grown an inefficient farmer's crop, but wasn't lost to the environment, because it ended up in the groundwater or even directly into the river in some cases.[39]

ML: As you say Richard, the Water Act was a visionary piece of legislation which appears – at the end of the day – as not being able to deliver on its vision and aspiration for restoring the environmental health of the Murray–Darling River Basin.[40]

This is a great tragedy not only for the health of our most scarce resource on a large scale but also for all the people who live in that basin and rely on it. There's no honesty nor transparency about the situation they're facing, and no attempt to be honest about how they might be assisted to adapt to the increasing climate-induced stresses that confront them.

RB: That's a really, really good point Michael. Whether there is a basin plan or not, effective or otherwise; the future for the people that live in the Murray–Darling Basin is hotter, drier and with less water. The government is going to have to help them adapt to that future and help the environment adapt to that future with, or without, a basin plan.[41]

Instead, there's very little movement in relation to that assistance and even acknowledgement of the reality of the coming situation. I say again, I'm a lawyer. I don't have all the solutions for that.[42] That's up to governments and it's particularly up to the politicians that represent the people in rural and regional Australia, and they're not doing a great job on it.

Conclusion

Despite over two decades of national water policy reform, legislation, institutional creation and over A$13 billion of public expenditure; Australia's single most precious environmental asset – the water of the Murray–Darling Basin – continued its historic degradation to an environmentally catastrophic and unsustainable condition.

Visionary and innovative water policy reform was undertaken in a federal-state system of government that rests powers over water and environment with the states. It was necessary for federal government legislation to override those powers of the states by invoking its constitutional international treaty powers.

Negotiated in consultation with the states, a federal basin management authority was established and charged with developing and implementing a basin-wide management plan. The plan was not accepted by all the states, was rejected by basin farming communities and was publicly burnt in the streets of country towns.

The legislation, which was founded constitutionally on international environmental treaty powers, empowered the newly established basin authority to develop and implement a basin plan based on the best available scientific advice. The objective was to return overallocated water rights in the form of restored environmental flows that would ensure the sustainable future of the river's key environmental assets.

The range of target-level return flows was based on detailed, expert multi-disciplinary scientific modelling, but was rejected almost from the start on the basis of farming, community and political protests. The target level decided upon was well below the lower range advised by the scientists as required for sustainable water management in the basin, and the analysis behind the modelling changes was not transparently made available. The basin authority was also alleged to have not required the inclusion of climate change impacts.

Arguably, the changes made were illegal in not adopting 'best available science' but equally important in this sorry tale of public policy management on a grand scale was the inefficient and ineffective expenditure of the A$13 billion budget. Overallocated water was to be taken back as enhanced environmental flows by one of two means: public investment in on-farm infrastructure for improved irrigation efficiency and voluntary auction-based buybacks of water allocations.

In the case of the former, even when water savings were realised, they were found not to be returned as environmental flows as well as the nominal 'savings' being 'double counted'. Voluntary water buybacks were successful in reaching set targets but ignited strong objections from communities that felt destroyed by losing water from productive farming use.

Water buybacks were not only more effective than irrigation efficiency, but the resulting return environmental flows were achieved more efficiently; and at a significantly lower cost per unit of environmental flow returned.

Both sets of measures were dogged by political controversy and suspended at various times, with new unsubstantiated 'projects' put forward for public funding. Sustainable environmental flow targets have not been met to date and political arguments continue to date between the newly elected Labor government, the Opposition, farming lobbies and communities.[43]

In a post-truth water world,[44] new approaches to complex basin-wide water governance on this scale are, arguably required, in both policy and modelling dimensions.

Notes

1 Beresford, Q. (2021) *Wounded Country: The Murray Darling Basin – A Contested History*, Sydney: New South Press
2 Simons, M. (2020) Cry me a river: The tragedy of the Murray-Darling basin, *Quarterly Essay*, 77, 23rd March
3 Davies, A. (2023) Murray-Darling Basin plan: Labor gives states more time to deliver water pledges despite El Niño Fears, *The Guardian*, 25th July www.theguardian.com/australia-news/2023/jul/25/murray-darling-basin-water-pledges-labor-extends
4 Beasley, R. (2021) *Dead in the Water: A Very Angry Book About Our Greatest Environmental Catastrophe – the Death of the Murray-Darling Basin*, Sydney: Allen & Unwin
5 Walker, B. (2019) *Murray-Darling Basin Royal Commission Report*, 29th January https://cdn.environment.sa.gov.au/environment/docs/murray-darling-basin-royal-commission-report.pdf
6 Dovers, S., Grafton, R.Q. and Connell, D. (2005) A critical analysis of the national water initiative, *Australasian Journal of Natural Resources Law and Policy*, 10 (1): 81–107
7 Van Dijk, A.I., Beck, H.E., Crosbie, R.S., De Jeu, R.A., Liu, Y.Y., Podger, G.M., Timbal, B. and Viney, N.R. (2013) The millennium drought in Southeast Australia (2001–2009): Natural and human causes and implications for water resources, ecosystems, economy, and society, *Water Resources Research*, 49 (2): 1040–1057
8 Salleh, A. (2009) No quick fix for river Murray acid problem, *ABC Science*, 20th May www.abc.net.au/science/articles/2009/05/20/2576085.htm
9 Skinner, D. and Langford, J. (2013) Legislating for sustainable basin management: The story of Australia's water act (2007), *Water Policy*, 15 (6): 871–894
10 According to a Murray–Darling Basin plan submission made by Deniliquin farmer Louise Burge prepared for Southern Riverina Irrigators: "Australia's water resources are also subject to a range of voluntary international agreements on the environment. International agreements affecting Australia's water resources include 'the Convention on Biological Diversity, the Convention on Wetlands (Ramsar, Iran 1971), the Japan/Australia and China/Australia migratory bird agreements (JAMBA and CAMBA), the Convention on Migratory Species, the Convention to Combat Desertification, the Commission for Sustainable Development and the United Nations Environment Program.'" (2011: 33) www.aph.gov.au/DocumentStore.ashx?id=852b6b16-1427-49dd-9689-eaed90e5b443
11 UN Convention on Wetlands (Ramsar) – Australia has been party to this Convention since 1975 www.ramsar.org/countries
12 Bilateral Migratory Bird Agreements www.dcceew.gov.au/environment/biodiversity/migratory-species/migratory-birds
13 UN Convention on the Conservation of Migratory Species of Wild Animals (Bonn) – since 1991 www.cms.int/en/parties-range-states
14 UN Convention to Combat Desertification – since 2000 www.unccd.int/our-work-impact/country-profiles/australia
15 Environment Victoria (2023) *How the Victoria Government Sabotaged the Basin Plan: A Timeline*, Blog, 26th July https://environmentvictoria.org.au/2023/07/26/how-vic-government-sabotaged-basin-plan-timeline/

16 Commonwealth Department of Sustainability, Environment, Water, Population and Communities (DSEW) (2012) *Australia's Obligations Under the Ramsar Convention: Legislative Support for Wetlands*, Fact Sheet www.dcceew.gov.au/water/wetlands/publications/australias-obligations-under-ramsar-convention-legislative-support-wetlands-fact-sheet
17 MDBA (2023) *Allocations: The Difference Between an Allocation and an Entitlement*, 4th July www.mdba.gov.au/water-use/allocations
18 Research Data Australia (2018) Key Environmental Assets (KEA) of the Murray Darling Basin, *Bioregional Assessment Program*, 12th December https://research-data.edu.au/key-environmental-assets-darling-basin/1436218
19 DSEW (2012), op cit
20 MDBA (2010) *Guide to the Proposed Basin Plan, Volume 1: Overview* https://cdn.environment.sa.gov.au/environment/docs/guide-to-basin-plan-vol-1-gen.pdf
21 Byrne, P.J. (2010) Cover story: Angry farmers burn Draft Murray Darling plan, *News Weekly*, 30th October https://newsweekly.com.au/newsweekly/cover-story/4564-cover-story-angry-farmers-burn-draft-murray-darling/
22 Rotche, T. (2023) We can't save the Murray-Darling without buying water – here's what you need to know, Blog, *Environment Victoria*, 10th September https://environmentvictoria.org.au/2023/09/10/we-cant-save-the-murray-darling-without-water-buybacks-heres-what-you-need-to-know/
23 Commonwealth of Australia, Water Act 2007, No 137, Compilation No 29, 15th November 2021 https://faolex.fao.org/docs/pdf/aus79228.pdf
24 Ker, P. (2010) Murray – Darling chair resigns, leaving reforms in turmoil, *Sydney Morning Herald*, 7th December www.smh.com.au/environment/sustainability/murraydarling-chair-resigns-leaving-reforms-in-turmoil-20101207-18nea.html
25 Wheeler, K.G., Robinson, C.J. and Bark, R.H. (2018) Modelling to bridge many boundaries: The Colorado and Murray-Darling River basins, *Regional Environmental Change* 18: 1607–1619
26 Young, B. (2011) The science behind the Murray-Darling Basin plan, *The Conversation*, 20th November https://theconversation.com/the-science-behind-the-murray-darling-basin-plan-4502
27 Alexandra, J. (2023) Climate risk assessment in the MDB – a review, *Australasian Journal of Water Resources*, 27(1): 18–30. See also Special Issue: Shared risks to water in the MDB (2023) *Australasian Journal of Water Resources* www.tandfonline.com/toc/twar20/27/1
28 Prosser, I.P., Chiew, F.H. and Stafford Smith, M. (2021) Adapting water management to climate change in the Murray-Darling basin, Australia, *Water*, 13 (18): 2504
29 McCarthy, M. and Sullivan, K. (2019) Conflicts, cost blowouts, time delays in Murray-Darling basin plan says productivity commission, *ABC News*, 29th January www.abc.net.au/news/2019-01-25/conflicts-cost-blowouts-time-delays-in-mdbp-says-commission/10749592
30 Davies, A. (2019) Murray-Darling buybacks 'twice as cheap' as efficiency projects, *The Guardian*, 14th March www.theguardian.com/australia-news/2019/mar/14/murray-darling-buybacks-twice-as-cheap-as-efficiency-projects
31 Kotsios, N. (2016) Murray Darling Basin job shock as water buyback hits farms, *The Weekly Times*, 3rd August www.weeklytimesnow.com.au/news/water/murray-darling-basin-job-shock-as-water-buyback-hits-farms/news-story/1e879f02487eb52d2475e46e3aa2ce3f
32 Berbel, J., Gutiérrez-Martín, C. and Expósito, A. (2018) Impacts of irrigation efficiency improvement on water use, water consumption and response to water price at field level, *Agricultural Water Management*, 203: 423–429
33 Grafton, R.Q. and Wheeler, S.A. (2018) Economics of water recovery in the Murray-Darling basin, Australia, *Annual Review of Resource Economics*, 10, October: 487–510

34 Wheeler, S.A. (2023) Water buybacks are back on the table in the Murray Darling basin, *The Conversation*, 24th February https://theconversation.com/water-buybacks-are-back-on-the-table-in-the-murray-darling-basin-heres-a-refresher-on-how-they-work-200529
35 Pittock, J. (2018) It's not perfect but implementing Murray-Darling plan in full can work, *The Guardian*, 6th April 2018 www.theguardian.com/environment/2018/apr/06/its-not-perfect-but-implementing-murray-darling-plan-in-full-can-work
36 Davies, A. (2018) The Menindee Lakes project: Who loses and who really wins? *The Guardian*, 11th April www.theguardian.com/environment/2018/apr/11/the-menindee-lakes-project-who-loses-and-who-really-wins
37 Walker, G.R., Horne, A.C., Wang, Q.J. and Rendell, R. (2021) Assessing the impact of irrigation efficiency projects on return flows in the South-Eastern Murray-Darling basin, Australia, *Water*, 13 (10): 1366
38 Linstead, C. (2018) The contribution of improvements in irrigation efficiency to environmental flows, *Frontiers in Environmental Science*, 6, June: 48
39 Pittock, J. (2011) Six reasons why the 2011 draft Murray-Darling basin plan fails, *Global Water Forum*, 21st December www.globalwaterforum.org/2011/12/21/six-reasons-why-the-2011-draft-murray-darling-basin-plan-fails/
40 Bell, S. (2022) The limits of federal-state capacity in managing Australia's Murray-Darling river basin, *Water Alternatives*, 15 (1): 129–149
41 MDBA (2023) *Adapting to a Changing Climate*, 27th June www.mdba.gov.au/climate-and-river-health/climate/adapting-changing-climate
42 Loch, A., Adamson, D. and Dumbrell, N.P. (2020) The fifth stage in water management: Policy lessons for water governance, *Water Resources Research*, 56 (5): e2019WR026714
43 Sullivan, K. (2023) Murray Darling basin plan revived with controversial water buybacks, but won't include Victoria, *ABC News*, 22nd August www.abc.net.au/news/2023-08-22/plibersek-brokers-new-murray-darling-basin-deal/102758998
44 Grafton, Q., Colloff, M., Marshall, V. and Williams, J. (2020) Confronting a 'post-truth water world' in the Murray-Darling basin, Australia, *Water Alternatives*, 13 (1): 1–28

19 Indigenous Agriculture and Sustainability Knowledge

The Great Australian Silence

Interview With Bruce Pascoe

Introduction

An emerging and fresh perspective on Australian Aboriginal and indigenous culture challenges the long-established and conventional view that they are a hunter–gatherer society. There is historical and archaeological evidence of elements of a sedentary way of life with villages and houses, and with knowledge associated with techniques of agricultural cultivation and the storage of agricultural products. This is a fascinating perspective, particularly in the context of the continuing debate prompted by climate change about Australian agriculture and its sustainability with increasingly disruptive droughts, fires and floods. There may be things that we can and should be learning from Indigenous Aboriginal people about their tens of thousands of years of continuous and sustainable lived experience on this continent.

Keywords: Aboriginal; agriculture; aquaculture; archaeology; bushfires; colonialism; cool burning; cotton, culture wars; domestication; droughts; fishing; fish kills; grains; history; houses; indigenous; irrigation; landscape management; native rice; native seeds; SDG 11; SDG 15; soil depletion; sustainability; *terra nullius*; tubers; villages; water management; water theft

Interviewee Profile

Bruce Pascoe (**BP**) is Professor, Indigenous Knowledge, University of Technology Sydney and has written an insightful book, *Dark Emu: Black Seeds, Agriculture or Accident.*[1]

The Interview

ML: Bruce, what motivated you to write this book and with what purpose in mind?

BP: I found it very frustrating that Australian history books in general, didn't refer to the Aboriginal past in the way that I understood it, or that most Aboriginal people understand it. It seemed to me that Australians were

DOI: 10.4324/9781003280316-22

missing out on a complete understanding of their country. That's what motivated me.

ML: What are you conveying by the title *Dark Emu: Black Seeds, Agriculture or Accident?* and the references it makes?

BP: The 'emu' is a creative spirit for Aboriginal people and when that creator finished work and left the earth, it went up into the sky and is visible as a shape within the Milky Way, quite visible at the moment, as it straddles Scorpio. With the 'black seeds', I was trying to convey that Aboriginal people were horticulturalists and agriculturalists.

'Agriculture or accident'? asks Australians the question, which some anthropologists or archaeologists tried to pose and seemed resistant to the idea that there was any Aboriginal agricultural management activity. Reading the history closely, it's hard to get away from the idea that this is regarded as a complex activity beyond an Indigenous society.

ML: What evidence and sources have you been able to bring to bear in highlighting the nature of this indigenous agriculture that goes back for nearly 60,000 years? In terms of the historical development of agriculture on a global scale, the time frames for its emergence, say in the Middle East, for example, in Mesopotamia and Egypt, are in the order of 5–10,000 years; that is, considerably later than the evidence of its existence among Aboriginal people in Australia. So, your basic proposition is most thought provoking.

BP: I was writing a book called *Convincing Ground*[2] about the Aboriginal Wars for the land which we lost, and our research came up with material throwing doubt on the idea that Aboriginal people were hunters and gatherers, simply wandering around the country. I was finding evidence of settled villages with substantial houses, and I'd never heard that before in studying the history of Australia as a university graduate.

I found evidence of Aboriginal people selling grain and tubers, harvesting both, and preserving food. Once I started down the rabbit hole through the archives, there was more and more evidence. It alarmed me that Australians knew so little about it and more than alarmingly, that our education system had perpetrated this idea that Aboriginal people lived an incompetent life. I wish I was writing *Dark Emu* now because there's so much more evidence available, because many archaeologists in the last five or six years have been doing incredible work, some of it provoked by *Dark Emu.*[3] Those findings are incredible and Australia is going to be fascinated by them.

For example, Jim Bowler, the archaeologist behind Mungo Man and Mungo Lady, and Jim Barlow's last excavation at Warrnambool, Point Ritchie, showed evidence of occupation of Australia of 10–20,000 years, probably longer by now.[4] That's an incredible date in world history, given our understanding that people left Africa 75,000 years ago, so that the age of 120,000 years is unexplainable in terms of the way history is taught around the world.

We need to take serious notice of this scientific evidence and try to come to grips with it. It's about our country itself – history with which Australians should be fascinated, not appalled, not doubting, not negative.

ML: Fascinated as I am by your material and the more recent scholarship, still the conventional views and people's understanding of those achievements is very limited. As you say, it's not taught in schools. It's not even accepted widely in science, anthropology and other disciplines. However, many of your sources are from early explorers' accounts, such as their diaries and journals. So even in the time following the initial occupation of the land by British colonists, there was an awareness which is still on the written record by those people of the remarkable achievements that you describe. For example, you mentioned the early explorers' accounts of seeing women harvesting yams, onions, and cultivating the land, and apparently there are records in Western Australia of yam fields stretching to the horizon. What is the evidence about the type and extent of crops that were harvested?

BP: When Major Mitchell, the colonial-era explorer,[5] wrote that he rode through nine miles of 'stoke' (sheafs) of grain, you have to be shocked because what he is talking about is agriculture.[6] He uses an agricultural term. The fellows travelling with him talk about how beautiful the villages were, how many of them supported 1,000 people, and that each of the houses was different and comfortable. Where does that appear in the history of Australia? It is there, it is documented, but I never learned about it.

Mitchell was in awe of the development of Aboriginal people, but that never translated into the common understanding in Australia. That is a factor of colonialism. Colonialism necessarily assumes that the occupants of the land are undeserving, that they are inferior to Christians, and that they should be relieved of their land and their life. And it's not just Australia. In South Africa, Cecil Rhodes imposed prison sentences for mentioning that the Shona had built the city in which they were living, in what is now Zimbabwe but that he called Rhodesia, after himself. That same deliberate misconstruction of history was going on in Australia.

ML: It's remarkable that Major Mitchell recorded seeing these extensive village developments with circular huts built around central poles, and bark and grass covered by clay with centre holes for chimneys. And, as you say, he estimated populations of the villages at over 1,000, with evidence that they'd been used for a very long time. It is interesting though, that when he came upon these places, he found them almost empty, because apparently the occupants decided to flee rather than confront the strangers.

BP: Yes, they obviously had experience with Europeans before and maybe not necessarily with the officials and the explorers, but rather with rogue British escaping from penal settlements or the like. Maybe the story of people like Dampier,[7] had spread across the country on the 'grapevine' so that when Europeans were encountered, they were avoided because of history.

ML: How can we bring forward greater knowledge, awareness, acceptance and adoption of indigenous knowledge? Why has it been so ignored in our history books, in our schools and in our culture? Perhaps it was because it would have provided evidence of occupation of what was argued to be *terra nullius*[8] in justification of the colonial land grab. Perhaps some of the indigenous ideas and practices for agriculture that might have previously been seen as a challenge might be adopted to enhance the sustainability of contemporary Australian agricultural policies and practices.

BP: I hope so and that the change will be led by Australian farmers of non-indigenous heritage because the drought is killing people. I live in rural Victoria and I've just come back from rural NSW; people on the land are desperate for answers because the prolonged drought is affecting businesses. It's certainly affecting farming.

People who have never read a book in their life are now talking to me about 'Dark Emu' because they recognise that agriculturally, we're in real trouble. Farmers are reading it because they understand that the way of farming for 230 years can't be sustained; that ploughing the land might work on good soils but that it can't be tolerated in our light, dry soils that simply blow away.

I've just come back from Brewarrina where I drove through 100 kilometres of dust because people were ploughing the land to grow that water-hungry plant, cotton.[9] That is why the fish die in the Murray–Darling Basin.[10] It is not drought as such because without these agricultural methods there would still be water in those rivers. The rivers have been dammed by the billionaires who are using assistance from the Australian government and the Australian people to grow cotton.[11] It's not because there's not enough water; it's because it's badly used.

ML: I'm intrigued by what you write about indigenous use of grains, grain harvesting, grinding of seeds into flour on quite a scale, and storage in secure vessels thousands of years before Mesopotamia and Egypt. I believe they also cultivated rice.

BP: Yes. We were making use of Australian flora for our food; 80% of the diet was vegetable so plant use was important. I've just come back from a trip to Ballina where I saw one of those storage vessels and we're starting to study it to find out what was stored in it.[12]

We know from preliminary research that rice was growing, but a formal study of it has never been done. The science for investigating practices in harvesting, sowing, preserving and storing food is incredible. Rice was discussed on ABC Radio about four or five years ago by a man steeped in knowledge of Australian grasses, but it had never occurred to him that Aboriginal people had domesticated them. Now that he and his fellow scientists are turning to look at it, they are finding that indeed Aboriginal people had domesticated the Australian rice and had been harvesting it for centuries before any other cultures.[13]

That doesn't mean though that we're the premiers at the top of the table. What it means is that Aboriginal life here began early, became sophisticated earlier, and was true to the Australian continent. We were not trying to grow northern hemisphere plants here; we are now, but Aboriginal people weren't. They were using what was around and domesticated the wild plants that they knew, which strange as it might seem, had become adapted to Australian conditions.

I'm growing yams and I haven't had rain on them for the nine weeks since I planted them, but they are flourishing. They love the drought. They're used to it and respond beautifully to this environment because they're Australian. We should all take a lesson from that and flourish in Australia. Don't be afraid of it.

ML: Indeed, that is remarkable because clearly these sources of food – the grains, the cereals, the rice – were indigenous and adapted to the conditions, presumably with a high degree of disease resistance, drought tolerance and able to adapt and survive here; and they sustained a society for thousands of years. In your book, you present a fascinating story about the way in which water was used for irrigation, through fish traps and aquaculture. What were the practices and knowledge to do with water, fish traps, weirs and irrigation?[14]

BP: I was transfixed by those early records that I read about water because I couldn't believe that researchers would use the word 'irrigation' in relation to Aboriginal people; not because I thought it was beyond us to think of something, but what stunned me was that we never talked about it. We knew it at one stage in our history, but we don't talk about it.

There are those ingenious means of collecting fresh water, for instance, where the wells were capped with perfectly fitting stones that had been ground for that purpose, so that vermin couldn't fall in the water and evaporation would be reduced. It made me sad for our country that we didn't know or appreciate it. There are incredible numbers of fish traps and many sophisticated trapping systems.

Donald Thomson took a photograph in Cape York of an incredible system that had been built by that community.[15] It must have taken weeks to build. It's a very deliberate construction and incredibly efficient but also very sustainable because fish couldn't pass through the trap in the periods when Aboriginal people weren't fishing and could continue with their daily life. It was meant to be sustainable and respectful of the fish. That's not how we fish today in the world where we're destroying our fishing grounds.

Over the last ten years in Australia, we've lost 30% of our reef species and if we go for another ten years at that rate, we will lose 60%.[16] Every Australian will be paying an absolute premium for fish. It'll be a part of our diet that will disappear because of overuse and yet Aboriginal people have been fishing sustainably for we don't know how long. It makes me feel sad to think that we've ignored that contribution to world knowledge.

ML: Arguably, we are already paying the price for the way in which our agriculture and food systems have effectively gobbled up thousands of years of sustenance of the land in a few generations of sustained exploitation verging on plunder.[17] It's almost like an extractive mining industry that we're engaged in rather than a renewable, sustainable process.

We can probably learn a few lessons of sustainability too when it comes to wildlife, landscape and vegetation management through controlled, cool burning.[18] This is a story that also has relevance to us now, isn't it?

BP: Aboriginal people 'control burnt' the landscape systematically. It wasn't *ad hoc* in any way. Everybody within hundreds of kilometres had to be consulted about the activity and methods. They had to be engaged in it. It had to reflect their needs. It was a transcontinental arrangement and its application differed from district to district. It was a consultative process so that your fire wouldn't endanger or prejudice the food production of another community, maybe 200 kilometres away. It was democracy in practice.

Aboriginal people mastered its application in recognition of the danger of using fire and the need to use it wisely. Superconscious of the needs of other people and careful in that regard, they used it as a regenerative tool, and the early European occupants referred to the Australian landscape as resembling a gentleman's park.

The book by Bill Gammage is a terrific read on this topic;[19] as is the book by Charlie Massy,[20] both of which I recommend. This approach to landscape management was evident to Europeans when they arrived here, but we stopped using fire in that way principally because of the constraints of private land ownership that prevents repeated burning so that the forest becomes scrub, and the scrub becomes flammable. So, here we are, on the brink of probably the worst fire season the continent has known in the past 200 years and this summer promises to be terrible.[21]

ML: As you look in prospect on the issues we have been discussing, are you optimistic about the opportunity for and the realisation of a better understanding and adoption of indigenous cultural knowledge, values and practices, and any progress towards more sustainable agriculture, land and water management?

BP: I have to be optimistic because I have four grandchildren. I'm not going to give up on the world before they get a chance to cure the ills that my generation produced. If I were to watch Channel 7 or Channel 9 commercial news, I'd be severely depressed, because they're so full of fluff, they avoid the big issues in the world so completely.

Even watching the SBS News, which is my favourite vehicle, can lead you to giving up, but we can't afford to. We've all got children. We've all got grandchildren, nieces and nephews. Our responsibility is to keep working hard to the end of our lives in order to give them a chance because the little kids I speak to – the eight-, nine- and ten-year-olds – are determined that under their watch things will be different and that gives me great hope.

ML: Well, that's an encouraging way to end this discussion. Are you working on anything in particular currently?

BP: I'm working on a film which talks about these very areas and so we're looking at the new research that is fascinating.[22] We're going to remote parts of Australia and seeing incredible things and we've got to dip our lids to the young archaeologists of the country who have turned their minds to these things that their elders had ignored.

An edition of 'Dark Emu' has been published for young readers and is being widely adopted by schools.[23] When I talk about archaeologists having ignored Australia, there were obvious exceptions including Peter Lax, John McDonald, Peter Veth and Michael Westaway.[24] They're doing incredible things, so I don't mean to demean their work in any way. I mean to applaud it, but in general terms, in Australia what weight has not been put behind the question of what were Aboriginal people doing to survive over those many millennia in a unique environment?

Conclusion

The Aboriginal peoples of Australia have survived and thrived in a harsh and ever-changing climate for at least 60,000 years and are the world's longest surviving culture. They have developed 'holistic' knowledge and practices that have enabled them to live sustainably throughout millennia by working with the flora, fauna, landscape and cosmos unique to the Australian continent.

There is much to be learnt from, and with, them about living sustainably on this vast and driest of continents. Sadly, history since colonisation in the eighteenth century not only ignored indigenous knowledge and culture but has sought to deny its existence, and has extended to its destruction. In particular, the First Nations' people made up of over 300 nations spread across the continent have been characterised simply as primitive nomadic 'hunter-gatherers'.[25]

Recent research and writing have provided evidence of significant elements of a more settled, agricultural and farming-based society governed by participative management practices geared to sustainable survival. Diaries of colonial explorers record long-ignored encounters with housing settlements and villages; agricultural cultivation and domestication of native plants, grasses, grains and seeds, along with their harvesting, processing and storage; aquaculture and fish traps; sophisticated landscape and water management practices involving cool burning and irrigation; and inter-community trading and social gatherings from across the continent.

Archaeologists have increasingly provided evidence in support of these practices. Modern, increasingly industrialised large-scale agriculture, farming and livestock practices are rooted in the agricultural practices and resources of the northern hemisphere and are demonstrably unsustainable in this 'great southern land'. They are based on the use of productivity-enhancing plant and animal varieties, industrial chemicals and pesticides, with extensive and well-known environmental impacts on biodiversity, carbon emissions, species loss, water pollution and soil degradation.

The historical and archaeological findings of the long-term sustainability of agricultural, land management and settlement practices of First Nations' peoples across the continent have been strongly challenged in some quarters of academia.[26] Nevertheless, there is broader mainstream and younger generation acceptance, engagement with and adoption of indigenous knowledge in agricultural, scientific and research domains.[27]

The long silence on indigenous knowledge inherited from colonial and Victorian eras and perpetuated in present times as a part of the broader 'culture wars' has been breached. This reflects and acknowledges the experience and lessons in sustainability on this unique Australian continent of the world's most ancient surviving culture, and its relevance to today.

Notes

1 Pascoe, B. (2018) *Dark Emu: Aboriginal Australia and the Birth of Agriculture*, Broome, WA: Magabala Books

2 Pascoe, B. (2007) *Convincing Ground: Learning to Fall in Love with Your Country*, Acton, ACT: Aboriginal Studies Press

3 Westaway, M. and Gorringe, J. (2021) How our new archaeological research investigates Dark Emu's idea of Aboriginal 'agriculture' and villages, *The Conversation*, 18th July https://theconversation.com/friday-essay-how-our-new-archaeological-research-investigates-dark-emus-idea-of-aboriginal-agriculture-and-villages-146754

4 McNiven, I. (2019) Moyjii mystery: Victorian site could force a 120,000-year rethink on Australian history, *Monash University Lens*, 8th July https://lens.

monash.edu/@politics-society/2019/07/08/1375658/moyjil-mystery-victorian-site-could-force-a-120000-year-rethink-on-australian-history

5 Baker, D.W.A. (1967) Sir Thomas Livingstone Mitchell (1792–1855), *Australian Dictionary of Biography*, Volume 2, ANU, National Centre of Biography https://adb.anu.edu.au/biography/mitchell-sir-thomas-livingstone-2463

6 Mitchell, T. (1848) *Journal of an Expedition into the Interior of Tropical Australia in Search of a Route from Sydney to the Gulf of Carpentaria*, Project Gutenberg https://gutenberg.net.au/ebooks/e00034.html

7 Collins, B. (2018) How explorer and pirate William Dampier's comments on aboriginal people in 1697 set the one for future sentiment, *ABC News*, 3rd November www.abc.net.au/news/2018-11-04/william-dampiers-terra-nullius-set-the-tone-for-australia/10420338

8 Banner, S. (2005) Why *terra nullius*? Anthropology and property law in early Australia, *Law and History Review*, 23 (1): 95–131

9 National Resources Access Regulator (NRAR) (2022) *Satellite Imagery Reveals Extent of Illegal Water Take on Farm*, 5th May www.nrar.nsw.gov.au/news/satellite-imagery-reveals-extent-of-illegal-water-take-on-farm

10 Australian Academy of Science (2019) *Investigation of the Causes of Mass Fish Kills in the Menindee Region NSW Over the Summer of 2018–19*, Report, February www.science.org.au/supporting-science/science-policy-and-sector-analysis/reports-and-publications/fish-kills-report

11 Speer, M., Hartigan, J. and Leslie, L.M. (2022) Cotton industry under the pump from climate change, *The Conversation*, 14th October https://theconversation.com/cotton-on-one-of-australias-most-lucrative-farming-industries-is-in-the-firing-line-as-climate-change-worsens-191864

12 Camper, J. and Camper, R. (2016) Fact checking Mr Pascoe's grain stores, *Dark Emue Exposed* www.dark-emu-exposed.org/home/2016/2/12/spruce-up-your-coffee-table-bny75-7kda3-mdef3-edb4x

13 Szabo, A.-M. (2019) Aboriginal foodways: Towards a return of native food in Australia, *Sustainable Food Trust*, 8th February https://sustainablefoodtrust.org/news-views/native-food-in-australia/

14 Jackson, S. and Moggridge, B. (2019) Indigenous water management, *Australasian Journal of Environmental Management*, 26 (3): 193–196

15 Wolmby, I., Peemuggina, N. and Sutton, P. (1990) Donald Thomson at Cape Keerweer, in Austin, P., Dixon, R.M.W., Dutton, T. and White, I. (eds) *Language and History: Essays in Honour of Luise A. Hercus*, pp. 271–282, Canberra: Australian National University (ANU), Department of Linguistics

16 Readfearn, G. (2023) Decline of more than 500 species of marine life on Australian reefs 'the tip of the iceberg', study finds, *The Guardian*, 23rd March www.theguardian.com/environment/2023/mar/22/decline-of-more-than-500-species-of-marine-life-in-australian-reefs-the-tip-of-the-iceberg-study-finds

17 Koch, A., Chappell, A., Eyres, M. and Scott, E. (2015) Monitor soil degradation or triage for soil security? An Australian challenge. *Sustainability*, 7 (5): 4870–4892

18 Skiba, R. (2020) Usage of cool burning as a contributor to bushfire mitigation, *Natural Resources*, 11: 307–316 https://shs.hal.science/halshs-02912744/document

19 Gammage, B. (2012) *The Biggest Estate on Earth: How Aborigines Made Australia*, Sydney: Allen and Unwin

20 Massy, C. (2017) *Call of the Reed Warbler: A New Agriculture – A New Earth*, Brisbane: University of Queensland Press

21 Kemter, M., Fischer, M., Luna, L.V., Schönfeldt, E., Vogel, J., Banerjee, A., Korup, O. and Thonicke, K. (2021) Cascading hazards in the aftermath of Australia's 2019/2020 Black Summer wildfires, *Earth's Future*, 9 (3): e2020EF001884

22 Screen Australia (2023) *The Dark Emu Story*, Documentary www.screenaustralia.gov.au/the-screen-guide/t/the-dark-emu-story-2023/35198/
23 Pascoe, B. (2019) *Young Dark Emu: A Truer History*, Broome, WA: Magabala Books
24 Balme, J. and Wilson, M. (2004) Perceptions of Archaeology in Australia amongst educated young Australians, *Australian Archaeology*, 58 (1): 19–24
25 Moore, R. (2020) The enduring myth of the hunter-gatherer, *University of Tasmania*, 3rd August www.utas.edu.au/about/news-and-stories/articles/2020/1043-the-enduring-myth-of-the-hunter-gatherer
26 Touma, R. (2023) The Dark Emu story: The legacy – and controversy – of Bruce Pascoe's groundbreaking book, *The Guardian*, 18th July www.theguardian.com/film/2023/jul/18/dark-emu-story-bruce-pascoe-controversy-legacy-abc
27 The Fenner Circle, Yindyamurra and the Dark Emu debate: A way forward for academic scholars, *Fenner School of Environment & Society*, ANU College of Science https://fennerschool.anu.edu.au/news-events/news/yindyamarra-and-dark-emu-debate-way-forward-academic-scholars

20 Regenerative Agriculture

Confronting Industrial Agriculture With Farmer-Led Sustainability Innovation

Interview With Charles Massy

Introduction

The innovation process is – at its simplest – a chain of events and processes starting with creativity, basic research and on through research and development. But at the back end, it's all about diffusion and adoption,[1] changing people's practices and confronting many cultural and institutional barriers in the process. Our topic is an amazing story about the process of trying to effect changes in traditional agricultural practices in Australia over a long-haul period. It is a very personal story of trying to bring regenerative agriculture to the landscape, an agriculture that's working with and in harmony with nature and ecosystems; and moving towards 'ecological literacy' and beyond sustainability in the long term.

Keywords: adoption; biodiversity; broadacre; carbon cycle; carbon capture; catchment management; cereals; complex adaptive systems; cropping; diffusion; emergent properties; enabling; extension services; grassroots movement; grazing; food supply; hydrologic cycle; human health; industrial agriculture; innovation adoption curve; kitchen table conversations; integrated land management; land care; regenerative agriculture; SDG 11; SDG 12; SDG15; self-organisation; soil biology; technology transfer; women

Interviewee Profile

Dr. Charles Massy (**CM**), OAM, is a New South Wales (NSW) fifth-generation farmer, scientist and author. His book, *Call of the Reed Warbler. A New Agriculture, A New Earth*,[2] charts his 'mistake-ridden' journey to regenerative agriculture. He is a well-known global advocate for 'regenerative agriculture'.

Charles holds a science degree from the Australian National University (ANU) and returned at an early age to his family property on the Monaro Tablelands around Canberra, running merino sheep and cattle for over 40 years. He was awarded a PhD (2009) from the ANU in human ecology where he is a Research Associate.

DOI: 10.4324/9781003280316-23

The Interview

ML: Charlie, your book is many things; but in part and very importantly, it's a story of a personal journey. It's been described as 'a brutally honest account of a personal journey of redemption'.[3] How would you describe the journey that you've undertaken?

CM: That description sums it up. I had to finish my university degree part-time when I was 22 because my father had a major heart attack, and I took over our farm not knowing how to manage it until I followed the practices of so-called 'lead farmers'.[4]

I proceeded to make all the mistakes you can make in farming. That led us into a major debt and we had to sell part of the farm because we tried to manage it the wrong way. It wasn't until I discovered the wonderful innovators involved in regenerative farming that I realised there was a better way. A way that didn't harm the land or put poison in our food and, in fact, works on some of the big systems to do with our planet. So, I guess it's a bit of redemption that we swung our own farm over to that sort of farming.

ML: Your farm might be called 'broadacre' on a few thousand hectares on the Monaro high plains country with sheep. Is that basically the perspective that you have on these issues?

CM: Yes, it's more like 1,000 hectares, mainly sheep; but occasionally, in a big season like this, one that might be we will bring in cattle to do an ecological mulching role. So yes, a traditional farm in that respect, but we do a lot of biodiversity work and other things that link in with getting our landscape working better.

ML: Where does the phrase, 'regenerative agriculture' come from in terms of science or practices?[5] It seems to have its roots in other strands of farming approaches, such as sustainability, permaculture, pesticide; and organic, herbicide-free farming. What is the underlying idea and concept behind it?

CM: Yes, good question Michael, and you're right, it is a 'broad church' with different strands. When I'm lecturing students and in my book, I describe four ways of understanding our landscapes; our system works essentially on four key landscape functions.[6]

First, the more grass, trees and shrubs we can grow; the more carbon we pull out through the solar cycle. Second, that puts sugars into the soil which in turn feeds into the soil biology. If you get the solar and soil systems right, then you improve the water and hydrologic cycle, which is the third component side.

With those three systems functioning in combination, you end up with a wonderful biodiversity. I've added a fifth function which is the 'human' dimension because all those different functions in the way our landscapes and gardens and everything work are totally interrelated as is the human.

Industrial agriculture simplifies and cuts across all those relationships, and its resulting 'monocultures' kill off the soil biology with too many fertilisers. It also interferes with the water cycle, gives you dead soil biology and not much biodiversity.

What we're doing in 'regenerative' farming is standing back and empowering nature to get on with what she's pretty good at after millions of years of evolution. Once you do that, you get a remarkable regeneration of those natural systems, a 'no brainer' given the arrogance of humans in thinking we can play the role better than nature.

In a nutshell that is 'regenerative agriculture'. Someone sent me a lovely card the other day with a Beatrix Potter-type scene of a rabbit that's got into the vegetable garden, lying on its back chewing a carrot, and the caption was 'all the best things in life are free'.

What we do in regenerative agriculture is maximising, empowering and making use of the three interrelated landscape functions that nature gives us: namely, rain, sunshine and soil biology, and the resulting biodiversity.

ML: As I understand it, regenerative agriculture applied with these landscape functions that you've described – this ecosystem if you like – is a process of revitalising and regenerating something that's being degraded, and that perhaps has been 'mined' in a sense. Is it, for example, in the case of soils the idea that somehow the mechanical, chemical-based agricultural decisions and practices lead to their degradation and non-renewable 'mining'? Are you critical of current farming practices in that sense?

CM: By implication, yes. I've been there. I've done that and I know when you're trapped in that paradigm you can't see out of it. There's no good in condemning individuals; the real story is that our Earth is entering the Anthropocene in which we've dangerously disturbed the key earth systems that sustain us. We have this suicidal, dominant worldview that now rules our planet, which is 'economic rationalism', that goes for growth for the sake of growth that means endless destruction.[7]

Behind that are the big multinational corporations and if you look at Australia and all modern economies, they determine government by their very power. Look at our politics and policies, totally predicated on that ethos for government departments, universities and colleges. We're all doing the one thing in a 'monoculture' sort of way,[8] which is simplifying and degrading the earth systems through 'industrial agriculture',[9] which is supported by all those institutions.

CM: 'Regenerative agriculture' has evolved as you said from many strands, such as biodynamics, healthy agroforestry, ecological or holistic grazing, and some wonderful new cropping developments, all of which rely on natural principles and natural inputs.

It is a real challenge for this enormous industrial agriculture power base. That's the big-picture context behind what's going on and the exciting thing is that the innovation is coming from the 'bottom-up', from the farmers. Whether it's from way back with biodynamics, from more modern, post-Second World War organics, or more recent cropping and grazing practices, it is essentially a farmer-led revolution and that's unique in the broad sphere of human innovation if you look at the twentieth and twenty-first centuries.

ML: It sounds like we have the knowledge base to inform adoption of these new more sustainable agricultural, 'regenerative' processes and practices. It doesn't sound like a big investment is required in research and knowledge. It seems that the name of this game is in the process of changing behaviours by farmers and modifying their decision-making so that they can adopt these different ways. Traditionally in agriculture, new innovations have been diffused from research and knowledge, often in the government sector, including public research institutions like the CSIRO, and agriculture departments through extension services,[10] and the like. However, now what? What role do such institutions have now in promoting and diffusing 'regenerative agriculture' methods, and what are the barriers?

CM: That's a perceptive question. The traditional agriculture extension innovation adoption is top-down where we the experts have developed this knowledge that we're now going to feed it down to you farmers at grassroots. You can sit there with an open mouth like a baby bird and take it.

That's the assumption on how the innovation adoption process works. Regenerative agriculture is based on an existing knowledge base. We know a lot and it's rapidly increasing now that farmers are working with topsoil biologists. We know a lot about how soil biology works, about the solar energy cycle and the carbon cycle. And we know a lot about biodiversity.

The point you made very early on is that this is really about the extension of that knowledge, and not an imperative for a whole lot of new research in a different field of knowledge. It's a total case of a dominant paradigm which is industrial and economic rationalist versus this emerging paradigm.

It's not new, in the respect that, for example, the United Nations recently did a survey that found 75% of the world food production – and industrial powers don't like to hear this – comes from peasant farms, five acres and less, and they're all run under natural biological processes.[11]

So, it's not like it's something new, but it is new for the industrial world, and an imperative because a key factor in the destabilisation of the earth systems that's pushing us into the Anthropocene is the 10,000 years of agricultural degradation and desertification.[12]

Nearly half of all agricultural land available for farming has now been desertified because we've just killed the biology, over-grazed. and over-ploughed it. That's what's behind this 'regenerative agriculture' movement. It has the potential to address and turn around some of the Anthropocene challenges. We can put a lot of carbon into the ground through healthy, developing healthy soils and healthy grazing. The other exciting thing is that once you start growing a lot of food off biologically healthy soil you've got a totally different type of food supply, full of nutrients and phytochemicals, which we're long coevolved for, and that's hugely linked to human health.

The escalating exponential rise of modern human health diseases parallels almost exactly in a carbon copy, the rise of industrial agriculture, pharmaceuticals and the chemicals that we put into our bodies and into our food.

ML: Charlie, you used the words 'movement' and 'grassroots'. It sounds like this innovation process of adoption and diffusion is being driven from the bottom-up outside conventional processes or institutions. You tell many stories of successful application by many different farmers, but these are relatively small islands of practice within the dominant paradigm, and have now been going on over a long period, haven't they?

CM: You're quite right. I deliberately call it an underground insurgency from the bottom-up. I'm not the great innovator; I am just the storyteller. It really is a bottom-up farmer-driven thing using basic principles. For many of us, our shift to regenerative came out of a major, often personal crisis. I interviewed some 80 people in doing my PhD that led to the book who'd swung over and in 60% of the cases it had been a major life shock that pushed them there, whether it was a bout of cancer, a chemical poisoning accident, or a major debt from a drought; there were sort of head-cracking events. That's a different form of innovation adoption, absolutely. It's not top-down but bottom-up and it's for different reasons.

If you look at the traditional innovation adoption curve,[13] you've got that chasm at about the 8 to 12% range where it's hard to break into the early majority. I'm not sure that model applies to regeneration, but if it does, I would say we're moving out of the 'early adopters' into that 'early majority'. It's absolutely taking off, and many of us are doing a lot of talking, travelling, and lecturing in this space. When I started a few years ago, if you'd get say 25 people and a couple of cattle dogs at a town hall, you're going well. Now, it's about a hundred to a 150 plus, so something's happening and the interest is alive. Just look at the traffic on web pages, etc.

ML: As you say, the traditional innovation diffusion adoption curve posits, and particularly in agriculture it's been true historically, that you have the leading innovators who are out front, the individuals who take the risks, pay the costs, break the new ground and others follow based on their example. The stories that you tell, including your own personal story, are of leading-edge innovators, leading by example, and they must pay a price for what they're doing in challenging the norms within their own communities and their own industries, mustn't they? What sort of a cost is faced by this advocacy and leadership that you and others have been doing on regenerative agriculture?

CM: Definitely you come under attack because you're threatening people's comfort zones and their traditional ways of thought. I think though that we've got to the stage now in Australia, where it is gaining respectability, and not just in Australia but in the international community among Americans, South Africans and Europeans. There's a lot of cross-fertilisation, talking, sharing, and it's very collaborative; we've got to the stage where it's beyond isolation. There's a growing community, and many organisations and support groups you can go to, and that's where the bedding down of an innovation occurs. You can do a course on grazing, or new cropping, and you've got mentors and case studies to draw on and provide support. The original innovators were all alone and they were getting fired at every time they put their head above the trench.

I'll give you a good example of just how radical this approach is. The traditional approach for cropping and industrial agriculture around the world is based on monoculture cereals, corn or soy, a lot of chemicals and fertilisers, and pretty much dead soil with a lot of problems. A couple in Western Australia farming a marginal semi-arid country came up with an innovation using worm juice and compost extract as their only fertiliser. Using no industrial inputs they are now getting equivalent yields to the industrial world but with much greater resilience. Their crops don't get dusted or a lot of water damage at harvest if it rains, and they're running more sheep and broadacre cropping, by using nature; about 30–40 thousand acres of crop and a lot of biodiversity along with it. It's quite radical and you can see why it's a threat to the establishment and a very powerful Department of Agriculture and the other government departments that promote industrial agriculture, as do our agri-political groups like the National Farmers Federation (NFF).

ML: These kinds of barriers to which you're referring are common in processes of innovation and disruption in whatever sector, confronting vested interests who are doing very nicely out of the existing system, and that can put up a stiff resistance. You and your fellow 'regenerative' farmer colleagues have come across some of that, no doubt in very telling and personal ways, but at the individual farmer level their planning and decision-making happens when sitting around that kitchen table.

How is the advocacy of regenerative farming going to reach into and penetrate that level of awareness and individual decision-making?

CM: Good questions Michael and not easy ones. I've done dozens and dozens of talks right across Australia and internationally: getting farmers into a room – initially in small numbers and now in their hundreds – and other groups and people such as Landcare[14] and catchment management.[15]

In many cases, the drivers and the organisers are the women, 30–40 maybe 50-year-old family oriented; they're the ones that are concerned about food and family. We males like to get into a machine and whip hell out of the country, because that's the way we're made but one of the avenues of change is that female concern for food, family and the Earth.

It's increasingly happening with males as well and that seems to be one of the key reasons why this adoption pathway is different to your traditional Department of Agriculture and extension. The other thing that's happened is that in many of the states now there is no extension coming out of the Department of Agriculture. The gap has been filled by the big chemical and industrial companies through the local stock and station or supply companies in country towns, so there is even more direct pushing of industrial agriculture.[16]

ML: Why is it that the states-based extension services that for decades in our history drove such important innovation and productivity in Australian agriculture are no longer in place?[17]

CM: I think it's cost savings for the government. They've cut the hell out of agricultural research, the Department of Agriculture has been stripped right down, etc. That would be my guess. They've defaulted to even more direct one-on-one extension people who are agents for the chemical and industrial sectors selling the products of the existing system.

ML: You mentioned as part of the dynamic of approaching these issues around the 'kitchen table';[18] that a lot of women and female farmers[19] are engaging with this. Perhaps more than some of the blokes. Is this in some sense, perhaps without getting sexist, a reflection of the fact that the 'regenerative' approach is what might be called an approach to a 'complex adaptive system'[20] in which you need to behave in very different ways to get outcomes? Do you need to understand how things work in a different way and with a different mindset?

CM: You're right. A nurturing mindset is needed in dealing with our landscapes, water, soils, solar energy and thereby diversity. It is a long, coevolved, complex adaptive system and when we stand back and allow it to work, what are called the 'emergent properties' that have evolved over millions of years of evolution, are allowed to provide the solution to that system becoming complex and healthy. To me that's exciting and my definition of 'regenerative agriculture' is the enabling of complex adaptive systems to function and allowing those emergent properties, their solutions, in other words, to revert to greater stability, diversity, richness and complexity. It's an important point you've made.

ML: Complex adaptive systems such as agriculture and the environment having among their attributes the features of 'self-organisation' and 'open-ended creativity'.[21]

Is 'regenerative agriculture' trying somehow to free up the whole system of any human intervention, or is it that humans need to act in these sorts of ways themselves? Such systems obviously look after themselves, but we're wanting to get agricultural outputs and productivity, aren't we?

CM: Great question. At the core of my definition of 'regenerative agriculture' is we farmers enabling that self-organisation to work; I don't see it as either or. By standing back we create an enabling function that allows those natural systems to self-organise back to health, stability and greater complexity. It's as simple as that; farmers becoming the enablers of complexity rather than the dominators and the simplifiers, who shut down that self-organisation.

ML: The title of your wonderful book, *The Call of the Reed Warbler*, reminds me in an interesting and positive way of the celebrated and influential book *Silent Spring* by Rachel Carson.[22,23] What is the idea behind the title of your book that advocates 'regenerative agriculture'?

CM: Great question, Michael. Having done a lot of psychology and a lot of writing, I am aware of the power of metaphors. My title came from a story in my research, when I visited a friend who had regenerated the creek on his property, which for 150 years had been flogged over and over again. When we drove out to have a look at the creek, his neighbour's farm above his on the creek was still that old fashioned, completely bare property in the area. Sheep hadn't been moved off. There was dust blowing. The creek wasn't running.

When we got to my friend's creek which was below the neighbour's, suddenly there was this huge green zone on either side of the creek. It's covered in beautiful reeds and the water was running again, and while we were standing down at the creek admiring this for the first time, a little patch of reeds had been brought in by water birds no more than the size of a suburban house at the most. And as we chatted, this reed warbler bird started to sing from among the reeds. That would have been the first time, probably in 150 years, that a reed warbler had returned to that creek. To me it was a metaphor. This farmer had enabled natural functions to get working again through his grazing and slowing down water movement and dumb nature started to respond. It is just a delightful metaphor; I thought that summed up that 'regenerative' process that we've been talking about.

Conclusion

'Regenerative Agriculture' enables the self-organising and self-creating natural systems of sun, soil and water, to regenerate landscape, plants and habitats of biodiversity and sustainability unimpeded by the constraints and environmental degradations of controlled, mono-cultural, industrial agriculture reliant upon chemicals and fertilisers. Output and productivity levels are maintained and even improved in a sustainable manner by enabling the 'emergent properties' of a 'complex adaptive system' without damaging the health and diversity of the underlying natural ecosystems, such as soil biology, carbon cycle, and plant and bird life.

The knowledge base and practices have developed over decades from multiple strands of sustainable farming practices such as organic farming, permaculture, agroforestry, landcare and minimum tillage. The historical reliance on knowledge generation, diffusion and adoption through state-funded research and extension services has been undermined by significant cuts to government funding and services closures. These public-sector roles have been largely ceded to commercial corporate industrial activities and outreach to farming communities by agents and sales forces in stock and station agencies, whose primary purpose is to drive business, sales and farming practices to productivity reliant on the dominant industrial agriculture paradigm.

Standing back and empowering the naturally regenerative systems to develop their own complexity and biodiversity is the farmer's role. The leading farming innovators and adopters are often driven by the need to confront personal or financial crises on the land, such as droughts and family farm succession. Regenerative agriculture is akin to a grassroots movement that promotes innovation and diffusion of awareness, knowledge and practice among farmers at the 'kitchen table', and 'town hall' meeting levels, often led by women and female farmers, who champion a nurturing rather than exploitative ethic. From a 'grassroots' level, the regenerative movement confronts and challenges the dominant paradigm and practices of powerful industrial agriculture and its leading practitioners and advocates can often pay a heavy personal and social price.

Notes

1 Miller, R.L. (2015) Rogers' innovation diffusion theory (1962, 1995), in Al-Squri, M.N. and Ai-Aufi, A.S. (eds) *Information Seeking Behavior and Technology Adoption: Theories and Trends*, pp. 261–274, Hershey, PA: IGI Global

2 Massy, C. (2017) *Call of the Reed Warbler: A New Agriculture, a New Earth*, St. Lucia: University of Queensland Press

3 Flannery, T. (2020) Call of the Reed Warbler, *Australian Book Review*, 395, October www.australianbookreview.com.au/abr-online/archive/2017/212-october-2017-no-395/4282-tim-flannery-reviews-call-of-the-reed-warbler-a-new-agriculture-a-new-earth-by-charles-massy

4 Ensor, J. and de Bruin, A. (2022) The role of learning in farmer-led innovation, *Agricultural Systems*, 197, 1st March: 103356

5 Sutton, S. (2021) The history of regenerative agriculture, *reNature*, 10th March www.renature.co/articles/the-history-of-regenerative-agriculture/

6 Newton, P., Civita, N., Frankel-Goldwater, L., Bartel, K. and Johns, C. (2020) What is regenerative agriculture? A review of scholar and practitioner definitions based on processes and outcomes, *Frontiers in Sustainable Food Systems*, 4, 26th October: 194

7 Stokes, G. (2014) The rise and fall of economic rationalism, in Uhr, J. and Walter, R. (eds) *Studies in Australian Political Rhetoric*, Chapter 10, pp. 195–220, Canberra: ANU Press https://library.oapen.org/bitstream/handle/20.500.12657/33346/1/502554.pdf

8 Kogut, P. (2020) Monoculture farming in agriculture industry, *EOS Data Analytics*, 20th October https://eos.com/blog/monoculture-farming/

9 Horrigan, L., Lawrence, R.S. and Walker, P. (2002) How sustainable agriculture can address the environmental and human health harms of industrial agriculture, *Environmental Health Perspectives*, 110 (5): 445–456

10 Marsh, S.P. and Pannell, D. (2000) Agricultural extension policy in Australia: The good, the bad and the misguided, *Australian Journal of Agricultural and Resource Economics*, 44 (4): 605–627

11 Fanzo, J. (2017) From big to small: The significance of smallholder farms in the global food system, *The Lancet Planetary Health*, 1 (1): e15–e16

12 Rastgoo, M. and Hasanfard, A. (2021) Desertification in agricultural lands: Approaches to mitigation, in Zhu, Y., Luo, Q. and Liu, Y. (eds) *Deserts and Desertification*, Intech Open www.intechopen.com/chapters/77379

13 LaMorte, W.W. (2022) Diffusion of innovation theory, *Behavioural Change Models*, November https://sphweb.bumc.bu.edu/otlt/mph-modules/sb/behavioralchangetheories/behavioralchangetheories4.html

14 Wilson, G.A. (2004) The Australian Landcare movement: Towards 'post-productivist' rural governance? *Journal of Rural Studies*, 20 (4): 461–484

15 Lockwood, A.C.M. (2000) Landcare and catchment management in Australia: Lessons for state-sponsored community participation, *Society & Natural Resources*, 13 (1): 61–73

16 Kuehne, G., Llewellyn, R., Pannell, D.J., Wilkinson, R., Dolling, P., Ouzman, J. and Ewing, M. (2017) Predicting farmer uptake of new agricultural practices: A tool for research, extension and policy, *Agricultural Systems*, 156, September: 115–125

17 Mullen, J.D., Vernon, D. and Fishpool, K.I. (2000) Agricultural extension policy in Australia: Public funding and market failure, *Australian Journal of Agricultural and Resource Economics*, 44 (4): 629–645

18 Douglas, R. (2014) Reasserting the public interest from Australians' kitchen tables, *The Conversation*, 25th August https://theconversation.com/reasserting-the-public-interest-from-australians-kitchen-tables-30755

19 Callari, M. (2021) Women are changing the rules of Australian agriculture, *Cosmos*, 5th November https://cosmosmagazine.com/earth/agriculture/women-farmers-are-changing-the-rules-of-australian-agriculture/

20 Nesheim, M.C. (2015) The US food and agricultural system as a complex adaptive system, in Nesheim, M.C., Oria, M. and Yih, P.T. (eds) *A Framework for Assessing Effects of the Food System.* Washington, DC: National Academies Press www.ncbi.nlm.nih.gov/books/NBK305181/ doi: 10.17226/18846

21 Rammel, C., Stagl, S. and Wilfing, H. (2007) Managing complex adaptive systems – a co-evolutionary perspective on natural resource management. *Ecological Economics*, 63 (1): 9–21

22 Carson, R. (1962) *Silent Spring*, Boston: Houghton Mifflin

23 National Resources Defense Council (NRDC) (2015) *The Story of Silent Spring*, 13th August www.nrdc.org/stories/story-silent-spring

Section IV

Governance Roles and Responsibilities

21 Silicon Valley Consensus

Self-fulfilling Technological Determinism

Interview With Michael Piore

Introduction

The term 'Silicon Valley Consensus' is a pervasive view about the ecosystem of ideas of innovation, creativity and disruption – originating from the Silicon Valley experience – and their implications for the future of work.[1] We live in an era where the 'mantra' of innovation, entrepreneurship, creativity and disruption is all around us. It drives a lot of business activity but also government thinking and policy, with immense political and social implications. But to what extent can we say that it might be responsible for and can explain some of the politics of the day, particularly in America and the rise of populism? Maybe, this reflects those who feel in the American labour market and in communities that they've been 'left behind' in all this with growing levels of inequality, lack of jobs and destroyed communities. And what's the way forward from this 'world view' of innovation and creativity and disruption? How do we find a path of 'structural adjustment' that's fair to everyone and spreads the benefits as well as the costs, and to what extent does this involve having to engage with the ideas behind the Silicon Valley consensus of a technical, technological digital revolution?[2,3,4,5]

Keywords: America; corporate governance; creativity; entrepreneurship; financialisation; inequality; innovation; jobs; Keynesianism; know-how; knowledge economy; left behind; market fundamentalism; policy paradigm; SDG 10; SDG 9; Silicon Valley Consensus; skilled immigration; STEM; skills; tacit knowledge; technology determinism; Washington Consensus

Interviewee Profile

Michael Piore (**MP**), Massachusetts Institute of Technology (MIT), Emeritus Professor, Political Economy, is an eminent economist and political scientist who has written for many years on topics such as labour markets, international affairs, the meaning of innovation, what makes for a creative economy and how can we move beyond an inherent 'technological determinism' and 'individualism' that resides in those views.

DOI: 10.4324/9781003280316-25

His particular interest is in labour economics and the structure of employment opportunities and wages in an economy driven by social processes of technology and globalisation to undermine employment in legacy industries.[6]

He has been faculty at MIT since his appointment in 1966 holds joint positions in Economics and Political Science, and among other responsibilities is Associate Director, Center for Technology Policy and Industrial Development. His many publications include the books *The Second Industrial Divide* (1986, Basic Books), *Innovation: The Missing Dimension* (1986, Basic Books), *Beyond Individualism* (1995 Harvard University Press) and *Root-Cause Regulation: Protecting Work and Workers in the Twenty First Century* (2018, Harvard University Press). Michael Piore has worked internationally and with many organisations including the US Department of Labor and the International Labour Organisation (ILO).

The Interview

ML: Michael, how have you come to formulating this view of what you've called the Silicon Valley Consensus? What's the 'problematic' and the issue that you're responding to by framing your policy-focused paradigm in this way?

MP: I and many of my colleagues have been thinking about this for some time. In the 1980s and 1990s, the economics profession and also the policymaking community was very much dominated by a view about markets that somehow the economy was going to be driven by competitive markets and that government intervention was only going to create inefficiencies in the economy. That's a view which was pushed very much by the United States and partly under that influence also in the broader sense by the international agencies, ranging from the UN to various kinds of international banks.[7]

Then, beginning in the 1990s this view of a kind of 'market determinism' was replaced by what I'm calling the Silicon Valley Consensus which became widely spread in the policymaking community, that technology rather than markets, was the dominant force driving the economy. But with both of those views we came to believe that these forces were inevitable and that you had to just let the economy be driven by them.

The result was that there was enormous displacement of labour in certain old industrial areas that we ignored or didn't pay attention to and where we thought it was the inevitable price of progress. And it was those old industrial areas that gave the margin of victory to Trump as President in the 2016 election.[8,9,10]

It was kind of a shock to all of us which forced us to look at and re-evaluate our own way of thinking. Certainly, that's what has pushed me to think hard about what is the real mechanism of technological change and how much is it inevitable and how much is it really something which can be controlled and moderated by public policy.

ML: So, you see the Silicon Valley Consensus as a sort of a 'technological determinism',[11] contrasted to perhaps the earlier 'economic determinism',[12] or 'market fundamentalism'. You describe innovation as a 'self-fulfilling' prophecy. What do you convey by that idea from an economic and social point of view?

MP: Innovation, almost by definition is an 'excursion into the unknown'. It's new. You don't really know and can't really predict where it's going. Research and development in trying to capture and shape the trends of technology is very much a self-fulfilling prophecy. We look for technology change where we think it exists. We've come to believe and we keep talking to ourselves almost, and preaching to each other, that technological change is going to be found in 'high technology', which requires increasingly high levels of education and is going to be driven by a kind of innovation in which individual entrepreneurs shake up the society. So if we believe that, then all business firms are busy out there trying to be the kind of entrepreneurial force that captures this high technology.

In fact though, in the United States at least half of the research and development funds are governmental funds and they're not driven at all by the market or by any underlying technological force.[13] They're driven by what government agencies think is the direction of technology.

Private companies are pushing to be the first to get to that place and it's the government sector which is trying to protect the country and make us the leading edge of new technologies. But everybody is working on the same set of beliefs and it's in that sense that we're kind of creatures of our own belief in innovation, whereas if we thought or believed that it was really important in order to reduce the educational requirements of technology, in order to look for technologies that bridge the gap between the machine and the man if you will. If we looked in a different direction, we would find different technologies. The direction in which we choose to look, where we should be pushing it seems to me, should be the welfare of society as a whole.

ML: Michael, the way you portray 'consensus' is like an ethos, a set of beliefs and a policy paradigm, if you like, a way of thinking which informs not only the role of government and the way it behaves and invests but also the private-sector players and the entrepreneurs. But you've also characterised it as typically a process that has pretty uncertain outcomes by its very nature. Can we open this up a bit perhaps with the question of the education needs to which you have referred as an 'obsession' with STEM (Science, Technology, Engineering and Maths) education?[14]

Where does this obsession with STEM education fit into this innovation paradigm or consensus critique of yours?

MP: It fits in in the sense that we have come to believe the Silicon Valley consensus that we're inevitably moving towards high technology and that in order to create the technology but also in order to staff it and have employment in the world into which we're moving, you have to be highly educated, you have to have essentially a technical education.

Particularly in my own country, there's this sense that if we don't have more science and engineering students, we're going to fall behind and we're going to be taken over by China, India or Japan, and so we have to educate people who can push us in this direction. Because we're educating people who can push us in that in this direction, we move in that direction, but in fact, half of the graduates of science and engineering programmes in universities in the States,[15] at least are working outside those occupations,[16,17] and in fact we're revising our immigration system so we can attract scientists and engineering students particularly from India and China.

ML: This seems a bit of a paradox that the US is promoting STEM and generating numbers of graduates in those disciplines, but they're not finding work, and yet, on the other hand, there seems to be a demand which is needing to be met in the case of America by immigration of these people who are being produced by the education systems in places like China and India?

MP: I think it is a paradox but one has to ask why are there so many scientists and engineers available from China and India and attracted to the United States, Europe and Australia as well. I think the answer is that China and India are also taken in by the Silicon Valley Consensus and believe that they need to have higher technical education. The result is an overproduction even in very poor countries of highly educated manpower that can't really find satisfactory employment in their own country and thereby a pool of labour that we draw on through our immigration system in order to facilitate movement in the same direction.

ML: A related point that you make is about the so-called 'knowledge economy'[18,19,20] which seems to be part of this Silicon Valley view of the world as a sort of monetised, commoditised version of knowledge in the digital era. What are your thoughts on that?

MP: Well, it's a belief that's dominated thinking about industrialisation for the last two centuries. We think of knowledge and education in terms of formal knowledge and formal education, whereas a lot of what actually is the 'know how' that's brought to bear in the day-to-day operation of the economy. It is what we call 'tacit knowledge',[21,22,23] when blue-collar people who pick it up on the job in the process of production. We call it 'clinical knowledge', a more elegant term, but it's really the same kind of process of knowledge generation when doctors are using their own 'experiential learning', and lawyers and professionals are using experiential learning. We've kind of underplayed that aspect of knowledge and so we've lost a set of ideas and really don't have a set of policies that preserve that knowledge, that validate it and that use it as a substitute for formal education.

ML: You're saying that the idea of the 'knowledge economy'[24] tends to undervalue this 'tacit knowledge', which you are saying is embedded through experience in communities, organisations and institutions, and that somehow the Silicon Valley view of the world, the policy paradigm that you say is the dominant one, ignores that experience. But we hear a lot too in this digital age of the very important role of 'entrepreneurs', following the ideas of the Austrian economist Schumpeter, that they are the real drivers of innovation and knowledge through their ideas, creativity, disruption and value creation. What's your take on the role of entrepreneurs in this Silicon Valley consensus mantra?

MP: Well, again, 'entrepreneurs' gives the impression that it is individuals who create new technology.[25] Schumpeter had the idea that society was very conservative and that it resisted change and new technologies, and you needed an unusual person who could come in and break with the dominant social consensus in order to change the way we did things in the world. But in fact, what we found in our studies, at least at MIT, is that innovation in the sense of changing the way we think about things and do things actually grows out of the community. That in fact, the way society evolves is like a language and you have to think of language as paradigmatic of what it means to be a human being. What distinguishes us from every other living creature is basically the ability to communicate with each other, and tacit knowledge evolves, and indeed even formal knowledge tends to evolve like a language in a communal sense. Instead of language being static and conservative in the way that Schumpeter pictures society, language, in fact, is always evolving and continuously changing, and our studies at MIT suggest that it is what you're doing when you deliberately go about creating new technologies.

For example, what we did in creating the cellular telephone, the Global Positioning System (GPS) or the World Wide Web (WWW), was to create a new community in a sense rather than their growing out of the market. The Web grew in the first place out of the development of large companies and government agencies that created 'intellectual communities' of people who knew how to learn through something that looks more like 'conversation' than research and development. They developed a new way of thinking about the world and the particular innovations that we now attribute to individuals like Steve Jobs grew out of these new 'intellectual communities'.[26,27]

ML: We're talking here about entrepreneurs and how that concept tends to overemphasise the role of individuals in innovation and creativity as against the community in a more institutionalised sense. But what about the role of enterprises themselves aside from entrepreneurs, and the role of corporate governance, and how they've been managed and how their practices have changed in the past couple of decades to take on board these changing perspectives of innovation.

MP: The US economy was dominated in the immediate post-war period by very large companies with a long existence that basically saw themselves as the important social players and that were relatively closed and internally managed.[28] We had a lot of problems with what that might mean for the structure of society and for the democratic process. But in fact what happened in the late 1970s and 1980s, and even more in the new century, was that these previously closed companies that used to finance research and development before it went into the marketplace, and that had internal managers, many of them have disappeared. They have been overtaken by new technology, but they no longer have this internal kind of structure that generates both innovation and over the long term.[29]

For example, Bell Labs and IBM used to have enormous research and development operations which were closed off from competitive pressure and where these new kinds of 'communities' developed shielded from competition.[30]

Now those companies are less and less investing in long-term research and development, while at the same time they have become increasingly, through what we call 'financialisation',[31] dependent on external financing and have boards of directors that are outside the company and really don't have independent judgement as to how the company should be moving.

They're much more dependent on 'fad-and-fashion' thinking; that if a company isn't investing the way other companies are investing in certain kinds of ideas in certain markets, then their board of directors wants to know why. Whereas, if you follow the 'fad and fashion' of business of the moment then the board of directors accepts your judgement.

ML: That's a fascinating perspective. You're suggesting or proposing that those formerly more 'closed institutions' in terms of outside directors, there not being so many outside directors as in more recent times, that they had people who were much closer to the business as against the corporate governance models of later time,[32] that opened them up to 'independent' directors.

And as you say, financialisation is basically maximising the short-term shareholder returns on the assets of the company, rather perhaps than thinking about longer-term innovation. This is a substantial critique of contemporary management but does it to any extent reflect the reason that many of the new big tech companies have chosen to go down the 'private company' rather than 'public company' structure and control path or not?

MP: To some extent that depends on which month or year you're looking at these companies because there is a kind of alternation between being highly dependent on outside financing and on outsiders to support the company when it goes to the market for funds and so on, and then partly as a reaction to that, the companies have moved to become private to be more able to avoid going to the market for financing. There's this kind of swinging back and forth in corporate governance, but relative to the immediate post-war period there's much more dependence on outsiders.

ML: So Michael, given your presentation of the Silicon Valley Consensus and critique of the structural adjustment problems that are being thrown up, particularly growing inequality and losses of jobs and communities, that leaves us with a big question. How do we go forward from here? In the past, as you've remarked, we've had a couple of major policy paradigms driving government thinking and business activity in the post-war period. We had the Keynesian ideas and the positive role of government in all of that in driving growth, and then in the 1970s and 1980s we had the Washington Consensus with its market-based focus.[33] Now we're caught up in this innovation mantra with the Silicon Valley Consensus. Do we need to rethink this and come up with a new policy paradigm? What's at stake here and what's the direction we need to be thinking?

MP: It's pretty clear from what I've been saying that I think we do need a new policy paradigm, that we need to understand not just the role of individuals, but that they're all part of the larger communities, and how do those communities develop and evolve overtime. But also, we need to think of who gets left out and of the existing communities. We have this tendency to think let the market or let private judgement play itself out, and then afterwards we'll pick up the pieces and will compensate people who suffer, who don't participate in this process. It's pretty clear that we can't continue with that approach, the result of which is that people don't get compensated, that some people do get left out. But it's really hard, almost impossible to make up for the ravages and the mark it leaves behind after the market has played itself out.

So, we need to understand better the role which communal institutions play in society and in the evolution of the economy. And then we need to think about who gets left out by those communal institutions and how to go about deliberately constructing a more egalitarian, not an egalitarian distribution of income but an egalitarian distribution of social goods. That's the paradigm and outcome that I would be advocating today. I don't think anybody really can provide that out of a cookbook but I think it's the direction we need to move.[34]

ML: That is a clear 'call to arms' that you're making, Michael. It sounds like quite a challenge for our times not least given the very polarised political climate of debate that we have of divided countries and citizens on these core issues, but there is also a great opportunity. As you say, in the previous 'paradigm shift' eras of Keynes and the Washington Consensus there were real turning moments achieved. Are you optimistic that both the political and the intellectual climate are up to coming up with some real answers and alternative ways at this point?

MP: No, I'm not optimistic at all when I look around what's happening in the political process. On the other hand, ideas like innovation are something new by definition. A new paradigm is something which you can't see coming and we didn't see that in the post-war period. We didn't see the shift towards the market happening in the 1970s until it was upon us and we didn't see the shift away from what we called the Washington Consensus to a kind of 'technological determinism' in the 1990s and at the beginning of the new millennium. One can only hope that there will be innovation in the way we think about policy in the same way that there's innovation in productive technology.

Conclusion

The Silicon Valley Consensus that has been driving innovation policy in the US has contributed to the displacement of individuals and communities, and has fuelled a divisive populist backlash in American politics. Based on a form of technological determinism underpinned by Washington Consensus 'market fundamentalism', it has created a large number of Americans who feel 'left behind' in the growth of the economy and by its accompanying growth in inequality without attention being paid to processes to easing the costs of structural adjustment in the economy. The Silicon Valley Consensus-based public policy is in effect a 'self-fulfilling' prophecy that posits high-technology disruption driven by individual creative entrepreneurs and demanding ever higher levels of education and skills formation in Science, Technology, Engineering and Maths (STEM). A paradox lies at the heart of this 'obsessive' STEM policy paradigm in that while producing increasing numbers of STEM graduates who cannot find high-tech work the country re-focuses its immigration programme on high-tech graduates from overseas to fill domestic vacancies while 'overproducing' graduates overseas that cannot be employed at home. In this monetised and commoditised 'knowledge economy', the values of 'tacit knowledge' and of 'experiential learning' are undervalued.

Changes in corporate structures and governance driven in part by the large-scale 'financialisation' of the economy have seen the financial services sector grow, while the manufactured goods sector has been hollowed out. Large corporations that previously funded substantial R&D programmes internally are now hostage to short-term returns and cut back long-term, high-risk research programmes. The new generation of high-tech companies from Silicon Valley operates in an environment that over-emphasises the role and significance of the individual private-sector entrepreneur rather than engaging 'intellectual communities' and promoting the broad welfare of society. A public policy 'paradigm shift' is needed to replace the prevailing Silicon Valley Consensus if innovation, competitiveness, job security, a more equal distribution of social goods, and social and political harmony are to be revived and sustained.

Notes

1 Armstrong, B. (2016) Unraveling the Silicon Valley consensus, *Boston Review*, 13th July https://bostonreview.net/articles/ben-armstrong-unraveling-silicon-valley-consensus/
2 Durand, C. (2020) *Technofeodalisme: Critique de L'Economie Numerique*, Paris: Editions La Decouverte
3 Escobar, P. (2020) No escape from our techno-feudal world, *Asia Times*, 3rd December https://asiatimes.com/2020/12/no-escape-from-our-techno-feudal-world/
4 Moore, M. and Tall, K. (2016) The Silicon Valley consensus: What it means for information professionals', *Online Currents*, 30: 89–95
5 Streinz, T. (2019) Challenging the Silicon Valley consensus: Data governance, *New York University, Law School*, 15th January https://law.yale.edu/yls-today/yale-law-school-events/challenging-silicon-valley-consensus-data-governance-tpp-usmca-and-beyond-thomas-streinz-new-york
6 Osterman, P. (ed) (2012) *Economy in Society: Essays in Honor of Michael J. Piore*, Boston, MA: MIT Press
7 Serra, N. and Stiglitz, J.E. (eds) (2008) *The Washington Consensus Reconsidered: Towards a New Global Governance*, Oxford: Oxford University Press
8 Alden, E. (2016) *Failure to Adjust: How Americans Got Left Behind in the Global Economy*, New York: Rowman and Littlefield
9 Frank, T. (2016) The Republicans and Democrats failed blue-collar America: The left-behind are now having their say, *The Guardian*, 6th November www.theguardian.com/commentisfree/2016/nov/06/republicans-and-democrats-fail-blue-collar-america
10 Frieden, J. (2018) *The Backlash Against Globalisation and the Failure of the Economic Order*, February, Harvard University, https://scholar.harvard.edu/files/jfrieden/files/frieden_future_feb2018.pdf
11 Technological determinism is the idea that technological development and innovation determine social, economic and political change and was coined by American sociologist Thorstein Veblen. For long-standing controversies and debates, see Marx, L. and Smith, M.R. (1994) *Does Technology Drive History? The Dilemma of Technological Determinism*, Boston: MIT Press
12 Economic Determinism is the idea that economics determines social, institutional and political structures, as well as being the driver of technology and innovation. First attributed to philosopher Karl Marx, it was elaborated by neo-liberals in the 1980s public policy in America as 'market fundamentalism' as a doctrine of *laissez-faire*, deregulation and small government. See, for example, Langmore, J. and Quiggin, J. (1995) *Work for All: Full Employment in the Nineties*, Melbourne: Melbourne University Press
13 Federal R&D funding has fallen from over 50% of total R&D funding in the 1950s to about 20% in 2010s as cited in American Association for the Advancement of Science (AAAS) (2022) *Historical Trends in Federal R&D* www.aaas.org/programs/r-d-budget-and-policy/historical-trends-federal-rd

14 Zakaria, F. (2015) Why America's obsession with STEM education is dangerous, *The Washington Post,* 26th March, www.washingtonpost.com/opinions/why-stem-wont-make-us-successful/2015/03/26/5f4604f2-d2a5-11e4-ab77-9646eea6a4c7_story.html
15 See Fayer, S., Lacey, A. and Watson, A. (2017) STEM occupations: Past, present and future, *US Bureau of Labor Statistics,* January www.bls.gov/spotlight/2017/science-technology-engineering-and-mathematics-stem-occupations-past-present-and-future/pdf/science-technology-engineering-and-mathematics-stem-occupations-past-present-and-future.pdf
16 Around 3.5M STEM jobs needs to be filled by 2025, see Lazio, R. and Ford, Jr., H. (2019) The US needs to prepare workers for STEM jobs, *SHRM*, 6th June www.shrm.org/hr-today/news/hr-magazine/summer2019/pages/the-u.s.-needs-to-prepare-workers-for-stem-jobs.aspx
17 Koch, W. (2014) Census: 74% STEM graduates don't get STEM jobs, *USA Today*, 10th July www.usatoday.com/story/money/business/2014/07/10/census-stem-graduates/12492079/
18 The 'knowledge economy' is the idea that the principal driver of the economy is human capital in the form of science, research skills, innovative ideas, intellectual property that find expression in knowledge-intensive activities, technologies, goods and services, that promote productivity and economic growth. Initially coined by Peter Drucker in his book *The Age of Discontinuity*, New York: Harper Row, 1969)
19 Foray, D. (2004) *The Economics of Knowledge*, Boston: MIT Press
20 Kahin, B. and Foray, D. (eds) (2006) *Advancing Knowledge and The Knowledge Economy*, Boston: MIT Press
21 The idea of 'tacit knowledge' as a pre-logical phase of knowing was initially contrasted to 'explicit knowledge' by social scientist and philosopher, Michael Polanyi (1891–1976) including in his books *Personal Knowledge*, Chicago: University of Chicago Press, 1958 and *The Tacit Dimension*, Chicago: University of Chicago Press, 1966
22 See also see Smith, M.K. (2003) Michael Polanyi and tacit knowledge, *The Encyclopedia of Pedagogy and Informal Education* https://infed.org/mobi/michael-polanyi-and-tacit-knowledge/ It formed the basis of 'knowledge management' which tackled the problem of managing tacit knowledge through its codification
23 Kimble, C. (2013) Knowledge management, codification and tacit knowledge, *Information Research*, 18 (2): paper 557 http://informationr.net/ir/18-2/paper577.html
24 O'Donovan, N. (2019) From knowledge economy to automation anxiety: A growth regime in crisis? *New Political Economy,* 25 (2): 248–266
25 Jones, G. and Wadhwani, R.D. (2006) *Schumpeter's Plea: Rediscovering History and Relevance in the Study of Entrepreneurship,* Harvard Business School Working Paper Series No 06-036, Boston: Harvard Business School www.hbs.edu/faculty/Pages/item.aspx?num=21421
26 Godin, B. (2008) In the shadow of Schumpeter: W. Rupert Maclaurin and the study of technological innovation, *Minerva*, 46 (3): 343–360
27 Lester, R.K. and Piore, M. (2006) *Innovation: The Missing Dimension*, Boston: Harvard University Press
28 Gross, D. and Sampat, B.N. (2020) *Inventing the Endless Frontier: The Effects of the World War II Research Effort on Post-War Innovation*, National Bureau of Economic Research, Working Paper 27375, June www.nber.org/papers/w27375
29 Arora, A., Belenzon, S., Patacconi, A. and Suh, J. (2019) *The Changing Structure of American Innovation: Some Cautionary Remarks For Economic Growth*, National Bureau of Economic Research, Working Paper 25893, May www.nber.org/papers/w25893

30 See Isaacson, W. (2019) How America risks losing its innovation edge, *Time*, 3rd January https://time.com/longform/america-innovation/. Isaacson revisits the history of post-war research-based companies based on his chapter in Aspen Institute (2018) *Technology and National Security: Maintaining America's Edge*, Aspen Policy Book Series www.aspeninstitute.org/wp-content/uploads/2019/02/2018-Tech-and-National-Security-FINAL.pdf
31 Krippner, G. (2005) The financialization of the American economy, *Socio-Economic Review*, 3 (2): 173–208
32 Clarke, T. (2014) The impact of financialization on international corporate governance: The role of agency theory and maximising shareholder value, *Law and Financial Markets Review*, 8 (1): 39–51
33 Rodrik, D. (2006) Goodbye Washington consensus, Hello Washington confusion? *Journal of Economic Literature*, 54 (December): 973–987 https://drodrik.scholar.harvard.edu/files/dani-rodrik/files/goodbye_washington_consensus_.pdf
34 Piore, M. (2008) *Second Thoughts on Economics, Sociology, Neoliberalism, Polanyi's Double Movement and Intellectual Vacuums*, MIT Industrial Performance Center, Working Paper Series 08-004 https://citeseerx.ist.psu.edu/viewdoc/download?doi=10.1.1.621.3000&rep=rep1&type=pdf

22 The Business of Climate Change

Reimagining 'Material Interests'[1] – And the Corporation

Interview With Bob Carr

Introduction

What is the role of business in addressing the climate change issues in Australia? Australian governments have been struggling for ten years or more to come to grips with the issues and to put in place a transition to a low-carbon economy in the face of campaigns of fossil fuel interests' 'climate denial'.[2,3,4] It seems though, that latterly, business generally is taking things into its own hands and stepping up to the plate with its own strategies and initiatives; supported or even urged on by institutional investors and activist shareholders to reposition business for low-carbon, sustainable development in the long term. The public, for its part, appears to have more trust these days in the capacity of business to do things than it does in its governments.[5] Is the public justified in placing this trust in business and can business deliver when governments appear to have failed?

Keywords: Abatement Certificate Providers (ACP); Australian Carbon Credits Units (ACCUs); Australian Chamber of Commerce and Industry (ACCI); Australian politics; Business Council of Australia (BCA); business lobby groups; carbon emissions trading; carbon lobby; carbon offsets; corporate governance; corporate social responsibility (CSR); eco-right; environmental, social and governance (ESG); fiduciary responsibility; fossil fuels; (NSW) Greenhouse Gas Reduction Scheme (GGAS); greenwash; (NSW) Independent Pricing and Regulatory Tribunal (IPART); institutional investors; Koch Brothers; lobbying; market-based mechanisms; Minerals Council of Australia (MCA); NSW Greenhouse Gas Abatement Certificates (NGAC); NSW Minerals Council; (US) Political Action Committees (PACs); SDG 9; SDG 13; SDG 17; shareholder value; stakeholder value; trust

Interviewee Profile

Bob Carr (**BC**) is Industry Professor at the University of Technology, Sydney (UTS), focusing on business and climate change. He's the longest-serving premier of NSW from 1995 and 2005, and subsequently Australia's Foreign Affairs Minister.

DOI: 10.4324/9781003280316-26

The Interview

ML: Bob, in your recent memoir,[6] among the many achievements that you talk about; you express pride in your achievements in environmental conservation, and particularly in respect of your declaring 1,000,000 acres of eucalyptus forest as reserves and protected, and introducing the first-carbon pricing scheme in Australia. What lessons might you have learned about dealing with business, and bringing them along on environmental issues?

BC: By focusing on market-based solutions. The NSW Greenhouse Gas Reduction Scheme (GGAS) which came into place in January 2003 – and was literally the world's first mandatory carbon-trading scheme[7] – created an obligation on electricity distributors to 'offset' any emissions above a certain benchmark. If they went beyond that, they had to make an investment in serious 'offsets' that might have been tree planting, but not any old trees anywhere in the state. It meant planting with a commitment so that trees were not to be logged for over 100 years, trees of certain species, and other obligations.

The methodology here was important.[8] If Australia had simply grown the NSW GGAS scheme instead of trying to establish more ambitious emissions trading, which was to be defeated in the Senate in 2009;[9] we would have been signalling to investors that we're pricing carbon, that they had to limit their emissions, but doing it in a way that consumers barely noticed it was a long-term price path for all carbon products.

I think 'incrementalism' is a big lesson. It was implicitly understood that investors would respond to governments giving them this long-term indication and consumers' responding to an uprising path, whether it's reducing water consumption or making arrangements about electricity. I think it's a tragedy that we didn't use this 'soft' approach to pricing carbon in Australia, and I think we've lost a lot of time as a result.

ML: Bob, you're saying that part of the key to dealing with the private sector and bringing them along was to adopt a 'market-based' approach that they can relate to in dollars and cents, and to set out a longer-term incremental vision and framework within which they can plan and invest.[10] What has motivated you in the past six months to take up this new position as an industry professor focusing on business and climate, as distinct from perhaps say, focusing on the role of governments and policies, not least given your background and expertise?

BC: It was an interesting coincidence that I took up the post at the time. It was becoming clear that government would be resistant or slow, but that business would be reaching through and driving innovation, not because they're all committed 'greenies' but because the legal pressure on directors is now unavoidable, and because institutional investors such as investment funds or superannuation funds have got to take account of climate risk before they commit the funds that they manage.

A third source of pressure is from individual shareholders making it known at annual general meetings that they don't want a company like a bank exposed to carbon because its future is very doubtful. Insurance companies are perhaps in a class of their own, facing huge, immediate and obvious risk from climate change and they'd be crazy if they didn't take account of the impact of changing weather patterns, for example, on their insurance payouts. It's created a situation where all the four big banks in Australia, for example, are getting out of thermal coal. They're not going to be exposed because they're calculating that climate change is real and that down the track in response to the big climate events, governments are going to be tightening up.

ML: You are saying that businesses are facing real business risks, and some of those risks are being played back into them by investors, insurance companies and various stakeholders. In a sense, they are responding in their own self-interest. But what in reality can business actually end up doing? In particular, their whole approach to corporate governance back to Friedman in the 1970s, as far as boards are concerned, is that the aim and role of a corporation are to maximise profits for their shareholders. Directors have a 'fiduciary responsibility' to do that, and by implication not to pursue other objectives. So, are there constraints here despite the apparently positive corporate rhetoric on climate change?

BC: Yes, there's now a body of law that says directors have a responsibility to manage risk and high on the list of risks, according to definitions by corporate regulators such as ASIC, APRA and the Reserve Bank in Australia, and by comparable organisations in jurisdictions overseas, is the climate risk. A director has to take account of that.[11]

On top of that, government agencies are saying company boards have that legal obligation in taking decisions to weigh climate risk; while institutional investors – including superannuation funds – putting money into a company, be it a bank or a manufacturer are saying their policy is not putting money into activities related to thermal coal or into coal-fired power. Just as these investors protect the reputation of their companies by not putting money into activities linked to child labour, they won't put money into anything that's degrading the planet through carbon emissions. So that is something we can believe.

Companies are steering away from carbon because it is now a clear legal obligation. Carbon-based businesses will lose money in a carbon-constrained world. In a world threatened by climate emergencies like the one that Sydney faces with its bushfire crisis,[12] governments are going to act, and they could be acting suddenly in a disorderly fashion, so you're not doing your job as a member of a board unless you're factoring that in.

ML: Right, so in your view, the framework for legal systems of our company law, corporate governance and regulation that date back to the market fundamentalist ideas of Friedman from the 1970s prioritising profit maximisation and shareholder primacy, can accommodate companies' responses to climate change within that framework, including directors' fiduciary responsibility. Do you believe that the legal corporate framework requires any attention or reform to ensure that corporate rhetoric is realised in their practice?

BC: Oh no, the lawyers are unanimous on this one. They're stating unanimously that a corporate board has got to take account of the climate risk.

ML: That's great that there seems to be a disposition among some areas of business to want to get out and do things on climate change, despite government inaction, and within a regulatory and legal framework that gives them a room to do that. But what are we to make of the incredible big money lobbying efforts on this issue over the last ten or 15 years in Australia,[13,14] and of course much bigger money over in the US – lobbying governments against policies in this domain?[15]

We have major industry associations in this country, including the Minerals Council,[16] both the Australian and the NSW operations, and the Business Council of Australia (BCA)[17] with its huge corporate members who are militating against effective climate change policies.

BC: I think it's very real. I think it's very powerful. I think it's very sinister. It's been effective as well. It's been effective above all in the United States, which ten years ago looked on the point of enacting on a bipartisan basis an emissions trading scheme. The McCain-Lieberman bill in the Senate was a manifestation of that, but the carbon lobby did it in.[18,19,20,21]

The notorious Koch brothers in America assembled funds through Political Action Committees (PAC) to undermine any political activism around climate and they subverted language to do it.[22] The industry, very early in the debate, said we don't like the 'global warming' term so started calling it 'climate change'. But that nomenclature is phoney; the climate has always been changing: here's been winter, spring, summer.

The fossil-business lobby knows we're talking about 'global warming' driven by human activity, in particular, the pumping of excessive quantities of carbon into the upper atmosphere in a way that changes the climate. But the soft language subverted that debate, and it was driven by a pro-carbon lobby. As a result, you've got a government in America today that comprises climate deniers, not only President Trump but more threateningly – because he can be dismissed as an eccentric – members of his cabinet like Pompeo and his Interior Secretary, and his Vice President, all of them mocking the idea that human activity is producing a change in weather patterns and other manifestations around the world.

The lobby has been very effective there and in Canada and Australia. Climate change denial, funded by the carbon lobby, has real influence over the way governments act and it's been a big factor on the conservative side of Australian politics. I'm interested in people on the conservative side of politics in Britain and a very small number in the United States known in America as the 'eco-right', including a former Republican Congressman, Bob Inglis, who has resisted the carbon lobby.[23] He says, I've been to Antarctica and have seen what's happening there. I want a carbon tax with all the proceeds being returned to taxpayers.

ML: Are you encouraged in any way that somehow the membership of these well-funded fossil fuel business bodies and their policies may alter these issues? Or are we stuck with these campaigns of climate-denying lobbying?

BC: There is movement as a result of shareholder pressure. BHP has changed. It has pulled out of some of these bodies. These bodies are still lobbying hard though and one of the recent thrusts has been to say coal is Australian and it's patriotic, making it look unpatriotic to contemplate an economy beyond coal.

There is some argument that it might be better if BHP were to stay inside the tent and to try to modify the behaviour of these lobby groups; but that's something to be considered by BHP and shareholder activists trying to influence BHP behaviour on a case-by-case basis.

ML: The rhetoric and positioning in the public policy arena from these lobbies have been one of threat, fear and uncertainty about science. It's a negatively based but powerful campaign. What are the opportunities that business sees in a transition to a low-carbon economy, particularly in Australia?

BC: Professor Ross Garnaut's latest book *Superpower* is bulging with ideas about how Australia can be an energy superpower in a post-carbon world.[24] He identifies, discusses and analyses a raft of opportunities where Australia has competitive advantage in a world responding to climate emergencies.

For example, you've got manufacturers in Japan, South Korea and Germany looking for a place to produce their products where they're not going to be indicted for using carbon. Garnaut argues that Australia is that perfect place because of the competitive advantage that renewables give us. I think that's one of the most important books to be published in Australia in the last ten years, because it lays down the opportunities for us as a carbon-dependent country and a great carbon exporter, but being even wealthier in a post-carbon world.

ML: Yes, it would be wonderful to see such a positive vision of opportunity taken up by Australian business. As you say, Ross Garnaut paints those opportunities vividly across just about every sector of the economy, from the added-value processing of minerals and energy, through the transport and electricity systems, and in the agricultural sectors with carbon farming and the like. To what extent though, can we believe or hope that these opportunities can be realised by business on commercial grounds in the face of government policies that are either not supportive; or in some instances, quite contrary to those opportunities?

BC: I think business is going ahead on its own but saying out of earshot that they're not getting guidance from Canberra. What we're looking at in Australia at the present time is business responding to shareholder pressure from investors, international pressure and pressure from business regulators like ASIC, APRA, the Reserve Bank (RBA). It is thinking that while Canberra fusses around about whether it's going to subsidise coal, we've just got to start planning for the post-carbon future, and we have to keep up with Europe because it's a big source of investment funds for this country.

ML: There's a long history over at least ten to 20 years of business internationally and here talking about corporate social responsibility (CSR),[25] ethical investment[26] and environmental, social and governance (ESG)[27] approaches against which many investors try to benchmark different companies for investment purposes.

How effective has all this been as distinct from being just corporate public relations talk and 'greenwash'?[28]

BC: We've got to be sceptical of the new orthodoxy from business. Some firms are changing seriously. Banks are winding back the money they put into thermal coal. That is significant and is going to be transformative. You need to go a step further though and challenge the banks.

Are you driving a transformation of the Australian economy and going well beyond what you're obliged to do by the shift in directors' responsibility to find a new norm in response to what regulators are saying? There's a debate to be had there: People employed by big corporations whose job is to add stuff to annual reports to give the impression the right things are happening.

On the other hand, the Commonwealth Bank (CBA), for example, is including in its annual report, a surprising amount of material about its carbon footprint and what it's doing about it, and this is a transformation of what used to be the case.[29]

ML: Bob, to what extent these developments we are discussing might necessarily involve a 'reimagining' of the corporation in respect of its role and purpose in society, and of the associated systems of corporate governance?

For example, the influential annual letters to investors from Larry Fink, CEO of BlackRock Investment which is probably the single biggest global investor, handling trillions of dollars of investment in companies. He talks about the repurposing and rethinking of corporations, and the need for that to be reflected in laws, regulations and codes.[30]

BC: I'm not sure. It is a bigger question than any I've wrestled with. I'm sure there's going to be a backlash and people will say 'your best contribution to society is to responsibly make a profit'. But I've got to say that the scale of this climate emergency we now face is serious enough to see a transformation in the corporation itself, and maybe you'll get it in America. Senator Elizabeth Warren, a candidate for the Democratic nomination, has legislation in the Congress that makes employees shareholders not just stakeholders.[31] She's a former professor of law at Harvard. This is a serious tilt in the way we've defined the corporation. Where it leads, whether there will be a backlash, whether it be reining it in, I don't know, but I do know that climate change is serious. It's all about us.

The fire crisis in Sydney while we speak, the reason I've got a cough and raspy, is just a sign of things to come. It's a climate event. There are going to be other climate events and they will force a reaction. This is what worries business but, in any event, they've got to be prepared for the reaction when it comes, in the 2020s or early 2030s. They've got to be ready for that.

Conclusion

Acceptance by the business sector of the state-based NSW Greenhouse Gas Reduction Scheme in 2003 amidst long-standing effective paralysis in Australian government action on climate change is a notable exception. This can be attributed to its reliance on a market-based mechanism that took a time-phased, incremental approach to electricity emissions reductions. It provided clear guidance from the government on the trajectory of required cutbacks and the resulting requirements for investment by business and price impacts on consumers.

This world first, mandatory carbon-trading scheme was based on trading of carbon credits as offsets to carbon emission. This state-based scheme preceded, by many years, the long-debated and ultimately rejected proposed full-blown national carbon emissions trading scheme in 2009.

Effective national targets and mechanisms were not successfully legislated until 2023 by the new incoming government but many challenges remain in terms of both developing new techniques of carbon reduction and new metrics and enforcement measures to ensure that carbon reductions are achieved.[32,33]

Fossil fuel-based, vested corporate interests mounted well-funded, successful political lobbying and public relations campaigns against effective climate action over many years that included the re-framing of public policy debate and language, for example, from 'global warming' to 'climate change', to minimise, question and knowingly obscure the long-standing scientific evidence.[34]

Somewhat ironically, having as a result contributed to a long-term loss of public trust in institutions and governments, the public has looked increasingly to the business sector more generally to take action where governments have failed. Under pressures from banks, investors, shareholder activists and corporate regulators, corporations are setting their own strategies and investments to manage the growing awareness and realities of climate change risks to the sustainability of their businesses and investments, their corporate liabilities under law and systems of corporate governance such as ESG, and the legal responsibilities of their boards and directors.

While there is inevitably evidence of corporate public relations 'greenwashing', and an absence of clearly defined standards and metrics backed by regulations and enforcement, there is a fresh questioning of the long-dominant views of corporate governance as rooted in bottom-line, short-term profit, maximising shareholder value;[35] and a renewed questioning and reimagining of the fundamental idea and role of the corporation, including as a response to achieving sustainability in the face of global climate warming.

Notes

1 Joseph Conrad's 1904 novel *Nostromo* was a critique of the power of 'material interests' of business and money, over politics and ideology

2 Crowley, K. (2021) Fighting the future: The politics of climate policy failure in Australia (2015–2020), *Wiley Interdisciplinary Reviews: Climate Change*, 12 (5): e725

3 Holmes, D. and Star, C. (2018) Climate change communication in Australia: The politics, mainstream media and fossil fuel industry nexus, in Leal Filho, W., Manolas, E., Azul, A.M., Azeiteiro, U.M. and McGhie, H. (2018) *Handbook of Climate Change Communication: Vol. 1: Theory of Climate Change Communication*, Chapter 10, pp. 151–170, Berlin: Springer

4 Wright, C., Nyberg, D. and Bowden, V. (2021) Beyond the discourse of denial: The reproduction of fossil fuel hegemony in Australia, *Energy Research & Social Science*, 77, 102094

5 Australian Institute of Company Directors (AICD) (2023) *Australia Looks to Business to Lead: Edelman Trust Barometer 2023*, 20th February www.aicd.com.au/good-governance/public-trust/organisation/australia-looks-to-business-to-lead-edelman-trust-barometer-2023.html

6 Carr, B. (2018) *Run for Your Life*, Melbourne: Melbourne University Press

7 Independent Pricing and Regulatory Tribunal (IPART) (2013) *NSW Greenhouse Gas Reduction Scheme: Strengths, Weaknesses and Lessons Learned*, July www.ipart.nsw.gov.au/sites/default/files/documents/nsw_greenhouse_gas_reduction_scheme_-_strengths_weaknesses_and_lessons_learned_-_final_report_-_july_2013.pdf IPART also publishes annual reports on the scheme

8 The NSW Independent Pricing and Regulatory Tribunal (IPART) between 2003 and the closure of the scheme in 2012 prepared and published a series of annual reports on the scheme. Electricity retailers purchased and acquitted NSW Greenhouse Gas Abatement Certificates (NGAC) by accredited Abatement Certificate Providers (ACP) who undertook the abatement activities. On review, at conclusion the level of compliance was found to be high throughout the life of the scheme www.ipart.nsw.gov.au/Home/Industries/Energy/Energy-Savings-Scheme/Greenhouse-Gas-Reduction-Scheme

9 The policy was a 'cap-and-trade' emissions trading scheme (ETS) called Carbon Pollution Reduction Scheme (CPRS). See Pearse, R. (2019) It's the ten-year anniversary of our climate policy abyss: But don't blame the Greens, *The Conversation*, 5th December https://theconversation.com/its-the-10-year-anniversary-of-our-climate-policy-abyss-but-dont-blame-the-greens-128239

10 A report by BCG and Shell noted 2022 as a record breaking year for voluntary carbon markets (166Mt) and expects it to be five times bigger by 2030. See Shell and BCG (2022) *The Voluntary Carbon Market: 2022 Insights and Trends* www.shell.com/shellenergy/othersolutions/carbonmarketreports.html

11 This article by the ASIC Commissioner states that disclosing and managing climate-related risk are a key director responsibility: Armour, C. (2021) *Managing Climate Risk for Directors*, 1st February https://asic.gov.au/about-asic/news-centre/articles/managing-climate-risk-for-directors/

12 Yu, P., Xu, R., Abramson, M.J., Li, S. and Guo, Y. (2020) Bushfires in Australia: A serious health emergency under climate change, *The Lancet Planetary Health*, 4 (1): e7–e8

13 Tham, J.-C. and Fui-Ng, Y. (2022) How to deal with fossil fuel lobbying and its growing influence in Australian politics, *The Conversation*, 19th August https://theconversation.com/how-to-deal-with-fossil-fuel-lobbying-and-its-growing-influence-in-australian-politics-188515

14 Lucas, A. (2021) Investigating networks of corporate influence on government decision-making: The case of Australia's climate change and energy policies, *Energy Research & Social Science*, 81: 102271

15 Lobbying expenditure of around USD2B in 16 years according to one study: Brulle, R.J. (2018) The climate lobby: A sectoral analysis of lobbying spending on climate change in the USA – 2000 to 2016, *Climatic Change*, 149 (3–4): 289–303

16 Morgan, E. (2020) Climate Change action stymied by Australian business lobby, *ABC News*, 22nd September www.abc.net.au/news/2020-09-23/business-lobby-groups-stymie-climate-action-uk-think-tank-finds/12695162 This article cites the Minerals Council of Australia as 'the single largest negative influence on Australian climate-related policy'. The Business Council of Australia (BCA), the Australian Chamber of Commerce and Industry and the NSW Minerals Council also get a mention

17 Kinnaird, G. (2019) *The Shady Climate-Wrecking Lobby Group You've Probably Never Heard of*, Australian Conservation Foundation (ACF), 26th March www.acf.org.au/business_council

18 Joy, K. (2003) McCain-Lieberman global warming bill rejected by senate, *Boston University Newswire*, 30th October www.bu.edu/washington/2003/10/30/mccain-lieberman-global-warming-bill-rejected-by-senate/

19 Lizza, R. (2010) As the world burns: How the senate and the White House missed their best chance to deal with climate change, *The New Yorker*, 3rd October www.newyorker.com/magazine/2010/10/11/as-the-world-burns

20 Knox-Hayes, J. (2012) Negotiating climate legislation: Policy path dependence and coalition stabilization, *Regulation and Governance*, 6 (4): 545–567

21 Layzer, J.A. (2007) Deep freeze: How business has shaped the global warming debate in Congress, in Kraft, M.E. and Kamieniecki, S. (eds) *Business and Environmental Policy: Corporate Interests in the American Political System*, Chapter 4, pp. 93–126, Boston: MIT Press

22 Mayer, J. (2016) *Dark Money: The Hidden History of the Billionaires Behind the Rise of the Radical Right*, New York: Doubleday

23 Kavate, M. (2022) Inside the climate fight: Who's funding the eco-right? *Inside Philanthropy*, 3rd November www.insidephilanthropy.com/home/2022/11/3/in-the-climate-fight-whos-funding-the-eco-right-more-big-names-than-you-might-expect

24 Garnaut, R. (2019) *Superpower: Australia's Low Carbon Opportunity*, Melbourne: Black Inc Publishers, La Trobe University Press

25 Rangan, V.K., Chase, L. and Karim, S. (2015) The truth about CSR, *Harvard Business Review*, 93 (1–2): 40–49 https://hbr.org/2015/01/the-truth-about-csr
26 Martini, A. (2021) Socially responsible investing: From the ethical origins to the sustainable development framework of the European Union, *Environment, Development and Sustainability*, 23 (11): 16874–16890 www.ncbi.nlm.nih.gov/pmc/articles/PMC8025062/
27 Atkins, B. (2020) Demystifying ESG: Its history & current status, *Forbes*, 8th June www.forbes.com/sites/betsyatkins/2020/06/08/demystifying-esgits-history–current-status/
28 de Freitas Netto, S.V., Sobral, M.F.F., Ribeiro, A.R.B. and Soares, G.R.D.L. (2020) Concepts and forms of greenwashing: A systematic review, *Environmental Sciences Europe*, 32 (1): 1–12
29 This article notes that Australia's largest bank, the Commonwealth Bank of Australia (CBA), released its first standalone climate report: Fox Koob, S. (2022) 'We're comparing apples, oranges and bananas': Climate disclosure by banks under microscope, *Sydney Morning Herald*, 23rd August www.smh.com.au/business/banking-and-finance/we-re-comparing-apples-oranges-and-bananas-calls-for-standardised-approach-to-banks-climate-disclosure-20220822-p5bbuc.html
30 Fink's 2022 annual letter to corporate America clarifies and defends his approach to social and environmental issues at the world's largest money manager: Ross Sorkin, A. and de la Merced, M. (2022) It's not 'woke' for businesses to think beyond profit, blackrock chief says, *New York Times*, 17th January www.nytimes.com/2022/01/17/business/dealbook/larry-fink-blackrock-letter.html
31 Klein, A. (2018) Sen Warren's accountable capitalism act rightfully challenges a central tenet of corporate governance theory, *Brookings Institution*, Commentary, 20th Augustwww.brookings.edu/articles/sen-warrens-accountable-capitalism-act-rightfully-challenges-a-central-tenet-of-corporate-governance-theory/
32 Chubb, I., Bennett, A., Gorring, A. and Hatfield-Dodds, S. (2022) *Independent Review of Australian Carbon Credit Units (ACCUs)*, Canberra: Department of Climate Change, Energy, the Environment and Water, December www.dcceew.gov.au/climate-change/emissions-reduction/independent-review-accus#toc_1
33 Morton, A. and Hannan, P. (2023) Chubb review recommends new integrity body for Australian carbon credits scheme, *The Guardian*, 9th January www.theguardian.com/environment/2023/jan/09/chubb-review-recommends-new-integrity-body-for-australian-carbon-credits-scheme
34 This book provides a detailed, analytical history of how the public relations industry has shaped the very idea of 'environment' in the minds of the public and policy makers, in serving the vested interests of its corporate clients: Aronczyk, M. and Espinoza, M. (2022) *A Strategic Nature: Public Relations and the Politics of American Environmentalism*, Oxford: Oxford University Press
35 Clarke, T. (2023) *Corporate Governance: Cycles of Innovation, Crisis and Reform*, London: Sage

23 Environment, Social and Governance (ESG)

Harnessing Capital to Sustainability or Just 'Woke' and 'Greenwashing'?

Interview With Pru Bennett

Introduction

Corporate governance[1] is about corporations and business enterprises, and the way in which they are managed, governed and held accountable. There have been significant developments in the way that corporations are viewed by society, their 'social licence' to operate,[2,3] and their reactions to their environmental and social responsibilities. The term ESG (environment, social and governance) has gained prominence in recent years as a way to understand and evaluate a company's impact and performance beyond the financial bottom-line measure.[4] 'Responsible investing' by banks, investors and asset managers is now rapidly growing globally to significant proportions.[5]

Keywords: Australian Stock Exchange (ASX); assets under management (AUM); boards; business culture; corporate governance; corporate regulators; corporate social responsibility (CSR); decarbonisation; directors; environmental, social and governance (ESG); governance; business ethics; (US) Financial Accounting Standards Board (FASB); greenwashing; institutional investors; International Financial Reporting Council (IFRC); International Integrated Reporting Council (IIRC); Integrated Reporting Framework (IRF); (UN) Principles for Responsible Investment (PRI); SDG 5; SDG 9; socially responsible investing (SRI); shareholders; shareholder activism; stakeholders; Sustainable Accounting Standards Board (SASB); wokeness

Interviewee Profile

Pru Bennett **(PB)** is a partner practicing in environmental, social and governance (ESG) services with the global corporate strategic advisory firm Brunswick Group that is headquartered in London with offices around the world, and in Sydney. Most of the top global corporate companies are their clients.

The Interview

ML: The traditional approach to corporate governance is the idea that the primary responsibility of boards and directors in overseeing companies

DOI: 10.4324/9781003280316-27

is that of protecting their shareholder interests by maximising profits. What is the nature of that basic idea and responsibility?

PB: My focus is on companies that are listed on say the ASX, the London Stock Exchange or other stock exchanges around the world. They raise capital through money provided by their shareholders, and they have a board of directors elected by shareholders that provides oversight of management on issues such as strategic direction and monitoring remuneration.

In considering a board of directors, first, you want competent people with a mix or diversity of skills and background. For example, if it's a mining company like BHP (Broken Hill Proprietary Ltd), you would expect to see independent directors with mining skills. If it's a bank, say CBA or National Australia Bank (NAB), you'd expect to see some of the independent directors with banking and financial services skills. But you don't want a mining company with a board made up of only miners or mining engineers; you want a diversity of skills and experience on that board.

You want directors as a centre of competence but also with intellectual honesty and that have a deep and inquiring mind so they can ask questions of management. They need to understand the strategy and how it is being implemented and be able to direct the strategy as 'stewards' on behalf of investors.[6] A director might be in that position for, say, six to nine years. They should leave the company in better shape than when they were appointed. They're there as representatives of the shareholders for whom they need to deliver long-term sustainable returns. They need to take a broader stakeholder view of their impact on the environment, on society and on their employees in order to be able to undertake that stewardship function on behalf of the shareholders whom they represent.[7]

ML: The directors have 'fiduciary' duties on behalf of those shareholders who invest in listed companies.[8] What does that mean? What are they accountable for? Does it just mean the stock price? And how are they held accountable?

PB: They are accountable for more than the stock price. Stock price is one way to measure the success of a company. Those boards that are very focused on short-term stock price are likely not managing the externalities of their companies' operations which will potentially catch up with them down the track. Board directors join as stewards, and they need to look after the company assets and deliver long-term returns for their investors.

Company profit and loss statements are one measure of success but that statutory requirement does not measure externalities which are those costs that are put on society. For example, delivery companies are calling their riders, contractors not employees. There have been some rider deaths which are horrendous. That's pushing the cost of the operations of those companies onto these riders and onto society because others have been injured as well, and that's not reflected in the profit and loss statement prepared under accounting standards. It's these external costs that need to be managed for long-term sustainable returns for investors. You need to have directors with what I term 'intellectual honesty' to understand those externalities and make sure that they are minimised.

ML: You've distinguished between short-term profitability and long term, and direct financial liabilities and what you call broader social and environmental externalities. How does the regulatory system work in those respects in Australia? Presumably, the corporate regulator ASIC holds directors responsible for the financial returns, including the dividend payments?[9] How are the externalities handled that don't impact on the financial bottom line?

PB: Shareholders have a powerful tool of accountability in that they are responsible for electing directors to the board. Directors are generally up for re-election every three years and shareholders can vote against their re-election; it is up to shareholders and particularly institutional investors.

The whole board's accountable for their actions, and so there's a bit of a test that comes up in the annual general meeting (AGM) when shareholders either vote for or against directors' positions. That's where accountability can lie, and I think that in the past, investors haven't used that tool enough. An example where that tool was used was with AMP at the beginning of the Royal Commission into misconduct in the financial services industry.[10] A lot of issues were raised at the Commission and investors felt that the board had not been accountable for their actions. As a result, two directors stepped off the board before the subsequent annual general meeting. There has been, since then, a significant turnover on that board. Investors have the power with this voting tool to make the boards accountable regardless of what regulations do or do not say.

ML: Shareholder activism is emerging as a powerful force these days, especially in the context of ESG.[11,12] It hasn't always been so.[13] On the other hand, we have been exposed over recent years in Australia – if not elsewhere, globally – to a lot of cases and revelations about the failure of corporate regulators, including ASIC, to effectively regulate the behaviour and governance of corporate boards.[14] What have we learned about the failure of regulators to hold corporate boards accountable?

PB: I think you're right in terms of the regulators, but I'd prefer to talk more about boards and look at what's happened in financial services and misconduct. The Royal Commission brought out many examples of misconduct and spoke a lot about company culture,[15] which it is a board's responsibility to create, but I don't agree with that view.

The board's role is to set and approve purpose, principles and values. Those have to be communicated throughout the organisation so that anyone working for that organisation has an understanding of the company values and that their behaviour should be in alignment, or you have misconduct and a bad culture.

But you can't create the culture. You've got to set the values and principles, and yes, you can blame regulation and the regulators for some of the things that happened, but you can't regulate for competence. I wish you could, but you can't. I think this is where shareholders and investors have a responsibility to engage with their investee companies and to ask questions, particularly the large institutional investors, because they have access to the board: What is your purpose? What are your principles and values? How are you communicating that through the organisation? How does the board know when there are cases of misconduct or serious misconduct? How does the board know that there are action plans in place to address incidents of serious misconduct? And this information needs to be provided on a continual basis to the board. If you read Commissioner Hayne's report, none of that was happening in the large banks.

ML: With regard to 'shareholder activism', including through large, institutional investment and finance funds; what's been happening recently and how effective are these shareholder interventions?[16]

PB: There are a number of what I call 'social shareholder activist' groups. The two key ones in Australia are Market Forces,[17] and the Australian Centre for Corporate Responsibility (ACCR).[18] They've been very successful over the last five to eight years in bringing shareholder proposals to annual general meetings (AGM) of Australian-listed companies. To bring a shareholder proposal requires 100 individual shareholders or owning 5%, so only large institutional investors would hold 5%, and most wouldn't even hold anywhere near that. So they've been very successful in garnishing, say 100 shareholders and putting proposals on agendas mainly relating to climate change.[19] They are currently targeting fossil fuel companies and in the last couple of weeks OilSearch, Santos and Woodside have agreed to put a climate change report to shareholders' vote. That's not stopping those such as ACCR tabling shareholder proposals on the agenda for this year's AGM for those companies to be forced to have it enshrined in their constitutions, but the companies have voluntarily come out and offered to do it.

ML: A recent report about the performance of banks is saying, though, that despite a lot of the talk, particularly from the big banks, they are not actually moving their patterns of investments away from fossil fuels.[20]

There's been a lot of discussion too about the 'social purpose' of corporations,[21] to distinguish from the idea that corporations are there just for the financial interests of their direct shareholders. What is this discussion about and who's leading it?

PB: A number of asset owners are leading this discussion but I think it also gets very confused. Directors have a fiduciary duty under Corporations Law to the company,[22] and again that comes down to the point that directors are 'stewards' of the companies' assets. But I'll keep coming back to the point that to discharge their fiduciary duty they need to take a broader 'stakeholder' approach; the company can't externalise its costs onto society or onto the environment in order to generate returns for investors because those costs aren't recorded in the statutory profit and loss statement. They will eventually catch up to the company in terms of fines or penalties and additional taxes or some other form which will impair that longer-term return for investors.

Companies operate within society, so they cannot simply impose externalised costs on society. It's almost the difference between right and wrong. Directors must have 'intellectual honesty' and understand this. If I compare boards today to boards 25 years ago, the period over which I have been involved with them, there's no doubt that previously boards were more focused on immediate shareholder return and dividends. Issues like human capital management and environmental and mental health are big issues that boards need to ensure that the company is taken care of particularly during COVID-19, which has raised many issues that weren't previously coming to attention of the board, with mental health a big one with employees working from home. They also need to take a broader stakeholder approach in order to discharge their duties. Noel Hutley SC has issued an opinion on the role of directors and climate change that it's part of a director's fiduciary duty to take into account climate change risk in company strategy.[23] This broader stakeholder approach is part of that fiduciary duty; and that interpretation, I think, has probably changed over the years.

ML: We hear a lot about 'sustainability', and you've referred to long-term business sustainability, which seems to be operationalised through environment, social and governance (ESG).[24] What is this idea and how is it being operationalised?

PB: I look at the term sustainability in terms of how a company makes its money and not what it makes as such. I'm working with boards and senior leadership teams to help them embed a sustainable approach in their strategy and how to communicate that internally. Internal communication to employees is important and something that I think companies have been over-looking for the last 20–30 years, as well as externally to investors and to the broader society.

The ESG acronym with G referring to the governance is unfortunate in that G is placed at the end. Best practice governance requires a board having competent directors with a diversity of skills and experience. It's important because a competent board will understand company exposure in terms of environmental and social risks and ensure that these are managed well. But with an incompetent board that doesn't have that level of understanding, there's a risk that exposure to environmental and social issues won't be managed as well. It comes down to an issue of risk management and I think that Australian companies are reasonably good at reporting on this. I've done a lot of work on this in Asia, with Hong Kong and Chinese companies, and that concept of incorporating ESG into the core of what the company does is still a challenge.

ML: Is it particularly a challenge because in part there are many definitions of what we mean by sustainability – let alone ESG – with many systems around the world, and corporations who adopt different metrics, definitions and reporting, and no effective regulatory framework?[25]

PB: Yes, you're absolutely correct and it is very challenging for listed companies because they may engage with one investor who says you should follow this framework and another investor that says we want you to follow another. Fortunately, globally things are changing and quite quickly.

I sit on the board of the International Integrated Reporting Council (IIRC)[26] that has oversight of the development of the Integrated Reporting Framework (IRF), which focuses on six forms of business 'capital': financial, physical, social, human, environmental and intellectual.[27,28] It's a highly interconnected way to report about 'value creation' of the firm, but there are many others out there. One is the Sustainable Accounting Standards Board (SASB), which is US based and is investor focused around 'materiality' of non-financial issues. The IIRC say they are in discussions with the International Financial Reporting Council (IFRC) about merging with them to develop a global Sustainability Standards Board[29] which would sit alongside the Accounting Standards Board.[30]

Sustainability reporting standards will go through a similar process to join with the accounting standards which in Australia are part of the Corporations Law, so companies are required to comply and this will help standardise disclosure of non-financial issues. From an investor perspective, it will provide more consistency and comparability to be able to assess risk and opportunities within investee companies.[31]

ML: There appears to be an active process of building an evolving consensus on how to measure, report and assess these broader externalities, whether you call it sustainability or ESG, and seemingly on a global scale. But are the 'global' accounting standards, for example, really global? Isn't there a fundamentally different approach between an American approach to corporate governance and a European approach? Or is that not a fair characterisation of the situation?

PB: Well, on accounting standards it is correct that the EU has not adopted international financial reporting standards as Australia and most of the rest of the world has done. The accounting standards are covered by the Financial Accounting Standards Board (FASB), which is US. There's not a huge difference between the two but from a governance perspective, US governance is quite different; and if you compare it to Australia, the standards are significantly lower. For example, in the US a combined chair and CEO role is common. What you do have in the US though, is a litigious environment that provides a check and balance on governance, where in Australia it comes down to the fact that investors or shareholders can vote directors off a board. For many US companies that is not the case, and you only need one vote for a director. You can't vote against a director and you can only withhold your vote. Some companies have adopted a majority vote which is the same as in Australia. It is a different system in the UK where governance structures are similar to in Australia. In Germany, they have a two-board system, a management board and a supervisory board. Again, it's quite different.

ML: Yes, Australia has followed primarily the UK European approach but we will see where it goes in the future. You mentioned diversity on boards and presumably having more inclusiveness on corporate boards is one of the challenges and metrics around ESG I imagine. What is the experience of diversity in Australia with women or ethnic groups, and are we seeing any moves and changes in that direction?

PB: In Australia, we've seen significant movement in gender diversity on boards and I've been researching this since 2011 when the stats were around 13% for the ASX 200 companies. That's now over 30% and has happened without quotas being introduced.[32]

It is a credit to asset owners and asset management for their engagement with Australian-listed company boards on this issue. Many directors have commented that having more women on the board has changed the conversation for the better around the board table. That's the start of getting diversity on boards and it's pleasing to see that. Boards are developing different processes to identify future candidates as opposed to sitting around the table and asking if anyone has any mates who have some free time to join our board. Now they're going to search firms and undertake a proper search as well as introducing the skills matrix,[33] as a reporting requirement, alongside corporate governance principles. I think this has helped boards to identify those skills I was talking about earlier alongside core industry skills.

We've seen many Australian-listed companies fail when trying to move into Asia or China. When I go back and ask the question of who on the board brings a strong Asian perspective and understanding of doing business in Asia or business in China, the answer is no one.[34] They rely on management and so the composition of the board in terms of skills, experience, expertise, diversity needs to reflect the underlying business and strategy. I do remember a listed retail company many years ago had no women on the board. Well, you know who's the best at shopping? Women. They changed and got to the point where I think they have all women on the board. The key questions for the board are: What's the underlying business? What's the underlying strategy? Does the board have the appropriate mix of skills, experience and diversity to understand it and to provide the necessary oversight of management when it comes to delivery?

ML: Pru, where are these trends in corporate governance taking us with respect to climate change, the environment and indeed with indigenous national heritage bearing in mind the recent controversy over the destruction of the Juukan Gorge caves by global mining giant Rio Tinto?[35,36] On the one hand, we have a situation where corporations seem to be moving quite fast to adjust their processes and investments to decarbonise in response to climate change, and on the other hand, we have a government that has spoken up on a couple of recent occasions, telling corporations to keep their noses out of social matters and to get on with their core business.[37] What is the tension here?

PB: I do sympathise with company boards at the moment about the lack of political leadership on national policy. On the other hand, I look at some of the changes that the boards are making, moving into battery technology and the investment that's going into renewables, and they're not waiting for the government. It is very difficult to make an investment decision without policy certainty. The pressure has come from investors around the transition to a lower carbon economy. We're seeing boards taking up that responsibility for what the world is going to look like going forward, as opposed to just waiting for legislation to materialise.[38,39]

Conclusion

A wave of revelations about unethical and even criminal behaviour of large corporations, particularly in banking and finance, mining and energy, pharmaceuticals, has put into question their accountability, transparency, the responsibilities of their directors, the lack of effectiveness of regulatory systems, and has prompted a 'crisis' in the basic approaches to corporate governance. The pressing issues of new technologies and climate change have heightened awareness of these corporate governance challenges.[40] Questions are raised about the role and responsibility for boards and regulators in creating sustainable businesses and ethical cultures.

Even in the absence of clear political leadership and policy guidance from governments on the need to invest in decarbonisation and renewable energy to tackle climate change, companies have been moving in those directions in response to shareholder activism and institutional investor pressures. More generally, corporate governance processes and requirements have been changing to reflect broader community interests, including from consumers, and a broader range of 'stakeholders' as against traditional 'shareholders', as a pre-condition of their 'social licence' to operate.

The new governance principles are known collectively as the ESG (Environment, Social Governance) approach and are seen as also underpinning long-term business sustainability in a profit sense. In the case of ESG standards, there is a proliferation of methodology, metrics, reporting and compliance for use by investors to assess accountability. In the absence of agreed standards, there is scepticism of corporate 'greenwashing' albeit with emerging attempts to set clear standards and harmonisation on an international basis.

However, in some instances, along the way there has been political questioning of the legitimacy of the boards and directors of corporations taking public positions on ESG-related issues rather than focusing on their directors' fiduciary responsibilities for short-term profitability and returns to shareholders. Latterly, in some jurisdictions there has been a strong backlash against the use of ESG as ethical investment criteria embedded in legislation,[41] and as a manifestation of 'woke' sensibility.

Notes

1 Corporate governance was developed to maintain the accountability, stability and performance of corporations, and displays considerable international institutional diversity in approaches. See Clarke, T. (2022) *Comparative Corporate Governance: A Research Overview*, London: Routledge

2 Introduced first in the mining industry in the 1990s, the term has gained wider acceptance among industries. See Dumbrell, N.P., Adamson, D. and Wheeler, S.A. (2020) Is social licence a response to government and market failures? Evidence from the literature, *Resources Policy*, 69, December: 101827

3 The following article refers to the concept as functioning whereby social norms can precede and supersede legal rules: Gehman, J., Lefsrud, L.M. and Fast, S. (2017) Social license to operate: Legitimacy by another name? *Canadian Public Administration*, 60 (2): 293–317

4 See Atkins, B. (2020) Demystifying ESG: Its history and current status, *Forbes*, 8th June www.forbes.com/sites/betsyatkins/2020/06/08/demystifying-esgits-history-current-status/?sh=681b405b2cdd Atkins notes that ESG was first mentioned in the 2006 United Nation's Principles for Responsible Investment (PRI) as required to be incorporated in the financial evaluations of companies. See also Saa, L. (2021) PRI reaches 4,000 signatories with emerging markets boosting RI uptake, *UNPRIBlog*, 14th June www.unpri.org/pri-blog/pri-reaches-4000-signatories-with-emerging-markets-boosting-ri-uptake/7823.article

5 Martin Adams, G. (2021) ESG assets may hit $53 trillion by 2025, a third of AUM (Assets Under Management), *Bloomberg Intelligence*, 23rd February www.bloomberg.com/professional/blog/esg-assets-may-hit-53-trillion-by-2025-a-third-of-global-aum/

6 See Contrafatto, M. (2014) Stewardship theory: Approaches and perspectives, in Costa, E., Parker, L.D. and Andreaus, M. (eds) *Accountability and Social Accounting for Social and Non-Profit Organizations*, Advances in Public Interest Accounting, Volume 17, pp. 177–196, Bingley: Emerald Publishing Limited. Contrafatto discusses a variety of approaches to stewardship theory as a basis for transition towards more sustainable governance compared to earlier agency theories

7 See Keay, A. (2016) Stewardship theory: Is board accountability necessary? *International Journal of Law and Management*, 59 (6): 1292–1314. Keay notes that despite embracing self-responsibility for the interests of others and trust of directors, as well as rejecting the fundamental problems of agency theory, board accountability is as relevant to stewardship theory as to agency theory

8 Black, B.S. (2002) The principal fiduciary duties of boards of directors, *OECD Third Asian Roundtable on Corporate Governance*, Presentation, 4th April, Singapore www.oecd.org/daf/ca/corporategovernanceprinciples/1872746.pdf Fiduciary was defined originally and primarily under common law as being the duty of loyalty and duty of care, but extended latterly to include duty of disclosure and duty of extra care when the company is a takeover target

9 Grant, R. (2005) Australia's corporate regulators – the ACCC, ASIC and APRA, *Research Brief*, no. 16, 2004–05, 14th June, Parliamentary Library of Australia. Grant discusses the establishment of these regulators in the 1990s, their responsibilities, rapid growth, strategies and challenges faced

10 Kells, S. (2019) The Hayne royal commission: An appraisal, *La Trobe University*, 20th March www.latrobe.edu.au/news/articles/2018/opinion/the-hayne-royal-commission-an-appraisal The Financial Services Royal Commission's final report was issued in February 2019 and ran to more than 76,000 words. It contained 76 recommendations and received more than 10,000 complaints about Australia's financial services businesses. It damned the banks' culture and the bankers' greed and pointed to the corrosive effects of conflicting interest among executives and directors: 'Experience shows that conflicts between duty and interest can seldom be managed, self-interest will almost always trump duty' said Commissioner Hayne

11 Liekefett, K., Gregory, H.J. and Wood, L. (2021) Shareholder activism and ESG: What comes next, and how to prepare, *Harvard Law School Forum on Corporate Governance*, 29th May https://corpgov.law.harvard.edu/2021/05/29/shareholder-activism-and-esg-what-comes-next-and-how-to-prepare/

12 Crowley, A.-J. (2023) Global shareholder activism sees record number of European campaigns, *Reuters*, 18th January www.reuters.com/business/global-shareholder-activism-sees-record-number-european-campaigns-report-shows-2023-01-18/

13 Fairfax, L.M. (2019) From apathy to activism: The emergence, impact, and future of shareholder activism as the new corporate governance norm, *Boston University Law Review*, 99 (3): 1301–1345 www.bu.edu/bulawreview/files/2019/06/FAIRFAX.pdf

14 Schmulow, A. (2018) APRA and ASIC have the legal power to sack bank heads, but they need willpower, *The Conversation*, 30th April https://theconversation.com/apra-and-asic-have-the-legal-power-to-sack-bank-heads-but-they-need-willpower-95772

15 Kells (2019), op cit

16 Hill, J.G. and Rowley, T. (2022) Australia: Fast-growing awareness and activism, *US-Asia Law Institute, East-West Studies*, 2 (4), 17th March https://usali.org/asia-pacific-symposium-essays/australia-fast-growing-awareness-and-activism#:~:text=There%20is%20an%20increasing%20level,ESG%20concerns%2C%20particularly%20climate%20change

17 Vincent, J. (2022) How shareholders can promote corporate decarbonisation, *Market Forces*, Speech to Foreign Correspondents' Club Japan, 27th www.marketforces.org.au/how-shareholders-can-promote-decarbonisation-fccj-address/

18 Sheehy, B., Pender, H. and Jacobsen, B. (2021) Corporate social responsibility/ESG shareholder activism in Australia: A case study of the Australasian centre for corporate responsibility, *Australian Journal of Corporate Law*, 36 (2): 156–177
19 This article summarises climate litigation cases in Australia: Pender, K. (2022) The environmental activists bringing the climate crisis to the courtroom, *The Guardian*, 12th February www.theguardian.com/environment/2022/feb/12/the-environmental-activists-bringing-the-climate-crisis-to-the-courtroom
20 This press release highlights the stark disparity between the largest banks' public climate commitments and their largely business-as-usual financing of fossil fuels, and reports that in six years since the Paris Agreement, the world's 60 largest banks financed US$4.6T, with US$742B in 2021 alone: Reclaim Finance (2022) *New Report: World's Biggest Banks Continued to Pour Billions into Fossil Fuel Expansion in 2021*, 30th March https://reclaimfinance.org/site/en/2022/03/30/new-report-worlds-biggest-banks-continued-to-pour-billions-into-fossil-fuel-expansion-in-2021/#:~:text=The%20report%20documents%20that%20in,%24742%20billion%20in%202021%20alone
21 Hsieh, N.H., Meyer, M., Rodin, D. and van't Klooster, J. (2018) The social purpose of corporations, *Journal of the British Academy*, 6 (s1): 49–73 www.thebritishacademy.ac.uk/documents/966/JBA-6s1-Hsieh-Meyer-Rodin-Klooster.pdf
22 Black (2002), op cit
23 Hutley SC, N. and Hartford Davis, S. (2019) Climate change and directors' duties: Supplementary memorandum of opinion, *Centre for Policy Development*, 26th March https://cpd.org.au/wp-content/uploads/2019/03/Noel-Hutley-SC-and-Sebastian-Hartford-Davis-Opinion-2019-and-2016_pdf.pdfThis was an update of the landmark 2016 legal opinion on how the Australian Corporations Act 2001 (Cth) s180(1) requires company directors to consider, disclose and respond to climate change
24 Atkins (2020), op cit; Saa (2021), op cit
25 McDaniel, P., Rosen, P., Chibafa, J. and Hancocks, T. (2022) Lack of uniformity in ESG ratings system poses risks, opportunities, *Bloomberg Law*, 16th May https://news.bloomberglaw.com/esg/lack-of-uniformity-in-esg-ratings-system-poses-risks-opportunities
26 See IIRC www.integratedreporting.org
27 Gibassier, D., Adams, C.A. and Jérôme, T. (2019) Integrated reporting and the capitals' diffusion, *Report Published by the French Accounting Standard Setter (Autorité des Normes Comptables)* www.anc.gouv.fr/files/live/sites/anc/files/contributed/ANC/3_Recherche/B_Appels%20à%20projets/2017/First_report_ANC_final_version_GIBASSIER_ADAMS_JEROME_2019-07-24.pdf
28 Dearnell, A. (2022) Are you ready for an integrated annual report? *Forbes*, 20th December www.forbes.com/sites/adriandearnell/2022/12/20/are-you-ready-for-an-integrated-annual-report/?sh=7122ebe4ec27
29 Global Reporting Initiative (GRI) *The Global Sustainability Standards Board* www.globalreporting.org/standards/global-sustainability-standards-board/
30 See Strickland, B. (2022) New year, new challenges: Preparing for sustainability disclosures, *Journal of Accountancy*, 23rd November www.journalofaccountancy.com/news/2022/nov/new-year-new-challenges-preparing-sustainability-disclosures.html
31 See Flower, J. (2015) The international integrated reporting council: A story of failure *Critical Perspectives on Accounting*, 27, March: 1–17. Flower argues that in the years since its formation in 2010 with the objective of promoting sustainability accounting it has abandoned as at 2013 that goal by adopting 'value for investors' not 'value for society', and places no obligation on firms to report harm inflicted on entities outside the firm, a victim of 'regulatory capture'

32 This summarises the research report, "Towards Board Gender Parity": UQ News (2021) *Australia One of Three Countries to Exceed 30 Per Cent Women on Company Boards*, University of Queensland, 30th July www.uq.edu.au/news/article/2021/07/australia-one-of-three-countries-exceed-30-cent-women-company-boards#:~:text=UQ%20Business%20School%20researchers%20Dr,33.6%20per%20cent%20in%202021

33 Governance Institute of Australia (2015) *Good governance guide: Creating and disclosing a board skills matrix* www.asx.com.au/documents/asx-compliance/creating-disclosing-board-skills-matrix.pdf

34 Wright, C., Cortese, C., Al-Mamun, A. and Ali, S. (2022) *The Whiteboard: Ethnic Diversity in Corporate Australia, Opinion and Blog*, Emerald Publishing, 31st May www.emeraldgrouppublishing.com/opinion-and-blog/whiteboard-ethnic-diversity-corporate-australia

35 Winning, D. (2020) Rio Tinto CEO to step down amid fallout over destruction of ancient rock shelters, *The Wall Street Journal*, 10th September www.wsj.com/articles/rio-tinto-ceo-to-step-down-amid-fallout-over-destruction-of-ancient-rock-shelters-11599782719 The CEO resigned under pressure from investors and a failure in governance processes

36 Kemp, D., Fredericks, B., Muir, K. and Barnes, R. (2021) Fixing Australia's shocking record of indigenous heritage destruction: Juukan inquiry offers a way forward, *The Conversation*, 20th October https://theconversation.com/fixing-australias-shocking-record-of-indigenous-heritage-destruction-juukan-inquiry-offers-a-way-forward-170212 The Parliamentary Committee inquiry found that the actions by Rio Tinto were legal but recommended changes to legislation that would make such actions illegal in the future

37 Knight, E. (2019) Social issues are no longer fringe for business or their customers, *Sydney Morning Herald*, 20th September www.smh.com.au/business/companies/social-issues-are-no-longer-fringe-for-business-or-their-customers-20190920-p52tc9.html This article reports remarks by Assistant Minister to then Prime Minister (Morrison) telling companies to 'keep their noses out of social issues' and concentrate their lobbying on business issues such as productivity, tax and industrial relations

38 Fox Koob, S. (2022) Going for woke: Companies treading a fine line on social licence, *Sydney Morning Herald*, 12th November www.smh.com.au/business/companies/going-for-woke-companies-treading-a-fine-line-on-social-licence-20221108-p5bwk5.html This article discusses the emerging public backlash to ESG, including political targeting in the US of ESG fund managers;. Anna Patty, "Companies shouldn't do their dirty 'woke washing' in public", *Sydney Morning Herald*, 27th January 2023 describing public cynicism about corporate and brand activism

39 Patty, A. (2023) Companies shouldn't do their dirty 'woke washing' in public, *Sydney Morning Herald*, 27th January www.smh.com.au/business/consumer-affairs/companies-shouldn-t-do-their-dirty-woke-washing-in-public-20230120-p5ce63.html This article describes public cynicism about corporate and brand activism

40 Clarke, T. (2023) *Corporate Governance: Cycles of innovation, Crisis and Reform*, London: Sage

41 Arjalies, D.-L. and Bansal, T. (2023) ESG backlash in the US: What implications for corporations and investors? *Financial Times*, 12th June www.ft.com/content/3f064321-138c-4c65-bbb9-6abcc92adead

24 Decarbonising and Transforming the Australian Economy

A Game-Changing Renewable Energy Opportunity

Interview With Ross Garnaut

Introduction

A leading international bank, Citibank, has issued a report about the sweeping and urgent decarbonisation of the world energy and power markets based on the rapid fall in incremental costs of going down the low-carbon pathway,[1] and the fact that the lowest costs now for power generation are found around the world in renewables, in wind and solar.[2]

Meanwhile, Australia has long been mired in the politicised debate on climate, energy and water that doesn't appear to be going anywhere very fast.[3] Australia is, at the same time, highly vulnerable to climate change disruption, while also, arguably, very well positioned to benefit from decarbonisation.

Keywords: AEMO; agricultural sector; carbon capture; carbon farming; carbon sequestration; carbon tax; carbon trading; climate change; climate wars; COP voluntary agreements; cost of capital; economics of renewable technologies; decarbonisation; exchange rates; gold plating; green hydrogen; green steel; indigenous land management; interest rates; *Laudato si;* LNG; low-carbon economy; quarry economy; renewable energy; SDG 7; SDG 11; SDG 12; SDG 13; smart grids; resources boom; soil carbon; solar power; trade protectionism; UNFCCC 2016; wind power

Interviewee Profile

Professor Ross Garnaut **(RG),** AC, is a highly distinguished Australian public policy economist who has made substantial contributions to public policy over many decades, including the major reforms of the Hawke government in the 1980s. Garnaut has been called 'our nation's most prophetic economist'.[4] He is a leading thinker on climate and energy policy and the author of the seminal 2008 report to the Australian government, the 2008 Garnaut Climate Change Review.[5] Ross is a Companion of the Order of Australia (AC) and is currently Professorial Research Fellow in Economics at the University of Melbourne.

DOI: 10.4324/9781003280316-28

The Interview

ML: Ross, you've said that the fog of Australian politics on climate change has obscured a fateful reality that Australia has the potential to become an economic superpower of the future post-carbon world. You develop this theme at length and in detail in your book *Superpower: Australia's Low Carbon Opportunity* (2022) in which you set out a crisp, compelling roadmap for progress on these issues.[6] It covers what could be said to be a total transformation of the Australian economy. What has prompted you to write the book at this time, and what has changed on these issues since you authored the landmark 2008 Climate Change Review?

RG: One of the things I do in the book Michael is to go back over what has changed in the dozen years since I was commissioned by all the governments of Australia – state, federal and territory – to do that first report. The science hasn't changed much, although there's been a lot of good science done that's reduced uncertainty about the outcomes, without changing our expectations of the most likely outcomes.

It has focused a bit more on the very large dangers of some of the feedback effects that could lead to extreme outcomes. For that reason, the science is leading us to focus more heavily on a 1.5 degree limit on increases in temperature rather than the 2 degrees that was more common a dozen years ago, but basically the development of the science has reduced uncertainty rather than changing expectations. There's been quite a lot of development on the ethics of climate change and a lot more thought given to it.

I discuss at some length these developments, including the very important contribution of Pope Francis in his encyclical *Laudato Si*,[7] which, as I say in the book, is based on first-rate contemporary atmospheric physics and he went to the best people for advice that's truly authoritative.[8]

There have been changes in the international framework within which we're discussing cooperation on this matter, and I've changed my mind on these things since a dozen years ago. We were looking at a top-down international agreement where we would allocate rights to use the atmosphere's remaining capacity to absorb greenhouse gas without great climate damage.

Now, we're looking at what I call 'concerted unilateral mitigation' or 'voluntary agreements' and relying on periodic meetings of senior government leaders to apply pressure that will ratchet up the effort over time to make sure we get as close as possible to the 1.5 degree objective.

The biggest changes and what's led to this book are changes in the economics; there are two very big ones. One is transformational reduction in the cost of renewable energy, wind and solar. A much faster rate of reduction of costs than I built into my modelling a dozen years ago. I expected falls in costs. For example, I built in expectations of a few percent per annum reduction in solar costs but what happened has vastly exceeded that; we have 95% reduction in solar generation costs over the first ten years since I did the modelling.[9] That's transformed the cost of generating electricity that we directly consume already but it is also transforming and decarbonising transport by reducing the costs of electrification of transport. It's also transformed our potential for the decarbonising of industry.

A lot of the use of energy-generating emissions now in industry is to provide heat and energy in forms that can be provided by electricity. Low-cost renewable energy now allows that to be done with zero emissions and at the same time it expands the range of industrial processes that become economic for Australia. We can look forward in a reasonable time frame to hydrogen being cheap enough to be competitive with coal. Using hydrogen-based renewable energy for reducing iron ore into iron metal, there will be zero emissions of primary steel.[10]

Another big change is better recognition of the opportunity for storing huge amounts of carbon in the landscape in soil, pastures, woodlands and forest plantations. I note in the book that there's more carbon stored in the first couple of metres of the earth's crust, than there is in the whole of the atmosphere and in the biosphere, with all the plants and animals on earth.[11]

If you can increase soil carbon by even a modest proportion, that can absorb a huge amount of carbon from the atmosphere. It happens that Australia has the lowest cost opportunities for producing renewable energy. We've got the world's best combination of solar and wind resources with nothing like it elsewhere on earth,[12] and that means zero net emissions in the zero-carbon world towards which we all agreed to head in Paris at the end of 2015.[13]

In that world, Australia will be the low energy cost country and the net-zero exporter by converting our mineral exports and final products whose processing involves a lot of energy. It also means that zero net emissions, from storing carbon in the landscape, can be a very large part of Australia's economic future.[14]

ML: What is the nature of the Australian asset base that's going to give us this potentially transformative competitive advantage based on the lower costs of renewable energies? You've mentioned that we are potentially a great energy source for renewables, and you've mentioned our landscape. Are these the two key elements that can drive our opportunities for the future?

RG: Our huge natural resources base gives Australia a natural comparative advantage rich in energy-intensive processing but also in carbon-based manufactures. All those chemical manufacturers, including all plastics, are currently based on natural gas and oil which generate carbon emissions. They will have to be using low emissions, biomass in which we will have great opportunities for relatively low-cost production.

The greater opportunity though is the low cost of renewable energy from the world's best combinations of wind and solar resources.

ML: If we're going to move down this path, there's going to have to be some big structural transformations. For example, what's required to happen to the electricity system and policies around it to realise and capitalise on these renewable generation technologies whose costs are dropping so fast?[15]

RG: We're going to have cheaper household transport with electrification through the 2020s and providing both passenger and freight transport from batteries, or hydrogen, would increase total use of power by about half in Australia. Converting only one-tenth of our iron ore into metal, which will be a natural thing to do in the zero-emissions world economy and just one-quarter of our aluminium oxide and ore exports into aluminium metal, will require trebling of our transport system and associated electricity system.

It's going to look a very different electricity system and we're not going to get such transformational expansion at a reasonable, globally competitive cost without a lot of that being through private, unregulated initiative. Then the crucial question will be about the terms on which that private provision interacts with the currently regulated system.[16]

ML: A part of that transformation to renewables generated electricity is the move towards what some call a 'Smart Grid',[17] which is better able to handle the variable renewable energy loads as compared to the traditional baseload systems that we've had. How is that going to be driven from a regulatory and financial point of view?

RG: There are really two questions. One is, how do we make the existing grid work more economically and better? That's the grid that provides millions of households in Australia with access to power into their homes, as well as to small businesses. As for big businesses using a lot of power, we will need a lot of flexibility. Many households and small businesses will become exporters as well as importers of power, requiring significant local storage and generation. At last, after being laggard for a long time the training system is starting to think about those things now led by the Australian Energy Market Operator (AEMO), which is looking into changes needed.[18]

Alongside, there will have to be a lot of high-volume transmission to service the big industrial users and this expansion is going to have to be mostly undertaken through private unregulated systems. Policy will not lead change, but good policy can help the change. Where good policy will be needed is in making sure we've got rational interaction at the points of connection between the regulated and unregulated systems. If we do that right, we can reduce the cost of providing transmission and distribution for both the regulated and the unregulated systems.

ML: Won't a lot of capital be required in this transition, not only for the electricity industry but in the transformation of transport, and of a whole range of minerals and energy processing industries that you've mentioned? Can Australia generate and access capital on that scale to invest in this transformation?[19]

RG: I expect this will be the least of our problems. We've got a reasonably sophisticated capital market that can mobilise large quantities of investment if people perceive two things, an opportunity for profit, and stability in the policy environment. We've had big investments into growing an LNG export capacity,[20] at the town of Gladstone, Queensland,[21] and in a relatively short period of time. We also significantly invested capital in the electricity transmission and distribution system when we provided private-sector incentives internally to counterproductive incentives that increased cost.[22]

We've just been through an immense resources boom where many hundreds of billions of dollars went into new resource projects.[23] I don't see the capital markets having any difficulty in providing the admittedly immense requirements needed for decarbonisation opportunities.

ML: That's reassuring. These investments need to be able to show good returns and fortunately too, we are living at a time of unprecedentedly low interest rates that can make them look even more attractive, can't they?

RG: That's right, and I neglected to mention earlier that one of the factors that brought down costs, not just a reduction in the cost of manufacturing the equipment for solar and wind and battery storage, is the cost of capital. The new technologies are zero-emissions sources of energy which are relatively high in capital costs and low in operating costs, whereas the old technologies using fossil energy are relatively high in operating costs, the cost of the gas or the cost of the coal itself rather than the initial capital cost. Accordingly, the costs of the former fall as global interest rates fall.[24] The price of capital has had immense effects in reducing the cost of the products of the new renewable energy-based industry.

ML: When it comes to the economy-wide industrial transformation that you're talking about, Australia has done very well for decades by extracting and shipping out bulk commodities. We've not been particularly good at adding value to our exports in these commodity areas you've mentioned. Is your scenario of low-cost, renewable energy available in bulk on a world-competitive basis setting out a framework for the possibility of adding real value to our minerals and energy commodities?

RG: That's right. I'm saying that the opportunity is there for Australia to benefit immensely economically from this renewable energy transformation. We do have to get away from the prevailing 'quarry mindset'[25] which we didn't always have. When pioneers of Melbourne business developed the Broken Hill deposits of lead, zinc and silver back in the late nineteenth century, those ores required substantial innovation in processing to bring them to market.[26] They joined with Australian technical people and scientists and introduced the 'flotation process' to maintain efficiency and production as mineral ore grades declined.[27]

One hundred and twenty years ago, Australia was a globally competitive producer of steel for various reasons.[28] We lost those capacities, partly with protection over 100 years,[29] because that systematically reduced investment in those industries which were potentially globally competitive but less profitable than the raw materials.

Protection helped concentrate our investment in raw materials because that was inherently more profitable and less damaged by high protection. Then the series of minerals booms culminating in the great China 'resources boom' of the first dozen years of this century,[30] made mining so profitable that processing and manufacturing was a poor cousin. Major companies in related sectors want to put their money into mining rather than steel-making or metal manufactures. The real exchange rate was pushed up so high by the China resources boom,[31] that it killed a lot of Australian manufacturing that would have survived with normal exchange rates, including parts of the car industry, for example, the Toyota plant.[32]

We have a bit of intellectual and cultural baggage to get rid of where we've come to think of ourselves as being a mining country that's no good at advanced manufacturing, but that's not what we've always been, and we've got the scientific and skill base to do much more than be a quarry. We lost our first chance, but we're being given a second chance.

ML: Low-priced renewable energy is, by its nature, widely geographically distributed as are Australia's natural and mineral resources generally, including in regional and remote areas. If we can achieve the transformation we have been discussing, much can be achieved too for those communities and economies. We might segue accordingly, from the theme of industrial transformation to the agricultural and primary industry sector. What opportunities and scenarios do you paint there in the low-carbon economy, for example, you speak of opportunities for a new carbon farming industry?[33]

RG: My first report in 2008[34] had a chapter on opportunities that captured carbon in the landscape and in my second report for the multi-party Parliamentary Committee on Climate Change chaired by Prime Minister Julia Gillard in 2011, I took that a bit further.[35]

The 'carbon farming initiative' that was subsequently legislated that allowed carbon credits from farming to be sold into the emissions trading scheme grew out of that.[36] What's happened since then is greater awareness around the world of the immense opportunity from carbon farming and just as we've got unparalleled resources in renewable energy, which can be the basis of international competitiveness. We've got far more opportunities for sequestering carbon in soils and in plants than any other country; a lot of that country doesn't compete directly with high-value agriculture and is at relatively low cost so we can readily make use of this opportunity.[37] Way back in 2011 I said that carbon farming could become an industry as big as the wool industry. In my latest book, I say that is a radical understatement of the opportunity.

ML: Well, that is a wonderful statement but what are the research and development challenges behind realising carbon sequestration and capture in soils and biomass, and are there also related opportunities for land managed by Indigenous Australians?

RG: Yes, in fact it's a marvellous opportunity for Indigenous Australia. All these are great opportunities for rural and provincial Australia. I spent some time recently with the leaders of Indigenous Business Australia (IBA) who are responsible for over 1,000,000 square kilometres of Australia; that's a landscape of over 100 million hectares.[38]

It will not be hard in my assessment, to manage that land in different ways. Sometimes in ways that are closer to indigenous management practices before white settlement. It would not be hard, for example, to do so in ways that we're adding a tonne or more carbon per hectare per annum. At the current price of carbon in the carbon-trading system in Europe, for example, if we were able to sell into that market just on that Aboriginal-managed land, you'd be talking about carbon credits of over $4 billion a year, so it's worth putting in a bit of effort into the research, development and knowledge to win a prize as big as that.

ML: The many and diverse low-carbon opportunities may need to be unlocked and supported by policy changes. For example, trying to win a share of carbon credit trading around the world must involve us in having to participate in international agreements on carbon pricing, and there must be many domestic reforms needed. What are the political prospects for driving the reforms that might be needed to realise the wonderful opportunities that you have detailed?[39]

RG: One point I make is that the opportunity is so large that we can make a good start without breaching the constraints that are placed by electoral commitments of the current Australian government, at least in this electoral term. For carbon farming, the biggest requirement is more investment in knowledge and research on the best ways of doing things, and especially research on low-cost ways of measuring carbon in the landscape, and the opportunity that comes from modern remote sensing to do that using satellite technology which also requires research and development.[40]

On the immense opportunity in industrial development, I make suggestions in the book, but none of them require us in the next few years to go outside the boundaries of current explicit political commitments. In the longer term, we will need to do more in the way of policy, but that will be in a political environment that's been transformed by early success.

Conclusion

The global imperative of decarbonisation has seen the rapid development of sustainable green technologies particularly in relation to replacing fossil fuel carbon-emitting energy sources with renewable energy sources primarily solar and wind power, in many consuming sectors of the economy, such as households and transport. Their adoption offers the opportunity to transform economies and industrial structures both as a sustainable energy source and as a green feedstock replacing hydrocarbons with green hydrogen for a range of industrial processes such as steel, aluminium and fertilisers. The agriculture and land management sectors have additional significant opportunities for global-scale carbon storage.

Australia is a case in point. Long reliant on traditional fossil fuel minerals and energy commodity exports to underpin its economic wealth it is now positioned to become a global renewable energy 'superpower'. Few countries are as well positioned with renewable energy assets of sun and wind which when combined with the country's globally significant minerals resources such as coal and iron ore could transform the industrial sector to domestic value-added processing and export of traditional commodities in the form of green steel, aluminium or fertilisers.

Industry, alongside finance and investment, is increasingly attracted by the rapidly falling costs of renewable energy technology and abetted by attractive cost of capital, thanks to prevailing low interest rates. The role of government is also proving of central importance in the transition to zero emissions. Many aspects of green technology, for example, in hydrogen and in carbon capture, require further substantial investments in R & D, including by governments. Australian experience with adoption and diffusion is clearly lagging behind the world due to the absence of necessary regulatory policies, incentives and investments in areas such as EV take-up and electrification grid infrastructure. As international climate agreements move to progressive ratcheting up to meet 1.5 degrees, there is hope that the long prevailing 'fog of Australian politics' on climate change issues will shift to support industrial and economic transformation into a decarbonised renewable energy 'superpower'.

Notes

1 Citi Global Perspectives and Solutions (2021) Global carbon markets: Solving the emissions crisis before time runs out, *Citigroup*, 8th December www.citigroup.com/global/insights/citigps/global-carbon-market
2 Wood, J. (2021) Renewable energy is cheaper than previously thought and could be a game changer in the climate change battle, Climate Brief SDG 13, COP26 Forum, *World Economic Forum*, 18th October www.weforum.org/agenda/2021/10/how-cheap-can-renewable-energy-get/
3 Crowley, K. (2021) Climate wars, carbon taxes and toppled leaders: The 30-year history of Australia's climate response, in brief, *The Conversation*, 15th October https://theconversation.com/climate-wars-carbon-taxes-and-toppled-leaders-the-30-year-history-of-australias-climate-response-in-brief-169545
4 Garnaut, R. (ed) (2022) *The Superpower Transformation: Making Australia's Zero-Carbon Future*, Melbourne: Latrobe University Press www.blackincbooks.com.au/books/superpower-transformation
5 This review has been described as 'one of the most important reports to be published in Australia for many years'. See also www.rossgarnaut.com.au/climate-change/
6 Garnaut (2022), op cit, in which he turns the superpower opportunity into a plan to reshape Australia
7 Pope Francis (2015) Laudato Si – on care for our common home, *Encyclical Letter*, www.vatican.va/content/francesco/en/encyclicals/documents/papa-francesco_20150524_enciclica-laudato-si.html
8 The 2015 Papal Encyclical *"Laudato Si: On Care for our Common Home"* motivated many to take action, but governments have lagged. See Bruggers, J. (2020) Five years after speaking out on climate change, Pope Francis sounds an urgent alarm, *Inside Climate News*, 7th August https://insideclimatenews.org/news/07082020/climate-change-pope-francis/
9 Roser, M. (2020) Explained: Why renewables became so cheap so fast, energy transition brief, *World Economic Forum*, 4th December www.weforum.org/agenda/2020/12/renewables-energy-price-cost-cheap-climate-change-sustainability/
10 Hieminga, G., Dantuma, E. and Stellema, T. (2023) Hydrogen sparks change for the future of green steel production, *ING Think*, 19th July https://think.ing.com/articles/hydrogen-sparks-change-for-the-future-of-green-steel-production
11 Eagle, A.J., Uludere Aragon, N.Z. and Gordon, D.R. (2022) The realizable magnitude of carbon sequestration in global cropland soils: Socioeconomic factors, *Environmental Defense Fund* www.edf.org/sites/default/files/2022-12/realizable-magnitude-carbon-sequestration-cropland-soils-socioeconomic-factors.pdf
12 Sims, R. (2023) Green energy is a bigger opportunity for Australia than the resources boom: Let's not waste it, *The Guardian*, 20th April www.theguardian.com/commentisfree/2023/apr/21/green-energy-is-a-bigger-opportunity-for-australia-than-the-resources-boom-lets-not-waste-it
13 UNFCCC, *The Paris Agreement* https://unfccc.int/process-and-meetings/the-paris-agreement
14 Finkel, A. (2023) *Powering Up: Unleashing the Clean Energy Supply Chain*, Collingwood, VIC: Black Inc. Books
15 Graham, P., Hayward, J., Foster, J. and Havas, L. (2023) GenCost 2022–23, *CSIRO*, July www.csiro.au/-/media/EF/Files/GenCost/GenCost2022-23Final_27-06-2023.pdf
16 Mercer, D. (2023) Billion-dollar brawl over power lines suggests Australia's energy transition is in full swing, *ABC News*, 20th April www.abc.net.au/news/2023-04-14/debate-over-australian-transmission-lines-energy-transition/102213470
17 Moreno Escobar, J.J., Morales Matamoros, O., Tejeida Padilla, R., Lina Reyes, I. and Quintana Espinosa, H. (2021) A comprehensive review on smart grids: Challenges and opportunities. *Sensors*, 21, October: 6978

18 AEMO (2021) *Standards Evolve to Support a Secure and Reliable Electricity Grid as Solar PV Continues to Grow*, 7th January https://aemo.com.au/en/newsroom/news-updates/aemo-welcomes-revised-inverter-standard
19 Murphy, K. (2023) Slow transition to renewables puts Australia at risk of losing 'attractive' investment, super funds warn, *The Guardian*, 1st December www.theguardian.com/australia-news/2023/dec/01/industry-super-funds-warn-slow-transition-to-net-zero-puts-australia-at-risk-of-losing-attractive-investments
20 ACCR (2023) *Australia's LNG Growth Wave – Did It Wash for Shareholders?* Report, 27th November www.accr.org.au/research/australias-lng-growth-wave-did-it-wash-for-shareholders/
21 Nelson, T. (2018) East-coast Australian gas markets – overcoming the lumpiness of capital allocation and temporal instability, *Economic Analysis and Policy*, 59, September: 103–112
22 Sawyer, M. (2022) Gold-plated Rorters: Power users gouged $10bn as big suppliers sobbed crocodile tears, *Michael West Media*, 5th October https://michaelwest.com.au/gold-plated-rort-power-users-pinged-10bn-as-networks-cry-crocodile-tears/
23 Kearns, J. and Lowe, P. (2011) *Australia's Prosperous 2000s: Housing and the Mining Boom*, RBA Annual Conference www.rba.gov.au/publications/confs/2011/kearns-lowe.html
24 Monnin, P. (2015) Supporting the energy transition: The role of low interest rates, *CEPII*, 1st October www.cepii.fr/blog/en/post.asp?IDcommunique=409
25 Mercer, D. and Marden, P. (2006) Ecologically sustainable development in a 'quarry' economy: One step forward, two steps back, *Geographical Research*, 44 (2): 183–203
26 Blainey, G. (2010) A brief history of BHP Billiton, *Journal of Australasian Mining History*, September, 8: 23–35
27 Nagaraj, D.R. and Farinato, R.S. (2016) Evolution of flotation chemistry and chemicals: A century of innovations and the lingering challenges, *Minerals Engineering*, 96–97, October: 2–14. The authors note that the great challenge of further innovation in flotation systems – if the minerals processing industry is to have a sustainable future
28 Kelly, D. (2011) Once upon a time, when Australia had a steel industry . . ., *The Conversation*, 24th August https://theconversation.com/once-upon-a-time-when-australia-had-a-steel-industry-2967
29 Anderson, K. (2020) Trade protectionism in Australia: Its growth and dismantling, *ANU Crawford School of Public Policy*, Working Papers in Trade and Development, Volume 10, May https://acde.crawford.anu.edu.au/publication/working-papers-trade-and-development/16630/trade-protectionism-australia-its-growth-and
30 Bishop, J., Kent, C., Plumb, M. and Rayner, V. (2013) The resources boom and the Australian Economy: A sectoral analysis, bulletin, March, *Reserve Bank of Australia* www.rba.gov.au/publications/bulletin/2013/mar/5.html
31 Freebairn, J. (2015) Mining booms and the exchange rate, *Australian Journal of Agricultural and Resource Economics*, 59 (4): 533–548
32 Durkin, P. and Evans, S. (2017) Toyota closure heralds the end of car-making in Australia, *Australian Financial Review*, 3rd October. The closure left Australia without a car manufacturing industry after more than half a century
33 Carbon Market Institute (CMI) (2022) *Carbon Farming: Scorecard Report*, April https://carbonmarketinstitute.org/app/uploads/2022/04/Carbon-Farming-Scorecard-Report.pdf
34 Garnaut, R. (2008) *The Garnaut Climate Change Review: Final Report,* Port Melbourne, VIC: Cambridge University Press
35 See Garnaut, R. (2011) *Weighing the Costs and Benefits of Climate Change Action*, January, Attorney-General's Department, Commonwealth of Australia https://

sustain.pata.org/wp-content/uploads/2014/12/GARNAUT-CLIMATE-CHANGE-UPDATE-1-Weighing-the-costs-and-benefits-of-climate-change-action.pdf This was the first of eight updates of his 2008 Review. The final update presented to the Australian Prime Minister on the 31st May 2011 was called *The Garnaut Review 2011: Australia in the Global Response to Climate Change* https://webarchive.nla.gov.au/awa/20190509030847/www.garnautreview.org.au/update-2011/garnaut-review-2011.html

36 The Carbon Credits (Carbon Farming Initiative) Act 2011 was a voluntary carbon abatement scheme run between September 2011 and December 2014 when it was integrated into the Emissions Reduction Fund (ERF) www.legislation.gov.au/Details/C2011A00101

37 Stitzlein, C., Baldock, J.A., Roxburgh, S.H., Mooij, M., Smith, D. and Fitch, P. (2023) Facilitating entry to land sector carbon abatement projects: The LOOC-C tool, *Carbon Management*, 14 (1): 2265156

38 Evans, M. and Polidano, C. (2022) First nations businesses; progress, challenges and opportunities, *Reserve Bank of Australia (RBA) Bulletin*, 16th June www.rba.gov.au/publications/bulletin/2022/jun/first-nations-businesses-progress-challenges-and-opportunities.html

39 Dawes, A., McGeady, C. and Majkut, J. (2023) Voluntary carbon markets: A review of global initiatives and evolving models, *Center for Strategic and International Studies (CSIS)*, 31st May www.csis.org/analysis/voluntary-carbon-markets-review-global-initiatives-and-evolving-models

40 Nikologianni, A. and Albans, A. (2023) The complex case of carbon-measuring tools in landscape architecture, *C: Journal of Carbon Research*, 9 (3): 69 www.mdpi.com/2311-5629/9/3/69

25 Public Interest Journalism

Vanishing Pillar for a Sustainable Democracy?

Interview With Allan Fels

Introduction

Digital technology has disrupted Australian media and journalism and been accompanied by misinformation and disinformation on social media. In particular, this has precipitated the decline in public interest journalism[1] and has created a problem for the sustainability of our democracy.

Keywords: AAP; ACCC; bargaining code; clickbait; COVID-19; cross-media ownership; cross-subsidy; digital platforms; disinformation; editing; fact checking; fair copying; fake news; freedom of the press; local news; market failure; media business model; media diversity; media ownership concentration; misinformation; newspapers; positive externality; public good; public interest journalism; Public Interest Journalism Initiative (PIJI); social media; SDG 16; SDG 17

Interviewee Profile

Professor Allan Fels (**AF**), AO, of Melbourne, Monash and Oxford universities is Australia's leading consumer crusader. Most prominently, and visibly, he was the first chairman of the Australian Competition and Consumer Commission (ACCC) from its inception in 1995; from 1991 he was Chair of the Trade Practices Commission that was subsumed under the newly formed ACCC, until he stepped down in 2003, some 14 years in all. He has been a regular feature on television screens over the years. His autobiography, *Tough Customer: Chasing Better Deals for the Battlers*, sums up what he's been doing throughout his eminent career.[2] He has chaired numerous public inquiries and as Dean of the Australia and New Zealand School of Government, and has trained top-level public servants for many years. Allan was recently appointed chair of the not-for-profit the Public Interest Journalism Initiative (PIJI),[3] in the face of a marked decline in public interest journalism. Allan is an eminent economist, lawyer, public servant and latterly academic.

DOI: 10.4324/9781003280316-29

The Interview

ML: What is public interest journalism and why is it important to us now?[4,5]

AF: By that, we're referring to any journalism on any form of media outlet whether newspapers, television or radio that concerns public matters. We put in 'public' to make it clear we're not particularly focusing on journalism about cooking or lifestyles, or that sort of thing, but about public matters in the broadest sense. If we're talking locally, it would include coverage of local matters, council matters, concerns of the local community, court matters and so on. And of course, nationally it would encompass all areas of similar journalism, including debates and discussions of a political kind.

ML: In what way is this role affected by the digital disruption of Australian mainstream and traditional media outlets across TV, radio and newspapers? We are familiar with the huge impacts on the traditional media business models, including the shedding of a huge number of journalists.[6] Even the other day, for example, we've seen the Australian Associated Press, that august instrument of news collection in the public interest, having to close down.[7,8] What is the connection between this digital disruption driven by the emergence of new media platforms, and the threats and renewed interest it has created in public interest journalism?

AF: Whilst acknowledging that the digital platforms and technology bring advantages to the media and to reporting, our concern is that it basically destroyed the old model upon which public interest journalism was based. The old model, in simple terms, was that taking newspapers; above all, they were funded partly by how much people paid for the cover price to get the paper, and partly but heavily by advertising revenue.

Now, the advertising revenue side has effectively collapsed because advertising has shifted over to digital forms, away from newspaper and other traditional media forms.[9] In the past and up till now, the revenue from advertising has in effect cross-subsidised 'quality' journalism, which may be a great 'public good'. But as a commercial property, it struggles to make a living, to earn enough content revenue to pay for itself.

It is now threatened by the loss of the advertising revenue and that is obvious from a couple of things you mentioned. The recent collapse of AAP, the poor profits of news media and TV, and the large number of closures of papers, for example, particularly in rural and regional areas, and among some suburban metropolitan papers, and in reducing the size of major news outlets. That has all led, as you mentioned, to a big decline in the number of journalists in Australia. It's been a dramatic fall in the last ten years and that has a bad effect on the quality of journalism.[10]

ML: While that traditional business model based on advertising has been substantially undermined, at the same time we've seen the emergence of new players in the media space in the form of digital platforms; particularly platforms like Facebook, which have taken over a lot of the advertising revenues, and the emergence of a whole new strand of news services through social media that have seen the emergence of these new, often international players onto our media scene.

AF: Yes, they do bring some additional good features though they do not generally support investigative journalists and in-depth reporting. They also tend not to have good 'intermediation' between information coming in and information being published. In the traditional press when information comes in, it's gathered fairly systematically, it's reviewed and assessed properly, and then it's published. Whereas, on social media, all sorts of fake news get through the system, and in general there's not an assessment over what is published and its effect. If you want reliable news, you're more likely to get it from established media sources.

ML: Have the old models of fact checking and editing been replaced by a move to attract eyeballs through what's called 'clickbait', which may be entertaining but perhaps may not ultimately convey substantial news stories, but does attract eyeballs and therefore advertising away from traditional media? As well as impacting on media organisations these developments have been surfacing as matters of public policy concern, including the establishment of a parliamentary Senate inquiry.[11] Where did the inquiry end up?[12]

AF: It set out the problems but it didn't really come up with solutions. By the way, I should also have mentioned that the media does a lot of detailed 'grubbing away' to find out things that you don't get on the Internet.

As I mentioned earlier, local reporters going to courts to listen for a few days to what's going on in a case, or attending local council meetings to report about matters of community concern. As far as your question about government action is concerned, we had the Senate inquiry and that subsequently led to the ACCC being asked to conduct an inquiry into the digital platforms,[13] with a particular emphasis on journalism.

The ACCC report has a large part devoted to the impact on the media,[14] and it concluded there is a serious problem; namely, that public interest journalism is a 'public good', to use economics jargon; it brings benefit to the public but the market itself is not funded adequately. There is therefore an emerging gap in the availability of good public interest journalism and the ACCC said something should be done about it.

ML: Is public interest journalism primarily about investigative, worthy reporting or is there a broader range of other stories that serve the broader public interest?

AF: Public interest journalism does go pretty wide, but it is worth mentioning that those core bits of public journalism have yielded large benefits to the public. For example, I think the Royal Commission on Banking would not have happened, but for investigative journalism from people like Adele Ferguson,[15] the Aged Care Royal Commission wouldn't have occurred,[16] the Institutional Abuse, the Family Violence, etc. All of that has been largely triggered by good investigative journalism,[17,18] but that doesn't mean that it pays for itself.

ML: The ACCC reports into digital platforms are a landmark,[19] I understand, by world standards in terms of the breadth of analysis and including looking as we're discussing, at questions of public interest journalism as well as the public interest role and responsibility of these emerging platforms. What specific recommendations have been made? Did they suggest financial assistance? Did they suggest taxation measures on these platforms? And where's the government decision-making in response to these things?

AF: There's some action on regional and rural, and metropolitan newspapers. The ACCC saw a problem everywhere, but the ACCC focused quite heavily on the short term, 'learning platform' that we have with rural and regional press, and with those suburban newspapers. They are closing down at an enormous rate.

There's also the AAP closure. AAP is not a newspaper but it's got huge numbers of reporters collecting information and then selling it thereby making it available to all the news media. If you're not familiar with the media, you get the impression that when stories break they're covered by the major papers. They are, to a point, but far more than that the AAP is always there. It covers a huge number of things and is a feeder service to newspapers big and small all around the country, so its loss is a big loss to everyone, but especially to smaller newspapers that rely on it.

ML: I understand that AAP is a private, commercially funded operation, not a government agency.

AF: That's right. It was essentially funded by News Corporation and now 9 Fairfax. They found that it was operating at a fairly big loss and they've cut it back. There is a slight possibility that it will survive, but at the moment it should have closed on 30 June. There has been some action by the government in recognition of rural problems with Paul Fletcher, the Minister for Communications and Arts announcing several pretty big measures. One of them was a $50 million fund for public interest newsgathering to support public interest journalism in rural and regional areas,[20,21] and possibly, but I'm not so sure about this, into suburban newspapers. He also extended a financial lifeline to AAP as it endeavours to build a new sustainable business model.[22] That is a recognition of the problem. It probably needs more funding than that, but at least it is a recognition that there's a terrible problem at the moment.

Of course, the government is hearing all the time from members of parliament in rural and regional areas about the near collapse of regional and rural journalism made worse by the coronavirus. The virus has led to a collapse of advertising revenue for all forms of media, from the collapse in travel and tourism advertising, real estate advertising, restaurants, entertainment, hospitality and so on, and the general economic decline.

The long-term problems caused by this digital disruption event were sharply accelerated by the recent COVID-19 crisis, and the government funding is as much in response to the virus as it is to the digital disruption.[23] They've also given other forms of relief, for example, some license fees for commercial TV and radio broadcasters have been removed for a year. There's also so-called 'red tape' relief and some recognition of the problems of having Australian content in the media. Some short-term relief there, but not a change in policy.

Short-term measures have been taken even if it is acknowledged that more needs to be done. I think to stop the collapse totally; the government should commit to spending more money overtime than it already is doing on public advertising. As a short-term measure, perhaps, subscriptions to newspapers could be made tax deductible; and some other short-term things to just keep the show alive.

ML: What about the bigger, longer-term picture given in the ACCC report about these digital platforms and their role and responsibility; and what sort of measures, if any, were being recommended more broadly and in the longer term to the government?

AF: That's also an important question. The government has said there's going to be a code of conduct, regulating the relationship between people like Google and Facebook, and the major media such as News Corp, Seven, 10 or 9-Fairfax.

The complaint by the big traditional newspapers is that their content is partly lifted by Google and Facebook onto their platforms without payment or without adequate payment, so they complain that their material is being misused under the fair copying laws that entitled them to make some use of that information often just at headline level.

The platforms' response is that it's actually helpful for newspapers that their material appears on their platforms but on the whole, the ACCC tended to be more on the side of the newspapers, and it recommended, and the government has accepted, that there should be a code of conduct negotiated between them all.

The code of conduct I think would, above all, aim for what might be regarded as delivering a fairer payment by the platforms for the use of material from newspapers. That seems to be what's going on, and we'll have to see what emerges from the negotiations over the Code of Conduct, but essentially the government has the final power to impose a code of conduct if the parties can't sort it out themselves.[24,25,26]

AF: That's the big development but there are no recommendations or suggestions anywhere in the system for a longer-term sustainable business model for public interest journalism, for example, perhaps to tax digital platforms or provide tax concessions and deductions to those providing public interest journalism,[27] or any fiscal measures like that.

With our own Public Interest Journalism Initiative (PIJI), we have made a number of proposals that include some kind of funding, I'll call it research and development type funding, to support media that take on additional journalists. We also support making it tax deductible if you subscribe to newspapers. We support several other measures but in respect of their funding we've not got involved in the question of whether there should be a tax on the digital platforms; that is firmly on the government and on global agendas as it should be.

ML: These issues link perhaps to what have been broader and always difficult questions of public policy in Australia in regard to competition or otherwise in our mainstream media, including concerns about the concentration of media ownership[28] and the media laws.[29,30] Haven't the mainstream media been lobbying recently for less regulatory restraints upon them on the grounds that existing media laws limit them from effectively competing with and responding to the digital platforms? Where does that line of lobbying stand and if responded to, how might that improve the position of public interest journalism?

AF: That's a serious question and you may well be right in the flavour of what you're hinting at. Many years ago, governments introduced two policies. First, the ACCC is there to prevent mergers and takeovers that are anticompetitive within particular industries. If, say, in newspapers, Fairfax and News wanted to merge that would probably be disallowed for sure. Same with television providers. But the ACCC legislation doesn't cover cross-media mergers, say between TV and newspapers. They can occur under the Competition Act. The government was concerned about the possibility of TV–newspaper mergers leading to a very concentrated market situation, so they brought in rules, basically stopping cross-media mergers.[31]

In recent times, the desirability of that legislation in the new digital technology situation came under question so under the Turnbull government, those cross-media restrictions were relaxed quite a lot, but not fully. The question now is whether they should go a step further and totally remove cross-media ownership restrictions. There is a geographic basis to the current restrictions. In some densely populated areas, mergers are not wanted; but in less populated, rural and regional areas, particularly those already facing decline in media accessibility, there is a case for permitting mergers and for further relaxation of the rules. Some of the important players in the industry are pressing for that and we'll have to wait and see what the policy outcome is.

ML: We've been discussing the threats to public interest journalism that we face as a result of a digital disruption, and you have mentioned a range of possible responses as we try to feel our way towards a society and a set up where we get a sustainable business model for public interest journalism. In closing, I wonder if we might consider whether the challenge to public interest journalism is of interest to the public as readers and consumers of media. If we produce this worthy investigative, accountability reporting under the name of quality journalism, will people want to read it and pay for it? Will they read it or will it end up being treated as some form of almost propaganda?

AF: Well, there are tricky policy dilemmas involved. To expand your point further, we are worried if the kind of funding that emerges is politically biased. We regard it as a key requirement that, however, it's done, the support be such that there is true independence with recipients and there's not bias in the allocation of money. Will the public read it? My belief is that the public will read it but in the present era, they're not willing to fully pay commercially to fund it. As I have said, the old revenue model of cross-subsidy from advertising is dying. People still read the stuff, but it doesn't pay newspapers to produce it as much. If I was telling you that story in relation to any normal good or service, that's the end of the story. The public is not willing to pay, but we regard public interest journalism as having a higher value, not fully captured by market forces.

It's long been recognised in economics that information is a rather tricky good because it can be reproduced at no cost, providing you can get around copyright laws and that sort of thing, and that therefore the market may not be able to capture the value that's embodied in the product, because it can be so easily copied.

ML: That's what's called a 'positive externality' that isn't captured by markets in market prices, and you do need perhaps various forms in the public interest to promote public interest journalism that would otherwise be underfunded and under provided.

Conclusion

In a democracy, open and informed public discussion and policy depend upon a free press able to pursue public interest journalism, including in regard to climate change and sustainability issues. The experience in Australia with respect to discussion of climate change has highlighted its importance and the challenges to its maintenance in the face of lack of media competition and ownership concentration, which was latterly exacerbated by the disruptive impact of digital technologies upon the mainstream media. The latter has essentially broken the traditional media's business model that relied upon cross-subsidy of the public interest and news content from the advertising revenues displaced by digital media platforms that are more cost-effectively able to target commercial audience segments, often in pursuit of clickbait. Social media has further undermined mainstream media while also giving freer rein to disinformation, misinformation and fake news.

As a result, thousands of journalists have been stood down from traditional media, particularly newspapers, and many print editions particularly in rural and remote areas have had to close down, resulting in an absence of local, community and public interest news coverage. Standards of journalism have also been compromised by pressures on editorial and fact checking resources. At the same time, media concentration, including loosening of cross-media ownership, has resulted in reduced competition, lessening of public interest journalism in favour of infotainment, and the readier media accessibility of powerful, well-financed and connected vested interests vis-à-vis the community.[32]

This contributed over time to the paralysis in public climate change policy in Australia that not even the presence of a national public radio and TV broadcaster was able to overcome.[33,34] Ironically, the COVID-19 pandemic has both highlighted the importance while further weakening public interest journalism.[35] While issues of media competition policy are still not fully resolved, the Australian government has been taking steps to promote public interest journalism; based in part on the work of the competition policy regulator ACCC, including agreement between digital platforms and traditional news media on payments from the former in recognition of their use of news content on their platforms.

Notes

1 Carson, A. (2017) Explainer: What is public interest journalism? *The Conversation*, 14th June https://theconversation.com/explainer-what-is-public-interest-journalism-78996

2 Fels, A. (2019) *Tough Customer: Chasing a Better Deal for Battlers*, Melbourne: Melbourne University Press

3 PIJI is a not for profit, non-partisan, specialist think tank focused on the sustainability of public interest journalism in Australia https://piji.com.au

4 Carson, A. (2017) What is public interest journalism? *The Conversation*, 15th June https://theconversation.com/explainer-what-is-public-interest-journalism-78996

5 Thompson, J.D. (2019) Defining the power of public interest journalism, *Pursuit*, University of Melbourne, 11th June https://pursuit.unimelb.edu.au/articles/defining-the-power-of-public-interest-journalism

6 Stanford, J. (2021) *The Future of Work in Journalism*, Centre for Future Work, Australia Institute, October. https://australiainstitute.org.au/wp-content/uploads/2021/11/Future-of-Journalism-WEB.pdf Stanford analyses the structural impact

of digital technology on newspapers and journalism, and makes the case for support of public interest journalism as a 'public good'

7 McGuirk, R. (2020) Australian Associated Press to shut down after 85 years, *AP News*, 3rd March https://sg.finance.yahoo.com/news/australian-associated-press-closes-85-032918014.html The article quotes Anthony Albanese, then Opposition leader, now Prime Minister as saying 'Today is a tragedy for our democracy'

8 Wake, A. (2000) The closure of AAP is yet another blow to public interest journalism in Australia, *The Conversation*, 3rd March https://theconversation.com/the-closure-of-aap-is-yet-another-blow-to-public-interest-journalism-in-australia-132856

9 This is a global phenomenon that had its impact over the first two decades of the 2000s. Grundy, A. (2022) *Service Annual Survey Shows Continuing Decline in Print Publishing Revenue: Internet Crushes Traditional Media*, United States Census Bureau, 7th June www.census.gov/library/stories/2022/06/internet-crushes-traditional-media.html

10 Media, Entertainment and Arts Alliance (MEAA) (2018) *Submission to the ACCC Digital Platforms Inquiry*, April. Their submission cites 3000 journalist positions have been lost since the growth and escalation of digital platforms www.accc.gov.au/system/files/Media%2C%20Entertainment%20and%20Arts%20Alliance%20%28April%202018%29.pdf

11 Senate Select Committee Inquiry (2018) *Future of Public Interest Journalism*, Commonwealth of Australia www.aph.gov.au/Parliamentary_Business/Committees/Senate/Future_of_Public_Interest_Journalism/PublicInterestJournalism

12 Radio Info (2018) *Future of Public Interest Journalism Inquiry Report Released: Detailed Analysis*, 13th February https://radioinfo.com.au/news/future-public-interest-journalism-inquiry-report-released-detailed-analysis/ This report outlines and discusses the recommendations and submissions made, while concluding that it recommended nothing unexpected and none directed at the large digital platforms

13 Downes, J. (2023) The ACCC's ongoing digital platforms services inquiry: Social media services, *Competition Policy International (CPI)*, 20th June www.pymnts.com/cpi_posts/the-acccs-ongoing-digital-platforms-services-inquiry-social-media-services/

14 ACCC (2019) *Digital Platforms Inquiry*, Final Report, 26th July www.accc.gov.au/about-us/publications/digital-platforms-inquiry-final-report

15 Ferguson, A. (2019) *Banking Bad*, Sydney: ABC Books

16 Connolly, A. (2021) ABC Investigations journalist Anne Connolly on her crowd-sourced probe into aged care and the shocking stories it uncovered, *ABC News*, 16th March www.abc.net.au/news/backstory/2021-03-16/anne-connolly-on-abc-investigations-aged-care-abuse/13251872

17 The importance and impact of public interest investigative reporting were subsequently taken up in the Senate Inquiry into Press Freedom that reported in 2021, making 17 recommendations including reversing the onus on journalists to prove public interest stories. See www.aph.gov.au/Parliamentary_Business/Committees/Senate/Environment_and_Communications/PressFreedom

18 Meade, A. (2021) Australia needs to strengthen press freedom laws and promote transparency, inquiry finds, *The Guardian*, 19th May www.theguardian.com/media/2021/may/19/australia-needs-to-strengthen-press-freedom-laws-and-promote-transparency-inquiry-finds

19 See Downes, J., Cameron, B. and Hick, J. (2023) The ACCC's ongoing digital platforms services inquiry (DPSI): Regulatory reform, *Competition Policy International*, 6th February www.competitionpolicyinternational.com/wp-content/uploads/2023/02/Oceania-Column-February-2023-Full.pdf The ongoing DPSI 2020–2025 follows the ACCC's original Digital Platforms Inquiry Final Report (published in July 2019 after requested by the Treasurer in December 2017) and is mandated to provide the Treasurer with an interim report every six months until it concludes by the 31st March 2025.

20 Hurst, D. (2020) Australian regional media to gain funding after 'catastrophic' ad revenue fall, *The Guardian*, 29th June www.theguardian.com/media/2020/jun/29/australian-regional-media-to-gain-funding-after-catastrophic-ad-revenue-fall This article subsequently revealed that the Public Interest News Gathering (PING) grants had been allocated politically using a federal seats analysis

21 Davies, A. and Meade, A. (2021) Regional Australian media outlets granted millions in federal support still slashed journalist numbers, *The Guardian*, 2nd December www.theguardian.com/media/2021/dec/02/regional-australian-media-outlets-granted-millions-in-federal-support-still-slashed-journalist-numbers

22 Visentin, L. and Samios, Z. (2020) Public Interest journalism is important: Government gives AAP $5m, *Sydney Morning Herald*, 18th September www.smh.com.au/business/companies/government-hands-aap-5-million-lifeline-20200918-p55wyy.html

23 MEAA (2021) A thousand journalists jobs gone as COVID bites, *Press Freedom Medium*, 1st May https://pressfreedom.org.au/a-thousand-journalist-jobs-gone-as-covid-bites-8383bc26ee4b The MEAA stated that more journalism jobs were lost in 2020 than in any other 12-month period

24 Legislation for the Treasury Laws Amendment (News Media and Digital Platforms Mandatory Bargaining Code) Bill 2021 was introduced despite the objections of Google and Facebook, and despite Facebook blocking news pages to its Australian readers (subsequently restored after a few days). This was reviewed by the Treasury in 2022 which concluded that the Code has been a success to date. See Treasury (2019) *News Media and Digital Platforms Mandatory Bargaining Code – The Code's First Year of Operation*, Review, 1st December https://treasury.gov.au/publication/p2022-343549

25 See also Fisher, C., McCallum, K. and Park, S. (2021) Is the news media bargaining code fit for purpose? *The Conversation*, 29th November https://theconversation.com/is-the-news-media-bargaining-code-fit-for-purpose-172224

26 See ACCC, *News Media Bargaining Code* www.accc.gov.au/by-industry/digital-platforms-and-services/news-media-bargaining-code/news-media-bargaining-code

27 Fels, A. (2020) Funding public interest journalism requires creative solutions: Tax rebate for news media could work, *The Conversation*, 21st September https://theconversation.com/funding-public-interest-journalism-requires-creative-solutions-a-tax-rebate-for-news-media-could-work-146563

28 Evershed, N. (2020) Australia's newspaper ownership is among the most concentrated in the world, *The Guardian*, 13th November www.theguardian.com/news/datablog/2020/nov/13/australia-newspaper-ownership-is-among-the-most-concentrated-in-the-world

29 Lidberg, J. (2019) The distortion of the Australian public sphere: Media ownership concentration in Australia, *AQ-Australian Quarterly*, 90 (1): 12–20

30 Dwyer, T., Wilding, D. and Koskie, T. (2021) Australia: Media concentration and deteriorating conditions for investigative journalism, in Trappel, J. and Tomaz, T. (eds) *The Media for Democracy Monitory 2021: How Leading News Media Survive Digital Transformation*, Volume 1, Chapter 2, pp. 59–94, Nordicom: University of Gothenburg www.diva-portal.org/smash/get/diva2:1557359/FULLTEXT01.pdf

31 Dodd, A. (2017) The sad history of Australian media reform, *Eureka Street*, 19th September www.eurekastreet.com.au/article/the-sad-history-of-australian-media-reform

32 Dwyer, T. (2023) *Stoush Over Media Bias Highlights the Need for Greater Diversity, Opinion, University of Sydney*, 1st March www.sydney.edu.au/news-opinion/news/2023/03/01/stoush-over-alleged-media-bias-highlights-the-need-for-greater-m.html

33 Armitage, M. and O'Shannessy, S. (2021) Data proves decades of lies in Murdoch media climate change coverage, *Echo*, 17th March www.echo.net.au/2021/03/data-proves-decades-of-lies-in-murdoch-media-climate-change-coverage/

34 Centre for Media Transition (2020) *News in Australia – Impartiality and Commercial Influence: Review of Literature and Research*, Sydney, NSW: University of Technology Sydney. This Australian Communications and Media Authority (ACMA)-commissioned report stated that 40% of Australians feel news content is biased and that media's reporting of climate change reveals significant partiality. www.acma.gov.au/sites/default/files/2020-01/News%20in%20Australia_Impartiality%20and%20commercial%20influence_Review%20of%20literature%20and%20research.pdf
35 Sweet, M., Williams, M., Armstrong, R., Mohamed, J., Finlay, S. and Coopes, A. (2020) Converging crises: Public interest journalism, the pandemic and public health, *Public Health Research & Practice*, 30 (4): e3042029

26 Public Confidence in Science

Building Trust on Understanding Scientific Method and Uncertainties

Interview With Aaron Mertz and Abhilash Mishra

Introduction

Public acceptance and confidence in science loom as a significant issue in Australia, not least because of the responses and acceptance of COVID-19 pandemic issues and the restrictions imposed on our society.[1] Before that, we had the issues of climate change which raised many questions about public confidence, trust and understanding of science, and in communicating science.[2] These issues also loom large in the United States of America from where we might glean some understanding and lessons about public understanding of science.[3]

Keywords: agribusiness; agriculture extension service; AI; Amazon deforestation; American Science Corps (ASC); anti-vaxxers; civic science; climate change; climate deniers; cognitive dissonance; communications training; community participation; COVID-19; COVID-19 masking; deficit theory; diploma divide; journalists; land-grant colleges; partisan politics; political leadership; public confidence; public trust; science communication; science education; science ethics; science journalism; scientific information; scientific method; scientists; SDG 4; SDG 16; SDG 17; trust; trust mechanisms; uncertainty; universities; vaccine hesitancy

Interviewee Profiles

Dr. Aaron Mertz (**AaM**) is the Founder and Director of the Aspen Institute, Science and Society Program, Yale University, New Haven, Connecticut where he gained his doctorate in Physics. Dr. Abhilash Mishra (**AbM**), founding Director, Initiative on Science, Technology and Global Development, Harris School of Public Policy, University of Chicago is a scientist, entrepreneur and educator

The Interview

ML: Aaron, late last year, you held a one-off event on the future of science,[4] and more recently you hosted a substantial global connection and

DOI: 10.4324/9781003280316-30

hook-up on communicating science.[5] Why was it a good time to be looking at the future of science?

AaM: Over the past several years, especially in the United States, many aspects of science have become very politicised and seen in ideological terms.[6] Science, in my view, has always been political, especially in the United States because it's largely funded by our government.[7] When it starts to be seen as a tool for just one part of our country, I think that's what we were responding to. I'm having these broader conversations about what role science should serve for our population, both in the United States and more globally.[8]

ML: What have been the trends in polling about society's understanding, acceptance and confidence in science?

AaM: It's been fairly consistent over the past few decades based on various polls that we've examined, and it hovers around 47%, so I would not say that's particularly high. That means we have about half of our population that is distrustful of the scientific process and its products.[9]

ML: What does the polling tell us about the demographics of public confidence and acceptance in science?

AbM: There's a clear 'diploma divide', which is that folks with a college degree and higher levels of education show greater trust in science; and folks without a college degree show lesser trust in science, which is not surprising.[10] But I think there's something deeper going on here. It's not just that they have trust in science, they just have a lack of trust in institutions and I think science is just a case in point. I would say, generally, that the demographics are clearly along the 'diploma divide' here in the United States.[11]

ML: Is political partisanship an indicator of levels of acceptance of science?

AbM: There again I see significant differences between Democrats and Republicans in the broad trust indicators. For example, a regular poll shows Democrats consistently trusting the science behind climate change at 30 points above Republicans, so there's clearly a huge overall partisan divide there.[12]

As a rejoinder to that statement, I would say that it's unclear how significant this partisan divide is because the leadership in particular parties are pro-science and anti-science, as against people overall being pro or con science. We saw this in the mask-wearing debate. Because leaders did not buy into the science behind masking and were peddling pseudo-scientific medicinal theories,[13] a lot of people who followed a particular party or that particular leader adopted unscientific beliefs. It is unfair and probably not appropriate to dub Republicans as anti-science and Democrats as pro-science, but there's definitely a clear divide between the two.

ML: So leadership is a factor in the partisan and political dimension, in that political leaders have a big influence. Do we draw the conclusion that people's attitudes towards science depend upon party political positioning?

AbM: Yes, absolutely.

ML: That puts a lot of responsibility on political leaders, doesn't it, to understand and communicate science?[14]

AaM: Yes, and not just communicating science from the perspective of an ideology but also communicating the method and process of doing science, its nuances. Dr. Anthony Fauci, Director of the NIH, is an example of someone who has truly tried to communicate the nuances of science in the pandemic, which I think is a great example of a scientific leader,[15] as opposed to going out there and saying 'I'm pro-science' or 'anti-science'. That doesn't really help the cause.

The role of leaders is to communicate the assumptions and the style of doing science that most people don't think about in their day-to-day lives. Early in the pandemic, the guidelines according to the science at hand were that masking was not necessary because at the time we did not know about asymptomatic transmission of COVID-19. Then, as we got more data and learned that there could be many carriers of COVID-19 who are transmitting the disease without a mask, then the new guideline was to wear a mask whether or not you're symptomatic and whether or not you're sick.

A lot of people interpreted that as bad 'flip-flopping' science when the messaging needed to be that this was actually science doing its job in responding to the data at hand, and revising the conclusions based on the new information that came in. I think it was on the leadership to say it's not that science is wrong or inconsistent, but that science is always reactive and evolving based on evidence. It's a continuous process, and I think that's where leadership needs to step up and communicate.[16]

ML: This highlights the question about the understanding among the public, and in the community, about the nature of scientific method and the related questions of uncertainty, knowledge and truth within the scientific method. I believe the polls generally show that those who have more knowledge of science, and the scientific method, tend to be more accepting and confident in science; whereas those who don't understand or know science, and its method, are less accepting.[17] Is that correct?

AaM: Absolutely, and what we've seen from research in psychology and sociology, is that understanding the process of science is actually the best way for people to be able to change their minds about long-held beliefs, even when they're in conflict with their personal, religious or family ideology.[18] It's not about bombarding them with new facts, data and statistics, but actually conveying to them the process of science.[19]

ML: Where do the responsibilities lie to get higher levels of understanding of the scientific method among political leaders and the general public?

AbM: It's important that scientists themselves recognise how we communicate science.[20] Often we scientists, especially when talking to the public at large, talk about science as 'the truth', whereas it is actually just a way of looking at the world and an ever evolving sort of toolkit through which we parse the world. That is the nuance that often gets missed when scientists talk in public. That pivot in communication is very urgently needed if we are to get people not just to be scientifically knowledgeable in terms of knowing a bunch of facts but also to think scientifically and to be able to deal with scientific uncertainty in a meaningful way.[21]

ML: Do scientists themselves have a significant responsibility for communicating the nature of science and the scientific method more generally?[22]

AbM: Absolutely, yes. It is important that scientists communicate the fascinating discoveries that we make and the facts of science. But it is even more important to communicate the method of science and the uncertainties around generating and developing scientific information. I think this eventually goes towards building trust in science, by acknowledging that scientific knowledge comes with a lot of uncertainty and that there's a systematic way of dealing with it. Uncertainty is a very important part of building that trust, which otherwise is not going to be built if we just go to the public and say here is a bunch of facts, here's the truth, accept that.

AaM: I agree and want to add that I think it's the duty of scientists to play that public role. As I mentioned earlier, science in the United States is largely federally funded by taxpayers' money. So I think there should be a public component to their work but they also need training on how to do that. It's something that is largely absent from the scientific training that we receive as graduate or postdocs:[23] how to boil our message down into an understandable format that's relevant to people's lives; how to convey the uncertainty and the scientific method that Abhilash just mentioned. So before scientists go out and do that work, they need to learn how to do so properly.

ML: Perhaps scientists are not skilled in communication because their main emphasis is on doing research and on communicating with their peers for peer review, evaluation and knowledge building, rather than speaking to a broader audience. This involves not only skills but a question about their access to resources to do that and their ability to get their messages out, even assuming that they're able to communicate in a good form. In these days of controversial media and social media issues these are highly contested domains in which to be trying to operate, aren't they?

AaM: It is and you raise a very important point that at least in the United States there are not a lot of incentives for scientists to do this kind of work. As you mentioned, there are so many other constraints on doing their research, writing articles that have to be peer reviewed, contributing to their writing to the community, and the incentives from universities are not there for them to go out and do this public engagement.[24] Towards that end we recently made a public proposal.

AbM: Aaron and I recently wrote an op-ed for *Science* magazine which called for the creation of an American Science Corps (ASC),[25] which would be a fully funded federal programme that would place early career scientists in communities that are traditionally not scientifically engaged. So think about rural communities and underserved communities which might not have access to scientific expertise. The proposal was to take early career scientific talent and place them in these communities so that they can pursue two big goals. One is to build public trust in science; and the second is to train communities that might not have access to a college education in skills that are relevant for the twenty-first-century innovation economy.

ML: We've been hearing in recent times out of India about the issues confronting the transformation of agriculture and the huge protests from the farming communities' right around the country against those reforms.[26] To what extent, if any, would you see the sort of points you're making as relevant to that sort of debate?

AbM: Part of the challenge in the Indian context was the lack of participation of communities in policymaking. A lot of conversation globally is about 'evidence-based' policymaking, which is the idea that policies, whether economic, social or scientific, should be driven by evidence which makes intuitive sense among scientists.[27]

What we sometimes forget about is who gets to have a say and who gets to participate in the evidence building itself. I think what we saw in India was a fracture in trust in terms of who is making the policies and who it was affecting.

The goal of the American Science Corps is to better foresee those kinds of fractures if we do not involve communities in the process of policymaking. But we need structures to enable that and one of the ways to do that would be through this American Science Corps. It's interesting that you bring up agriculture, because the ASC proposal is based on the US Agricultural Extension Service,[28] which was a policy innovation in the early part of the twentieth century. It brought together academics at land-grant universities and farmers creating this network between the two, which led to a highly cooperative way of doing research and innovation.[29] We need a similarly new institutional structure like the ASC which goes back to these cooperative roots in the way of doing science and technology together for the larger public good.

ML: Abhilash, this raises the question of power in science policy decision-making because in that context, as distinct from research, what we see is the involvement of many vested interests.

I'm thinking particularly of the climate change debate and before that, of course, we had the tobacco debate – where public perception of science and scientific evidence was thrown into huge doubt by big money campaigns from vested interests.[30] Where does this fit into your picture of how we can build better public acceptance and understanding of science?

AbM: What you're describing is a much deeper challenge of who gets to shape the conversation about science. Obviously, there are challenges around who funds scientific research and information campaigns and whether they might be biased by commercial interests. That is why I think an agency or a mechanism by which you have a truly democratic process of communicating science, which is not driven by commercial or partisan interest but is there just for the public good, is essential. That was the big animating vision behind why we need something like an American Science Corps.

AaM: We hope that initiatives like the ASC and work being done by others in the field of 'civic science'[31] will help diversify the pipeline of individuals going into science policy and research, and also into those big invested stakeholders who can have a big influence across different sectors. In that way, we're hoping that in the future we'll see more voices at the table that have been absent from previous discussions about the role that science should play in our society.

ML: Abhilash, you mentioned in the context of agriculture, the importance of the extension-type service ideas that were around in the public interest in earlier decades of the last century. Australia pioneered and had strong agricultural extension networks that drove huge increases in productivity off the back of public research. However, we don't have that system of public extension anymore.[32]

What we do have is a privatised model where the big agricultural conglomerates and their agents, whether it's in machinery, seeds, chemicals or fertilisers, are the people now disseminating and purveying extension and advice about science in agriculture.

AbM: Yes, a similar trend has been observed here in the US and actually, my understanding of the Agricultural Extension Service came from my work in global development. Many Americans don't know about the Agricultural Extension Service primarily because agriculture has become an enterprise with a smaller number of people involved. The Extension Service which was a prominent part of the land-grant universities has been replaced by other research priorities at those universities.[33]

What has been lost in the process, however, is the central ethos of taking the university to the people, which was the core vision of the extension programme. The goal of the federal government in establishing these universities, through land grants, was that these universities in return would provide public goods through their extension programmes. We need similar approaches now for the science that is being developed at these universities to provide public goods to the community in cooperation with the community. That again requires appropriate institutional structures, and it's probably time to revive some of those older structures that existed and were hugely successful in the past century.

ML: How do we confront issues that have again arisen strongly in the COVID-19 context but which we also saw surfacing strongly in the climate context, of large bodies of public opinion, that could be characterised as 'deniers'. These people seem to have a complete set against science, with perhaps different views of the world, whether they're moral, ethical or political. We're seeing it here in Australia and around the world not so much as 'anti-vaxxer' denialism itself, but in the form of 'vaccine hesitancy'.[34] In respect of these deeply in-bred, almost pseudoscientific, anti-scientific bodies of thought in the community, what are the appropriate responses to these positions and from whom?[35]

AaM: It's very important to try and this is a really good point. There are two ways to approach it. When it's something so egregious and imminently of harm to others, we need to try to shut it down immediately. But it's different when people are coming from their own belief system and are genuinely concerned about their families' health and well-being.

When we talk about 'anti-vaxxers', there are a lot of parents who want the best for their children. The best approach is to listen to where they are, meet them where they are, and then talk about the issues through stories and through emotion.[36] These are the ways that people can really connect with something that is generally very abstract when it's rooted in data and statistics, and biology and physics, and so on.

AbM: In the past two decades, we have had a lot of optimism and enthusiasm about access to information, and access to scientific information is very easy today. But we need to distinguish between the fact that access to information does not ensure trust in information. Trust fundamentally relies on interpersonal connections. It involves face-to-face communication. The dynamics of building trust is fundamentally different to simply accessing a website where you might get a bunch of information.[37]

So it's also important for us to recognise that often – when we talk about scientific distrust – we are puzzled by the fact that while there's so much information out there saying that vaccines work, why don't people believe it? We are baffled because we do not pay attention to the trust mechanisms that are essential to believe in this information which is a whole different game than merely accessing information.[38]

ML: Artificial intelligence (AI) and data raise important issues and questions of ethics and morality, ranging from surveillance through personal data and control. What's the role for public policy, in regulating and getting the messages out about these AI ethical domains?

AbM: We are just starting to see what happens when the public does not trust data as we have seen, for example, in the case of information around COVID-19. This kind of distrust is going to accelerate when we start using data to recruit people and to test who needs to be admitted to a hospital.

There's already a lot of evidence that the way in which artificial intelligence systems are built today are extremely biased, and that bias is automatically going to lead to distrust in these tools in the first place.[39] If we truly want to achieve the potential of AI in the next two decades, it is absolutely imperative that we build trust in these tools. A tool is not useful if people don't use it and people are going to use it only if they trust it, and the way in which people will want to trust it is by making sure that these tools are unbiased and not unfairly treating people.

For that, we need public policy and a mechanism by which AI tools that are deployed in the market are using data and ethical ways and making sure that they are heterogeneous enough in their training datasets so that they can be fair and unbiased. A step in the direction you raised is coming up with a policy to regulate AI algorithms. I believe a controversial memo about such was leaked yesterday.[40] Public policy has a huge role to play in making sure that people trust AI, because unless and until people trust AI these tools are going to be useless.[41]

ML: Data and information isn't necessarily knowledge. What is the role of journalists and the media in communicating science?[42]

AaM: Journalism has a very important role in providing rapid, on the fly, information to the public while acknowledging that this information might be in flux. We see this with COVID-19 where there are potential treatments or possible interventions, and then just yesterday in the United States, the Johnson and Johnson vaccine was put on hold.[43] Conveying to people thoughtfully and carefully the thought and regulatory processes that go into those decisions is extremely important.

The main point I want to make is that science is not a complete endeavour that's all wrapped up and tied with a bow. It's an ongoing endeavour, a pursuit of new knowledge and then applying that knowledge towards the public good. It evolves and it changes and it's really important for journalism to convey those changes thoughtfully and to talk about uncertainty in a way that the reader can understand.[44]

ML: Gentlemen, you've used the phrase 'standing up to power' during your global congress on communicating science. When it comes to building public acceptance, confidence and understanding of science – what does that mean? Who's got to stand up to power and how?

AaM: All of us need to 'stand up to power' and have the confidence and courage to call out entities and activities that are not consistent with our values and with science. The conference that you were referencing took place about a month ago. We drew together a wonderful network of about 100 science communicators and advocates from over 50 countries.[45]

Our keynote speech was given by Mariette DiChristina, who's the former editor in chief of the magazine *Scientific American*.[46] She was in conversation with Ricardo Galvão, who is a Brazilian physicist, who stood up to power for science by calling out the Brazilian government, and specifically President Bolsonaro, for not listening to the data that were showing the devastating effects that were harming the Amazon rainforest.[47] As a result, Ricardo lost his job over standing up to power and standing up for science. That was the discussion about how we all have to 'stand up to power' whether we're coming at it from the vantage point of a federal government position, as a scientist or as a layperson.

Conclusion

The experiences with climate change and COVID-19 highlight that a key to building public trust and confidence in science is communicating the nature of the scientific method, its uncertainties and risks. Science's ongoing assessment and reassessment of 'the truth' in the light of newly available data must not be misunderstood as the equivalent of political flip-flopping, as characterised by changing decisions on masking and vaccines.

The access to, and provision of, scientific data and facts is important but in themselves although now widely available through internet and online sources on the assumption that this can fill some knowledge 'deficit' on the part of the public is not sufficient.[48]

In addition, it is necessary for scientists and those that they advise to participate in an ongoing conversation or dialogue that not only addresses the diversity of situations, values and emotions in the community but seeks their active engagement and participation using multiple communication channels. Talking at people does not bridge their 'cognitive dissonance' gap even among sustainability scientists themselves and risks their disengagement or even alienation.[49] A new model of community-based cooperative research, development and extension may be required.

Scientists have a social responsibility to communicate their work for the 'public good',[50] but they need appropriate training, incentives and institutional support. At times of crisis and political divisiveness, they may need to 'stand up to power'. Science journalists have a vital information role particularly during crises and are challenged by new media in building engagement and trust with their readers. Science has always been closely involved with politics, and politicians have a responsibility to both heed scientific expert advice in policy-making and without being tempted to use scientific advice as a cover for their own responsibilities. Emerging concerns about bias inherent in AI algorithms demonstrate how easily public trust can be eroded and how dependent it is on the development of effective government regulations.

With traditional political demographics now fuelled by an emerging strong 'diploma divide' based on levels of education,[51] building public trust in science is proving even more challenging in an increasingly polarised and partisan political climate.

Notes

1 Hyland-Wood, B., Gardner, J., Leask, J., and Ecker, U.K. (2021) Toward effective government communication strategies in the era of COVID-19, *Humanities and Social Sciences Communications*, 8 (30) www.nature.com/articles/s41599-020-00701-w

2 Torok, S., Goldie, J. and Ashcroft, L. (2021) Communicating climate change has never been so important, and this IPCC report pulls no punches, *The Conversation*, 12thAugusthttps://theconversation.com/communicating-climate-change-has-never-been-so-important-and-this-ipcc-report-pulls-no-punches-165252

3 Funk, C. (2020) Key findings about Americans' confidence in science and their views on scientists' role in society, *Pew Research Center*, 12th February www.pewresearch.org/short-reads/2020/02/12/key-findings-about-americans-confidence-in-science-and-their-views-on-scientists-role-in-society/

4 Aspen Institute (2020) *Future of Science in America Summit*, 12th November www.aspeninstitute.org/events/future-of-science-in-america-summit/

5 Aspen Institute (2021) *Science Communicators and Advocates from 50+ Nations Gather for Global Congress on Scientific Thinking*, 15th March www.aspeninstitute.org/news/global-congress-on-scientific-thinking-2021/

6 Druckman, J.N. (2022) Threats to science: Politicization, misinformation, and inequalities, *The ANNALS of the American Academy of Political and Social Science*, 700 (1): 8–24

7 Mandt, R., Seetharam, K. and Cheng, C.H.M. (2020) Federal R&D funding: The bedrock of national innovation, *MIT Science Policy Review*, 1, August: 44–54

8 West, D.M. (2022) R&D for the public good: Ways to strengthen societal innovation in the United States, *Brookings Institution*, 10th October www.brookings.edu/articles/rd-for-the-public-good-ways-to-strengthen-societal-innovation-in-the-united-states/

9 Kennedy, B., Tyson, A. and Funk, C. (2022) Americans' trust in scientists, other groups declines in 2021, *Pew Research Center*, 15th February www.pewresearch.org/science/2022/02/15/americans-trust-in-scientists-other-groups-declines/
10 Burakoff, M. (2023) Confidence in science fell in 2022 while political divides persisted, poll shows, *AP News*, 15th June https://apnews.com/article/trust-science-medicine-social-survey-725ab3401f27900be6cc957eec52e45e
11 Williams, J. (2020) How the 'diploma divide' helps explain the US election result, *The Spectator*, 5th November www.spectator.co.uk/article/how-the-diploma-divide-helps-explain-the-us-election/
12 Tyson, A., Funk, C. and Kennedy, B. (2023) What the data says about Americans' views of climate change, *Pew Research Center*, 9th August www.pewresearch.org/short-reads/2023/08/09/what-the-data-says-about-americans-views-of-climate-change/
13 Niburski, K. and Niburski, O. (2020) Impact of Trump's promotion of unproven COVID-19 treatments and subsequent internet trends: Observational study, *Journal of Medical Internet Research*, 22 (11): e20044 www.ncbi.nlm.nih.gov/pmc/articles/PMC7685699/
14 Sutherland, W., Spiegelhalter, D. and Burgman, M. (2013) Policy: Twenty tips for interpreting scientific claims, *Nature*, 503, November: 335–337
15 Bibbins-Domingo, K. (2022) Dr. Anthony Fauci – communicating science in a polarized era, interview, *JN Learning*, 8th September https://edhub.ama-assn.org/jn-learning/video-player/18721249
16 Vallejo, J. (2021) The CDC didn't change': Anthony Fauci defends flip-flop accusations after shifting mask guidance, *The Independent*, 29th July https://news.yahoo.com/cdc-didn-t-change-anthony-000430540.html
17 Lackner, S., Francisco, F., Mendonça, C., Mata, A. and Gonçalves-Sá, J. (2023) Intermediate levels of scientific knowledge are associated with overconfidence and negative attitudes towards science, *Nature Human Behaviour*, 7 (9): 1490–1501
18 Belliizzi, K.M. (2022) Cognitive biases and brain biology help explain why facts don't change minds, *UConn Today*, 16th August https://today.uconn.edu/2022/08/cognitive-biases-and-brain-biology-help-explain-why-facts-dont-change-minds-2/#
19 Maher, R. and Murphet, B. (2020) Community engagement in Australia's COVID-19 communications response: Learning lessons from the humanitarian sector, *Media International Australia*, 177 (1): 113–118
20 Cormick, C. (2019) *The Science of Communicating Science: The Ultimate Guide*, Clayton, VIC: CSIRO Publishing
21 Castillo, M. (2010) The uncertainty of science and the science of uncertainty, *American Journal of Neuroradiology*, 31 (10): 1767–1768
22 Reddy, D. (2021) Scientific literacy, public engagement and responsibility in science, *Cultures of Science*, 4 (1): 6–16
23 Dudo, A., Besley, J.C. and Yuan, S. (2021) Science communication training in North America: Preparing whom to do what with what effect? *Science Communication*, 43 (1): 33–63
24 Rose, K.M., Markowitz, E.M. and Brossard, D. (2020) Scientists' incentives and attitudes toward public communication, *Proceedings of the National Academy of Sciences*, 117 (3): 1274–1276
25 Mertz, A.F. and Mishra, A. (2021) Science's new frontier, *Science*, 371 (6533): 967
26 Curtis, J. (2021) Farmers protests in India and agricultural reforms, *House of Commons Library*, no. 9226, 13th December https://researchbriefings.files.parliament.uk/documents/CBP-9226/CBP-9226.pdf
27 Gueguen, D. and Marissen, V. (2022) Science-based and evidence-based policy-making in the European Union: Coexisting or conflicting concepts? *Bruges Political Research Papers*, 88, September, College of Europe: Department of European Political and Governance Studies www.coleurope.eu/sites/default/files/research-paper/wp88%20Marisen_Guegen.pdf

28 Jones, G.E. and Garforth, C. (1997) The history, development, and future of agricultural extension, in Swanson, B.E., Bentz, R.P. and Sofranko, A.J. (eds) *Improving Agricultural Extension: A Reference Manual*, Chapter 1, Rome: Food and Agricultural Organisation www.fao.org/3/W5830E/w5830e03.htm
29 Wang, S.L. (2014) Cooperative extension system: Trends and economic impacts on US agriculture, *Choices*, 29 (1): 1–8
30 Oreskes, N. and Conway, E.M. (2011) *Merchants of Doubt: How a Handful of Scientists Obscured the Truth on Issues from Tobacco Smoke to Global Warming*, London: Bloomsbury Publishing
31 Elizabeth Good Christopherson et al (2018) The civic science imperative", *Stanford Social Innovation Review*, Spring www.ssir.org
32 Hunt, W., Birch, C., Vanclay, F. and Coutts, J. (2014) Recommendations arising from an analysis of changes to the Australian agricultural research, development and extension system, *Food Policy*, 44 (February): 129–141
33 Gavazzi, S.M. (2020) The land-grant mission in the 21st century: Promises made and promises to be kept, *Animal Frontiers*, 10 (3): 6–9
34 Troiano, G. and Nardi, A. (2021) Vaccine hesitancy in the era of COVID-19, *Public Health*, 194, May: 245–251
35 Dobson, G.P. (2022) Wired to doubt: Why people fear vaccines and climate change and mistrust science, *Frontiers in Medicine*, 8, January: 809395
36 Diethelm, P. and McKee, M. (2009) Denialism: What is it and how should scientists respond? *The European Journal of Public Health*, 19 (1): 2–4
37 Mont'Alverne, C., Badrinathan, S., Ross Arguedas, A., Toff, B., Fletcher, R. and Nielsen, R. (2022) *The Trust Gap: How and Why News on Digital Platforms Is Viewed More Sceptically Versus News in General*, Oxford University, Reuters Institute for the Study of Journalism, https://ora.ox.ac.uk/objects/uuid:42cc0bd8-f737-4a79-947f-e528e8116926
38 IHatamleh, I.H.M., Safori, A.O., Habes, M., Tahat, O., Ahmad, A.K., Abdallah, R.A.Q. and Aissani, R. (2023) Trust in social media: Enhancing social relationships, *Social Sciences*, 12 (7): 416
39 Deloitte Center for Integrated Research (2021) AI model bias can damage trust more than you may know: But it doesn't have to, *Deloitte Insights* https://www2.deloitte.com/content/dam/insights/articles/US164503_CIR-AI-model-bias-within-the-internal-organization/DI_CIR-AI-model-bias-within-the-internal-organization.pdf
40 Ramlochan, S. (2023) The leaked OpenAI memo: A revelation of the company's stance on AI regulation, *Prompt Engineering Institute*, 21st July https://promptengineering.org/the-leaked-openai-memo-a-revelation-of-the-companys-stance-on-ai-regulation/
41 Heikkilä, M. (2023) Suddenly, everyone wants to talk about how to regulate AI, *MIT Technology Review*, 23rd May www.technologyreview.com/2023/05/23/1073526/suddenly-everyone-wants-to-talk-about-how-to-regulate-ai/
42 Carr, T. (2019) Revisiting the role of the science journalist, *Undark*, 15th July https://undark.org/2019/07/15/science-journalism-communications/
43 Hsieh, Y.L., Rak, S., SteelFisher, G.K. and Bauhoff, S. (2022) Effect of the suspension of the J&J COVID-19 vaccine on vaccine hesitancy in the United States, *Vaccine*, 40 (3): 424–427
44 Moss, R., Schneider, S., Hassol, S.J. and Katzenberger, J. (2008) Characterizing and communicating scientific uncertainty: Aspen Global Change Institute, Report, *Aspen Institute Global Change Workshop*, 31st July–8th August https://citeseerx.ist.psu.edu/document?repid=rep1&type=pdf&doi=c9279b5f99d7a039871c2cf3bafc41565021cc5f
45 Aspen Institute (2021), op cit
46 DiChristina, M. Stories by, *Scientific American* www.scientificamerican.com/author/mariette-dichristina/

47 Showstack, R. (2019) Ousted head of science agency criticises Brazil's denial of deforestation data, *Eos*, 20th August https://eos.org/articles/ousted-head-of-science-agency-criticizes-brazils-denial-of-deforestation-data
48 Dutilh Novaes, C. and Ivani, S. (2022) The inflated promise of science education, *Boston Review*, 6th September www.bostonreview.net/articles/the-inflated-promise-of-science-education/
49 Schrems, I. and Upham, P. (2020) Cognitive dissonance in sustainability scientists regarding air travel for academic purposes: A qualitative study, *Sustainability*, 12 (5): 1837
50 Daedlow, K., Podhora, A., Winkelmann, M., Kopfmüller, J., Walz, R. and Helming, K. (2016) Socially responsible research processes for sustainability transformation: An integrated assessment framework, *Current Opinion in Environmental Sustainability*, 23, December: 1–11
51 Sosnik, D. (2023) The 'diploma divide' is the new fault line in American politics, *New York Times*, Opinion, 17th April www.nytimes.com/2023/04/17/opinion/education-american-politics.html

27 Systems-Based Governance

For a Complex Sustainable Future

Interview With Ray Ison

Introduction

How can we explain the collective failure of our institutions to respond to the global climate emergency and crisis, and why can't our institutions seem to respond for the collective good and sustainable future? This is an important and systemic question.

Keywords: adaptive learning; anthropocene; biosphere; climate emergency; command and control; complex adaptive systems (CAS); constitutional conventions; corporate lobbying; COVID-19; COVID-19 travel bubbles; crisis management; emergent properties; end-state fallacy; first-order change; governance; incremental change; ICAC; IFSR; institutional failure; integrity ecosystem; Landcare; requisite variety; river catchment management; royal commissions; SDG 11; SDG 13; SDG 16; SDG 17; second-order change; self-organising; separation of powers; stationarity; subsidiarity; sustainability; systematic change; systemic change; systems thinking; technosphere; tracking and tracing; transformative change

Interviewee Profile

Ray Ison (**RI**) is Professor of Systems at the Open University in the UK and spends time regularly in Australia on university exchanges. He is an Australian-British cybernetician and systems scientist known for his work on systemic governance and the design and practice of learning systems. Formerly Professor of Sustainability Systems at Monash University, he is also President of the International Federation for Systems Research (IFSR). Ray and his colleague, Ed Straw, recently published an insightful new book, *The Hidden Power of Systems Thinking: Governance in a Climate Emergency*.[1] It is a critique of institutional governance failure and the need for institutional innovation and a new way of managing our institutions in the Anthropocene.

DOI: 10.4324/9781003280316-31

The Interview

ML: Ray, what is the nature of this institutional governance failure, particularly in the context of the climate change emergency? What are the symptoms of this failure?

RI: Good question Michael. Let me start by unpacking the word 'institution'. That word gets used and abused somewhat. I use it in the sense that institutional economists use it, which is about the norms and rules of the game that we humans have created.[2]

These can be formal rules like you drive on the left-hand side of the road, and that we have a three-year Parliament and we vote in particular ways. Or they can be informal rules like our family has dinner at six pm and if you're late, you could be in trouble. Those are institutions in the sense that I use them and I differentiate them from organisations, but both ideas are central to why our governance systems are failing today.

To get to the nub of the question, you've got to begin to imagine how or what a governance system might look like and many people find it hard to talk about the different elements of a governance system. The one we have come up with and talk about in our book is that we identify five high-level elements.

One, of course, is the state and I should say here that we differentiate between the term governance and government. We're not talking about government, but governance. It's within the state. It can be a one-party state, it can be a federation, it can be a democracy. There are various forms of operating the state and the different elements within states like the executive, the bureaucracy, and the Parliament, the Communist Party of China if you're talking about China, and all of the other things that the state owns and controls.

Then you have the judiciary, the law of the legal system, which has many components as well, such as courts, barristers, justices, etc. And historically, we tended to confine the idea of our governance system to what in Latin was known as the political. The relationship between the executive, the Parliament and the law.

But if you want to understand how we're governed today, and particularly in the context of an emerging Anthropocene,[3] then you have to add into the state and the law, the private sector. We live in a world now where some of the large multinationals are more powerful than 70% of nation states. We can no longer leave them out of our governance.[4]

The other element is the civil society. We all belong to different civil society organisations, and often innovation comes largely from civil society.[5]

The final governance system element is the media which tends to float around historically but is now very much aligned with the private sector. Certainly in this country, there is a big debate about where the private sector sits, where the media sits, and if the power rests within the News Corporation.[6] In China, where there's a one-party state the media power sits there and the news is aligned with the state.

Those are the key elements of the governance systems that we talk about in our book and we make the argument that all of the institutions, the norms, the rules of the games that we humans have invented and invested in our governance systems are really up for grabs in the Anthropocene. The idea that we humans are a force of nature and changing whole earth dynamics means that what we've done in the past has to be up for critical scrutiny.

There is a set of innovations that we have built into our governance systems that are probably not suiting us all that well. I've talked about the power of the private sector and multinationals. When we built our institutional arrangements, we didn't see the rise of global connectivity through technology, the rise of the technosphere. For example, the social dilemma about the power of social media and how social media tends to use us rather than us use it.

There are other distortions in the thinking that sits behind many of our institutional arrangements. For example, it's almost impossible with a three-year political election cycle for Parliament to deal with the complexity of most of the issues with which we have to deal. We have a constitution in this country that was invented in 1900 or thereabouts and it has rules that are no longer 'fit for purpose'[7] and yet we have a poverty-stricken way of reinventing our Constitution.[8] As in the US, for example, there's a great struggle between the executive and the judiciary over the appointment of a Supreme Court judge. These are some of the examples of our dysfunctional systems of governance.

ML: Why do you refer to the 'systems thinking' approach as the 'hidden power'? How does this help us understand in an analytical sense, some of these governance failings of which you've given examples? And how does this approach differ from the way in which we've constructed our institutions and rules of the game in the past?

RI: Well again, a good question. Let me give two recent examples with which your listeners may be familiar. As we speak, we are experiencing the after-effects of the so-called COVID-19 'travel bubble' established between New Zealand and Australia.[9] Although apparently this was done in consultation between states and communities, there's contestation over what was agreed and what wasn't. Quite clearly what wasn't done was the design or the building of a system in which everyone had a stake, a common understanding and a clarity of purpose because the arrangement broke down. For example, what happens if suddenly there's a series of outbreaks of COVID-19 in New Zealand? When does the plug get pulled? There's a failure to design a system that is 'fit for purpose'.

The inquiry in Victoria again exemplifies a classic case of systemic failure and lack of clarity of purpose.[10] Why were security guards brought in? Who was responsible? What was the purpose? Was it an oversight? How do you make sure it's effective and fit for purpose? These are all questions related to systems thinking, systems design and the enactment of systemic governance. Unfortunately, there is too much of what we call 'systematic thinking' rather than 'systemic thinking' within our body politic and in society in general.[11]

ML: As you say, there are many examples, and COVID-19 is a case in point, where a crisis has challenged many of the 'rules of the game' and the associated organisational forms and behaviours, and have opened up new possibilities and opportunities for change.[12] Could one characterise the previous ways of thinking and organising as essentially a form of 'command and control' and hierarchical efficiency based, and might a 'systems' way of thinking create different rules and structures to tackle crisis?

RI: Absolutely. You've put your finger right on the nub of the issue. The concept 'systemic' or the idea of being 'systemic' means that things have to be in relationship with each other and fit together for a purpose. By contrast, the 'command-and-control' model is the classic, simple cause-and-effect idea of power model that has dominated, particularly in the Westminster system. For example, there's a classic power struggle going on at the moment in Britain, between the Prime Minister of Britain, on the one hand, and the Mayor and local government of Manchester in respect of COVID-19 responses.[13] It is a struggle over centralised command and control that has played out in Britain as a complete failure of governance at a central level as against a more distributed decision-making and action around tracking and tracing that has had more success.[14]

COVID-19 'tracking and tracing' is a really interesting application for systems and cybernetics thinking. To monitor and control effectively in this system, you need timely feedback, and the best way of getting that is for the feedback and actions to be distributed and localised.[15] And there was a lovely example reported a few weeks ago of citizens in Colac, Victoria.[16] A COVID-19 outbreak occurred around the meat works and the citizens created their own isolating regimes and tracking and tracing systems being aware that the centralised system in Melbourne was not capable of doing the job quickly enough. That is a great example of a systems theory known as Ashby's law of 'requisite variety', which says that 'only variety, can manage variety'.[17]

ML: We're dealing here with very complex systems such as the biosphere,[18] societies and the technocracy that are highly unpredictable and uncertain.[19] Are we trying in a sense to control or govern them using 'command-and-control' approaches that are not up to the job? Isn't our very notion of 'the job' part of the problem? It is based on what, I believe, is referred to as an 'end-state fallacy'[20] in the way we think about how to manage these 'complex adaptive systems'.[21]

Don't we need to think in a different way about what we're trying to achieve in managing and changing these large-scale, complex systems?[22] Not just in terms of ideal, unique end states that we set up as our policy objectives and then try to implement?

RI: Absolutely. Unfortunately, much of the thinking on which our contemporary governance arrangements are made is based on this end-state fallacy. I've done work in water and river catchment governance in which the hydrology profession and discipline have been central.[23]

That work has been built on the concept of 'stationarity'; the idea that you can use data from the past to model and predict what's going to happen in the future.[24] However, within the Anthropocene, what is absolutely certain is the certainty of uncertainty and we can no longer rely on 'stationarity'. There's a well-known paper published in Science magazine titled 'Stationarity Is Dead',[25] which means that we have to 'learn' our ways into the future.

We've got to have localised ways of knowing, as well as being open to much more rapid change and innovation; and it's why we can't be tied down to static constitutional forms. It's why, for example, three-year parliamentary cycles are totally inadequate; and why the pursuit of party interests within our government systems are not necessarily in the interests of a nation, as typified by the climate debate and the carbon taxing issue.

ML: This suggests the need to reinvent and reimagine the institutions for governance with a systems thinking approach. That path seems to require a move away from command and control to a distributed model that you've mentioned involves notions of self-regulation and learning, rather than current ideas of governance based on compliance with a set of rules that are supposed to lead us to a desired end state. Is this what is involved in moving to the systems thinking approach to governance that you have in mind?

RI: Well, you've just described a tremendous amount of the content of our book because it has those ideas right throughout it. You're absolutely right. A good example that we talk about in the book is the distortion of our governance systems at government, corporate and other levels by the fallacy of target or goal setting. This is often done with the idea that the particular target or the goal is going to stay static, and that you can optimise its pursuit centrally. Alternatively, it's the example I mentioned earlier, of responding to COVID-19 in Colac. While the high-level, collective imperative was to survive and do the best we can for the economy, it was left to localised action to devise the means adopted. This was a self-organising, bottom-up innovation process that capitalised on variety management.

ML: How can we effect that sort of change within our very entrenched institutions with their strong hierarchical power relationships? What skills and capacities are required at the leadership, organisational and community levels to implement the systems thinking and social learning that you're talking about?

RI: Well, there are some. There are different examples that can operate in different domains of our governance systems. We could imagine the creation of a constitutional committee, or deliberative institution that inquired into how we were going to govern ourselves as a nation into an Anthropocene future, and that this inquiry was set up in perpetuity.[26]

It's amazing how often we set up royal commissions and commissions of inquiry and their sheer number in recent years is itself a measure of how bad our governance systems are. But the problem with inquiries is that their recommendations are often not given institutional effect or even not acted upon, and their potential impact is often dissipated; as is happening, for example, with the Banking Royal Commission.[27]

This means that we've got to invent new institutions. Starting with high-level ones like constitutions,[28] we have to change practices at all levels, in various organisations and arms of government. We really do have to think about whether the Westminster system of government, which gives power to the minister based on a command-and-control design, is fit for purpose. What rules would we have to invent to allow a greater sharing of power with citizens and more citizen-based power?

We have some good experience to draw on in Australia. Citizens came together to build a federation and construct the first constitution.[29] We also have a lovely example in Landcare in Australia which was a citizens' driven initiative to cooperate across countryside and river systems to build greater sustainability.[30] It was unfortunately then, albeit with good intentions, taken up by the government and institutionalised and appropriated by the government which felt because it owned it and was going to pay some of the bills, that it should dictate what happened. So rather than a bottom-up, self-organising, adaptive-learning system that it was initially, it became co-opted into a command-and-control institution.

ML: The issue of power and its location and distribution are at the centre of trying to effect the sort of changes and innovation required by systems thinking and constitute a barrier to institutional reform. It is an often-observed phenomenon that people on the frontline of organisations compared to their leaders can often see and acknowledge the systemic implications and need to change things more clearly than their more remote leaders. The pathway to institutional change needs to confront power and leadership issues and your book sets out 26 principles for systemic governance. What's at the core of those principles?

RI: They fit into groups and the very first principle that has to be addressed, and I haven't perhaps paid enough attention to it in this interview thus far, is that our governance systems are missing three essential elements. The first is the centrality of the bias.

In the Anthropocene, we have to re-admit the biosphere as the central feature of our ongoing existence. Unless we invent institutions that place the biosphere as essential to our ongoing existence then the quality of our life and our coevolution with the biosphere is really questionable.

David Attenborough has ignored this over a long period, but in his last programme he has at last come out publicly and said that it's not the earth we're trying to save but ourselves in relation to the earth.[31] That's the central thing that we have to design to build into our future governance systems.

The second group of principles relates to democracy and subsidiarity,[32] as we have been discussing.

The other group of principles is what my co-author Ed Straw calls the 'fourth separation of powers' and, that is, that the world can't be allowed to run on lies, which tends to be happening in many parts of the world at the moment. One of the emergent failures of our current government system is what is known in some circles as 'state capture',[33] or preferential 'lobbying',[34] and there's a lot being written about that.[35] For example, the discussion about the federal ICAC is about the prevalence of preferential lobbying in this country.[36] However, that discussion is not following the principles of building a systemic approach to governance. Focusing solely on a single institution, as it does, doesn't take account of where that fits in the different relations with other parts of government and governance, and it is accordingly unlikely to succeed. It may only become a band aid.[37]

ML: How do you see the prospects for reinventing our governance in this more systems-based way? The current COVID-19 crisis seems to be overturning many of our governance norms and practices in the short run emergency.[38,39] Does that crisis afford an opportunity for change?[40] Are you optimistic about the prospect for systemic governance reforms?

RI: I wish I could say I was really optimistic. Certainly, crises present opportunities, but there's a great danger that comes out of crises. People merely use the same ways of thinking and acting to do what the systems community would say is to keep 'doing the wrong thing, righter' rather than reinventing a new thing.

We would talk about coming out of COVID-19 as demanding 'second-order change' to change the whole system. It's not about 'first-order change' which is just about trying to make the current system better.[41] We need to have a conversation about this and this is what our book is designed to do,[42] in the way that citizens talked about making this nation they eventually called Australia – unfortunately, without Indigenous people as part of that conversation.

We need to have another national conversation about who we are and what we want to be in the post-COVID-19 world in which the systemic consequences of a virus pandemic point to the breakdown of human relationship with the biosphere, with each other and with many other species.

Conclusion

Systems thinking offers an innovative approach to respond in a sustainable manner to the institutional and governance failures in the face of the global climate change emergency in the Anthropocene era. The COVID-19 viral pandemic crisis has shown both the need and opportunity for transformational changes to prevailing governance approaches with respect to our relationship both to the biosphere and to the kind of institutions within which we operate.

The existing rules and norms of governance based on notions of command-and-control hierarchy are not sufficiently adaptable to cope with the emerging complexity and uncertainty of the existential sustainability challenges that we face. They are premised on an 'end-state fallacy' that envisages a single solution or point of equilibrium drawing on projections of historic experience and data in the face of the 'death of stationarity'. The future is not simply and uniquely deterministic and is on a scale that requires decentralised data gathering, feedback and responses that can adapt continuously through adaptive learning.

The scale and nature of institutional and governance changes needed in response to the global climate crisis need to move beyond 'first-order', systematic changes that do the same things incrementally better; to second- and third-order transformational changes that conceive and deliver systemically new ways of thinking and acting.

Decentralised, distributed and empowered governance at the local and community levels can better deliver the 'requisite variety' and 'subsidiarity' required to meet the challenges of the 'complex adaptive systems' of the biosphere, technocracy and political governance. Redistribution of constitutional and institutional power and control in response to the 'path dependence' of vested interests in corporations, the media and in government means a move towards a 'fourth separation of powers' with more transparency, accountability and empowerment of civil society, communities and citizens.

Systemic governance offers an innovative approach to an emergent path to a sustainable future for the biosphere and society as a complex adaptive system characterised by learning and self-organisation.

Notes

1 Ison, R. and Straw, E. (2020) *The Hidden Power of Systems Thinking: Governance in a Climate Emergency*, London: Taylor and Francis
2 Samuels, W.J. (1995) The present state of institutional economics, *Cambridge Journal of Economics*, 19 (4): 569–590
3 Malhi, Y. (2017) The concept of the anthropocene, *Annual Review of Environment and Resources*, 42, October: 77–104
4 Ruggie, J.G. (2018) Multinationals as global institution: Power, authority and relative autonomy, *Regulation & Governance*, 12 (3): 317–333
5 Percival, R.V. and Huiyu, Z. (2013) The role of civil society in environmental governance in the United States and China, *Duke Environmental Law and Policy Forum*, 24: 141
6 Muller, D. (2023) A reciprocating engine of money, power and influence: How Australia's 'media monsters' used journalism to cement their empires, *The Conversation*, 20th June https://theconversation.com/a-reciprocating-engine-of-money-power-and-influence-how-australias-media-monsters-used-journalism-to-cement-their-empires-206757
7 Kelly, B. (2023) *The People's Constitution: The Path to Empowerment of Australians in a 21st Century Democracy*, Sydney: Australian Community Futures Planning
8 Holbrook, C. (2022) The sentimental deficit: Australians and their constitution, in Beilharz, P. and Supski, S. (eds),*The Work of History: Writing for Stuart Macintyre*, Chapter 23, pp. 279–295, Melbourne: Melbourne University Press
9 Sun, X., Wandelt, S. and Zhang, A. (2023) Why are COVID-19 travel bubbles a tightrope walk? An investigation based on the Trans-Tasmanian case, *Communications in Transportation Research*, 3, December: 100089
10 Rundle, K. (2021) A year after the Victoria hotel quarantine inquiry, one significant question remains unanswered, *The Conversation*, 27th August https://theconversation.com/a-year-after-the-victoria-hotel-quarantine-inquiry-one-significant-question-remains-unanswered-166100
11 Williams, A., Kennedy, S., Philipp, F. and Whiteman, G. (2017) Systems thinking: A review of sustainability management research, *Journal of Cleaner Production*, 148, April: 866–881
12 Hazaa, Y.M.H., Almaqtari, F.A. and Al-Swidi, A. (2021) Factors influencing crisis management: A systematic review and synthesis for future research, *Cogent Business & Management*, 8 (1): 1878979
13 Stewart, H., Halliday, J. and Walker, P. (2020) Chaos and fury as Boris Johnson forces curbs on Greater Manchester, *The Guardian*, 21st October www.theguardian.com/world/2020/oct/20/burnham-says-government-playing-with-peoples-lives-as-tier-3-covid-rules-imposed
14 OECD (2020) The territorial impact of COVID-19: Managing the crisis across levels of government, *OECD Policy Responses to COVID-19*, 10th November www.oecd.org/coronavirus/policy-responses/the-territorial-impact-of-covid-19-managing-the-crisis-across-levels-of-government-d3e314e1/
15 Juneau, C.E., Briand, A.S., Collazzo, P., Siebert, U. and Pueyo, T. (2023) Effective contact tracing for COVID-19: A systematic review, *Global Epidemiology*, 9th March: 100103
16 Preiss, B. (2020) Cases linked to Colac abattoir outbreak jump, *The Age*, 24th Julywww.theage.com.au/national/victoria/cases-linked-to-colac-abattoir-outbreak-jump-geelong-infections-rise-20200724-p55f96.html
17 Naughton, J. (2017) Ashby's law of requisite variety, *Edge*, www.edge.org/response-detail/27150

18 Voulvoulis, N., Giakoumis, T., Hunt, C., Kioupi, V., Petrou, N., Souliotis, I. and Vaghela, C.J. (2022) Systems thinking as a paradigm shift for sustainability transformation, *Global Environmental Change*, 75, July: 102544
19 Siegenfeld, A.F. and Bar-Yam, Y. (2022) A formal definition of scale-dependent complexity and the multi-scale law of requisite variety, *arXiv*, June: 2206.04896 https://arxiv.org/abs/2206.04896
20 Cordesman, A.H. (2016) The 'end state' fallacy: Setting the wrong goals for war fighting, *Centre for Strategic International Studies (CSIS)*, 26th September www.csis.org/analysis/end-state-fallacy-setting-wrong-goals-war-fighting
21 Naylor, A., Ford, J., Pearce, T. and van Alstine, J. (2020) Conceptualizing climate vulnerability in complex adaptive systems, *One Earth*, 2 (5): 444–454
22 Inigo, E.A. and Albareda, L. (2016) Understanding sustainable innovation as a complex adaptive system: A systemic approach to the firm. *Journal of Cleaner Production*, 126, July: 1–20
23 Kundzewicz, Z.W. (2018) Quo vadis, hydrology? *Hydrological Sciences Journal*, 63 (8): 1118–1132
24 Yang, Y., Roderick, M.L., Yang, D., Wang, Z., Ruan, F., McVicar, T.R., Zhang, S. and Beck, H.E. (2021) Streamflow stationarity in a changing world, *Environmental Research Letters*, 16 (6): 064096
25 Milly, P.C., Betancourt, J., Falkenmark, M., Hirsch, R.M., Kundzewicz, Z.W., Lettenmaier, D.P. and Stouffer, R.J. (2008) Stationarity is dead: Whither water management? *Science*, 319 (5863): 573–574
26 Glasser, R. (2023) Government must be up front with Australians about climate risks, *The Strategist*, 21st March www.aspistrategist.org.au/government-must-be-up-front-with-australians-about-climate-risks/
27 Butler, B. (2021) Banking royal commission: Most recommendations have been abandoned or delayed, *The Guardian*, 19th January www.theguardian.com/australia-news/2021/jan/19/banking-royal-commission-most-recommendations-have-been-abandoned-or-delayed
28 Kelly (2023), op cit
29 Winterton, G. (1998) Australia's constitutional convention, *Agenda: A Journal of Policy Analysis and Reform*, January: 97–109
30 Robins, L. (2018) More than 30 years of 'Landcare' in Australia: Five phases of development from 'childhood' to 'mid-life' (crisis or renewal?), *Australasian Journal of Environmental Management*, 25 (4): 385–397
31 Hoare, B. (2023) How David Attenborough has championed climate change, *Discover Wildlife*, 7th March www.discoverwildlife.com/people/david-attenborough-climate-change
32 Latimer, T. (2018) The principle of subsidiarity: A democratic reinterpretation, *Constellations*, 25 (4): 586–601
33 Australian Democracy Network (2022) *Confronting State Capture: How Corporations Have Eroded Our Democracy, and What We Can Do About It*, February https://australiandemocracy.org.au/statecapture
34 Ng, Y.F. (2020) Regulating the influencers: The evolution of lobbying regulation in Australia, *Adelaide Law Review*, 41 (2): 507–543
35 dela Rama, M.J., Lester, M.E. and Staples, W. (2022) The challenges of political corruption in Australia, the proposed Commonwealth Integrity Commission Bill (2020) and the Application of the APUNCAC, *Laws*, 11 (1): 7 https://doi.org/10.3390/laws11010007
36 Knott, M., Smith, A. and Rabe, T. (2022) 'Public autocracy': Morrison warns of integrity commission risks, *Sydney Morning Herald*, 4th May www.smh.com.au/politics/federal/public-autocracy-morrison-warns-of-integrity-commission-risks-20220502-p5ahq3.html

37 dela Rama, M., Klettner, A. and Lester, M. (2019) *Cui bono?* Corrupters and the corrupted – corporate governance and corruption, in Ellis, J. (ed) *Corruption, Social Sciences and the Law*, Chapter 5, London: Routledge
38 Lester, M., dela Rama, M. and Crews, J. (2021) COVID-19 governance, legitimacy, and sustainability: Lessons from Australian experience, *Corporate Governance and Sustainability Review*, 5 (1): 143–153
39 dela Rama, M. and Lester, M. (2022) The end of neoliberalism? The response to COVID-19: An Australian geopolitical perspective, in Oberoi, R., Halsall, J.P. and Snowden, M. (eds) *Contestations in Global Civil Society*, pp. 79–95, London: Emerald
40 Moore, M.L., Hermanus, L., Drimie, S., Rose, L., Mbaligontsi, M., Musarurwa, H., Ogutu, M., Oyowe, K. and Olsson, P. (2023) Disrupting the opportunity narrative: Navigating transformation in times of uncertainty and crisis, *Sustainability Science*, June: 1–7
41 Bartunek, J.M. and Moch, M.K. (1987) First-order, second-order, and third-order change and organization development interventions: A cognitive approach, *Journal of Applied Behavioral Science,* 23 (4): 483–500
42 Termeer, C.J., Dewulf, A. and Biesbroek, G.R. (2017) Transformational change: Governance interventions for climate change adaptation from a continuous change perspective, *Journal of Environmental Planning and Management,* 60 (4): 558–576

28 Political Reform and Public Engagement

Necessary Sustainable Path for Confronting Climate Change

Interview With Barry Jones

Introduction

Our discussion is about the big existential issues that Australia faces as a country, and as a society, is political governance. We have lost trust in our political system.[1] At the same time, we are facing the existential threat of climate change that requires a strong and timely political response that has not been forthcoming.[2]

We explore a path forward into the future as set out in a book called, *What Is to Be Done? Political Engagement and Saving the Planet* by Barry Jones, which addresses these issues.[3]

Keywords: accountability; authoritarianism; Clive Palmer; code of silence; compulsory voting; constitution; corporatisation; corruption; democracies; election funding; gambling industry; higher education; independent politicians; indigenous rights; integrity; lobbying; lobbyists; lucky country; Mafia; mining industry; national treasure; *omerta*; party factions; policy paralysis; political activism; political disengagement; political dysfunction; political trust; privatisation; SDG 4; SDG 16; social media; transparency; veto power; the Voice referendum

Interviewee Profile

The Hon Dr. Barry Jones (**BJ**), AC, is a prominent and eminent Australian public intellectual, lawyer, writer and activist of over 70 years and a lifelong member of the Labor Party and politician. He is a 'National Living Treasure'[4] and has been recognised for his contributions to society with the award of Companion of the Order of Australia (AC). He was, for 26 years, a Member of Parliament (MP) in state and federal parliaments; and for seven years a minister, including the longest serving Minister for Science (1983 to 1990). He is a former National President of the ALP (1992–2000, 2005–2006).

The Interview

ML: Barry, your latest book *What Is to Be Done?*[5] is a stimulating and important read. Could we start by going back to an earlier landmark book that you wrote before you became a minister? *Sleepers, Wake!*[6] is a very

DOI: 10.4324/9781003280316-32

prescient take on the impact and potential of technology in our society. Looking back, do you think that Australia grasped the opportunities and challenges that you presented?

BJ: No, we certainly did not. We failed conspicuously, I think. I owe a great debt of gratitude to Donald Horne for his even earlier and great book called *The Lucky Country*.[7]

The term 'Lucky Country' was intended as an irony. He was saying that Australia was run by 'second-grade' people. There are some exceptions, but every time we looked as if we were facing a crisis, the luck returned. For example, things looked pretty bad in the Second World War but then the Americans came to our rescue and we survived.[8] We survived the war and the economy wasn't going too well, but suddenly we discovered enormous mineral deposits in WA which transformed the very nature of the economy.[9]

Horne made the point which I picked up in *Sleepers, Wake!* to say that this was a danger and that we might think of Australia as simply being a quarry and a farm.[10] In other words, although we have one of the most urbanised societies on earth, we might also say that the cities aren't really contributing that much to our economy.[11] After all, the important thing is what we dig up and sell off in huge volumes to the world. But since then, world trade has changed dramatically and Australia is still concentrating on the sort of things that we were good at in the 1970s and the 1980s.[12]

It's as if the transformation of the twenty-first century and as we move towards a post-carbon society[13] is something for which our politicians on both sides of the fence lack any enthusiasm. You mentioned that I was a long-serving member of the Labor Party, but I'd have to say all the major political parties think that way. They haven't seized the opportunity to act courageously and to act with vision.

Sometimes Australia performs very well, for example, in the case of COVID-19,[14] but I think initially it was geography and isolation more than anything else that saved us from having a heavy death rate; and in New Zealand it was the same. But more recently, the handling of the distribution and access of the vaccines has been confused and muddled,[15] and we ought to be performing better.

ML: A major theme in your new book that you explore, develop and about which you put forward propositions is that democracy is undergoing an existential crisis,[16] which in part you put down to the dysfunctionality of our political system, including both political parties.[17] What is the nature of this existential crisis that you believe democracy faces?

BJ: We have an extreme example in the United States in the Trump era. But now that the United States is backing off from the extremes of that four-year period, perhaps I need to rethink my level of pessimism there.[18] If you take Europe, for example, it was assumed that after the fall of the Berlin Wall at the end of the Soviet bloc in Eastern Europe you would get the operation of a kind of liberal democracy. In fact, instead of having liberal democracy, you've had the development of an authoritarian democracy.[19]

In Australia, there are a surprising number of people actually quite attracted to the idea of authoritarian leadership. In Europe, countries like say Hungary have gone hard right in adopting a populist authoritarian nationalism with a heavy emphasis on keeping foreigners out.[20,21,22] This is the idea of identifying an enemy and saying that they are threatening us.[23,24,25] You can see that with the hostility that's been generated towards refugees in Poland, Belarus and Russia itself.

You can see authoritarianism increasing in China,[26] which has changed tremendously in economic and social terms. Chinese life expectancy has changed dramatically over a comparatively short period, from about 35 years to more than 70 years. It's effectively doubled in only one and a half generations. That's an extraordinary achievement, but it's an authoritarian government.

In countries like Brazil, you've had the rise and rise of authoritarian leadership,[27] invoking notions of 'my country, right or wrong'. We don't care what happens in the rest of the world and we're opposed to any kind of global cooperation.

Coupled with that, there's been the withdrawal of a very significant number of people from being part of the political process. They say, well, I don't mind going along every three or four years to cast a vote for a political party but don't ask me to get involved. Then, they wring their hands and say 'oh isn't it dreadful what they're doing' and 'aren't they dismal leaders'. You have to challenge people and say, but what are you doing about it? Well, I'm so busy with other things. I'm busy with my professional preoccupations, the family, my vineyard, my yacht or in the days when people used to travel overseas, with my overseas travel.

Take the case of Kevin Andrews who was unloaded as the Liberal member for Menzies in Victoria.[28] It's extraordinary that at the last federal election he polled more than 50,0000 primary votes: 50,863 to be precise, and yet after 30 years, getting rid of him as a member involved a vote of a total of 282 people who turned up. In other words, 0.5%. So, 99.5% of people in Menzies said 'I don't want to be involved'. That's terrible.

ML: You have written in this context of the existential crisis in democracy about how the digital world and technology has changed everything. How does digital technology impact on the issues that you're discussing about political disengagement and the existential crisis in democracy?

BJ: Well, you know I got a lot of things right in *Sleepers, Wake!* back in 1982 but one of the things I got wrong, and virtually every other person writing in the area got wrong as well, was the assumption that the expansion of tertiary education would raise the quality of political engagement; but in fact, it's been quite the contrary.

The expectation was that tertiary education would raise the quality of political debate, embrace the universal, put more emphasis on the long term and adopt scientific methods. Well, it hasn't worked out like that.[29]

What's happening is that to a very large extent, people say: well, look, because I'm so busy and I haven't got time to do things, rather than find something where there's serious analysis of a topic. They say, I know what my general views are about, let's say refugees, whether you are hostile or sympathetic to them; and you say, well look, all I want to read is material, which reinforces my point of view.

And if I look up on the web and find there are 4,000 sites which are anti-refugee, and maybe 5,000 sites which are sympathetic to refugees, people say, I'll just plug in to one of those and I will simply look for reinforcement over and over and over and over again.

The result is that to a very large extent people are picking up their view of the world, their understanding of the world, not by looking out the window or by direct personal experience, but by simply gazing at a screen, everything that comes via the screen.[30] The result is that in a way they pick up views which are somebody else's views but which are crafted in order to appeal to them. So don't think about the issue, we'll provide a solution for you. A ready-made solution that you can immediately adopt.[31] That's the real threat.

And I would say it's extraordinary when you reflect on what's happening in our politics, particularly in the Parliament. When I was in the Parliament, you had a comparatively small number of people with degrees but what they did have was life experience.[32]

I was struck by how many Members of Parliament when I was there first might have had perhaps a few fingers missing, or might have been missing an eye, or might have suffered from burns. They were people who've had life experience that's been pretty tough, and they decided to try and improve the quality of working life, for example, but now you find there's a very high percentage of people in Parliament who have formal qualifications.

Their primary loyalty is to a political faction, then party branch. Policy now doesn't seem all that important. I'm struck by the fact that so many of the really important issues like emissions, in the environment; to say, issues about foreign policies are not discussed.

We haven't had a serious debate on foreign policy in the Commonwealth Parliament for more than a decade. We haven't had a serious discussion about defence spending. Take the case of the acquisition of the controversial submarines.[33,34] There's never been a debate about it because they say on this something the executive decides.

The result is that nobody ever says what the reason is for having 12 submarines. Why not 11 or some other number? What's magic about the number 12?

And, if you're only having 11, you could instead say, spend a billion dollars improving tertiary education. We never had that discussion. People don't realise that.

One of the things for which Australia deserves a gold medal is the shortness of the sitting year of the Australian Parliament.[35] Compared to New Zealand, Canada, Britain, the United States, Germany, and France; Australia's right at the bottom. That's because political parties and governments on both sides regard the Parliament as a confounded nuisance and they don't really want to have a serious debate.

ML: Why do you think that there's been such a significant drop in public trust in our system of politics or politicians and our institutions?[36] Is it just that they're not getting on with the job or are there other reasons?

BJ: To a very large extent, both political parties are quite happy with the current situation. The last thing they want is to have large numbers of well-informed people who are rocking the boat.

The major political parties have essentially become privatised, like private companies such as Woolworths or Coles. You've got habitual users who turn up but who don't necessarily want to get involved in the management. Our political leaders don't want to encourage large numbers of people to come in because they might start asking awkward questions.

I'm actually in favour of compulsory voting although strictly speaking it's not compulsory voting as such; it's compulsory registration and compulsory turning up because when you actually cast your vote it's a free vote. You could vote if you like or otherwise you could vote informally or strike a line through the ballot paper; not that I'd encourage people to do that but you're not compelled to vote, you're compelled to turn up.

The other thing is public funding for elections which is quite generous on the basis of how many votes a party achieved in the previous election.[37] That being the case, you don't really need to engage with the community as a whole but you do need to engage with lobbyists and their role is profound.

Think of the role of Clive Palmer who admits to having put $123 million in not primarily for the purpose of securing the election of his own candidates, but to prevent a change of government.[38] That means that the role of lobbying, for example, the gambling industry has been absolutely profound in its social impact.[39]

It has been very deleterious I think, but nevertheless, the gambling industry is a big employer, and it does make some contribution to revenue, but it's been extraordinarily powerful. You might find a large proportion of people in the community want gambling to be regulated or controlled far more, but it won't happen because both major political parties are caught up in it.[40]

ML: Barry, you speak in your book of 'political paralysis' and of almost a 'code of silence' among our political classes in not addressing some very key issues. You compare it to the *omerta* of the Mafia[41,42] and suggest that it reflects a certain sense of neglect and complacency. What is at the heart of this 'political paralysis' and 'code of silence'?

BJ: The code of silence is about not wanting to offend somebody that is supporting you. Take, say, the role of the mining industry at a time when increasingly we're concerned about global warming and about reducing CO_2 emissions.

A few strategically placed mining lobbyists have a tremendous impact on the government.[43] Also, there is the influence of a number of trade unions with affiliations in construction work associated with mining.[44] It means that both political parties have been hesitant about taking a really courageous stance. They say, if we do, we're going to disturb or anger people who are related to our political base or who are our major financial contributors.

ML: You paint a fairly bleak picture of the political parties and our political system in the sense that they've become very isolated from, and lacking in, engagement with ordinary people. It sounds deep seated and I get the impression that you're not even sure it's capable of reform.

You speculate about and call for the need for a new party which you call the courage party. Do you really think that we're not likely to be able to resolve these problems of lack of engagement of our people in society through the existing political party system?

BJ: It's what I've called the zero-point-zero two percent (0.02%) problem. There are about 15 million voters in Australia but if you add up the number of people who are aligned and can be regarded as more or less politically active that number is likely to be about 30,000.

In other words, you've got 15 million people who feel completely passive or isolated, and you've got 30,000 people who are actively involved. People feel we're outnumbered. While there's 15 million of us and only 30,000 of them; that 30,000 are strategically placed to influence the government.

I've been interested in talking to a number of people who are very seriously considering putting up candidates as independents at the next federal election.[45] They say Helen Haynes is wonderful in Indi and Zali Steggall in Warringah with both of which I agree. But when you reflect, you ask how much effort is needed to get an independent electable to win a marginal seat, leaving aside the question of whether you really want Parliament made-up largely of independents[46] – and who are simply competing with each other for resources for their own electorates. That's a different kind of problem.

But if in each federal electorate you had 1,000 committed and active citizens, that's not even 1%, then you would transform and revolutionise the political parties. You wouldn't even need a 'courage' party because both political parties would be courageous through their active membership.

ML: Barry, you set out an interesting list of possible policies and reforms. How important are the reforms that you articulate in the areas of our constitution; and in terms of anti-corruption and public accountability, responsibility and recognition of the public interest and the public good?[47]

BJ: At the moment, it's a scandalous situation about the lack of transparency and there's no sense of accountability. In the case of the present federal government, obviously I don't want to be too partisan because of my Labor Party priors, you can see I am critical of the government.

I'm critical of both major parties, but I consider with the present government there are at least a dozen non-performers and several ministers who are really invisible. I'm not even sure that they are even alive or not, you can never find them. It was extraordinary in the last federal election, the then Minister for the Environment (Sussan Ley) was completely invisible. She never came. She never answered a single question in the course of the election campaign. Although there are serious issues about the environment, she was not seen once to be talking; so whatever her views were, they were completely mysterious, maybe even to herself.

The starting point has to be accountability but the other thing is, we've gotta be honest with ourselves about issues like race. We've gotta be honest with ourselves about our history and about the Constitution.[48,49]

In some ways, the republican debate has been rather limited.[50] It should be a much more wide-ranging debate.

People look at the 1901 constitution and they say 'if it ain't broke, don't fix it'. Well, in a sense it was broken right from 1901.[51] It's amazing people, for example, including monarchists never quote the Constitution. They never read it out and say, we agree with this, and this.

For example, in Britain, the last time a sovereign vetoed an act of Parliament was 1707, and that was actually on the advice of ministers.[52,53] In the Australian Constitution, the power of the queen as monarch, the veto legislation is expressly preserved.

Now, is there any monarchist in Australia who can say, oh yes, we defend that? We think it's absolutely right that Queen Elizabeth over there, the now-widowed queen in Windsor, should be able to exercise the power of veto. It's there in the Constitution and then people say, oh no, oh no, the Prime Minister runs the show but the Prime Minister isn't even mentioned in the Constitution.

ML: Barry, your recurring theme is that if we're going to get more political engagement of the people, which you clearly believe we need to do, we need a lot more openness both in government and in the political parties. You say that we need to face up to some difficult moral choices, to debate them and take a longer view. In particular, you talk about climate change. How central is it to this discussion that we address the climate change issue?

BJ: It is absolutely central. Australia – because it's the largest per capita producer of CO_2 – has a moral responsibility to take a lead.[54] We look completely hypocritical if we say, well, we're going to leave it to the other bigger emitters to play a role. We can't play the role. Of course we are small, but we can be very important among middle-sized powers to say we've got to act courageously if we're going to preserve the planet. We should think of the limited amount of time we have. The next 10–15 years are going to be absolutely critical. Otherwise, the situation may become quite irreversible.

Conclusion

The democratic political system is dysfunctional as evidenced by falling levels of public trust in governments and the disengagement from politics of the people. Parties of both colours are content, if not complacent, as a duopoly, with the present situation which entrenches their positions of power while effectively excluding the rise of alternative more courageous parties.

In the past, Australia has been the 'lucky country' prospering despite our 'second-rate' leadership. However, the prospects of constitutional and governance reforms to our political system needed to tackle the big long-term issues such as climate change and sustainability are not encouraging.

Many countries have been turning to authoritarian nationalistic leaders. Movement towards effective reforms, such as to election funding, integrity, transparency and lobbying, in the liberal representative democracies appear to be enmeshed in a form of 'political paralysis'.

Increasing levels of education have not raised the level and quality of public debate as had been widely expected; people are politically disengaged and increasingly turning inwards to their own lives, careers and families. While prepared to vote in elections, they are not prepared to become politically active or engaged.

Social media has acted as an 'echo chamber' where people seek confirmation of their existing views rather than seeking out objective policy analysis. The political field is left to party factions, a small number of party activists, and to vested interests, including business and unions, and the influence of monied lobbyists.

There is a 'scandalous' lack of political transparency and accountability which are minimal and ineffective. A 'code of silence' resembling the Mafia's *omerta* characterises the lack of real public debate on key issues. The lack of sufficiently robust and timely political responses to climate change pose a moral challenge of existential proportions for the world. Can the 'lucky country' bank on being 'lucky' once again?

Notes

1 Stoker, G., Evans, M. and Halupka, M. (2018) *Trust and Democracy in Australia: Democratic Decline and Renewal*, Report, Democracy 2025, 6th December, www.democracy2025.gov.au/documents/Democracy2025-report1.pdf
2 Crowley, K. (2021) Fighting the future: The politics of climate policy failure in Australia (2015–2020), *Wiley Interdisciplinary Reviews: Climate Change*, 12 (5): e725
3 Jones, B. (2020) *What Is to Be Done: Political engagement and saving the planet*, Melbourne: Scribe Publications
4 Barker, G. (1998) Respected by all, feared by none, *Financial Review*, 31st July www.afr.com/politics/respected-by-all-feared-by-none-19980731-k86q6
5 Jones (2020), op cit
6 Jones, B. (1982) *Sleepers, Wake! Technology and the Future of Work*, Oxford: Oxford University Press
7 Horne, D. (1964) *The Lucky Country: Australia in the Sixties*, Camberwell, Victoria, Penguin Books
8 Barclay, G. St. J. (1977) Australia looks to America: The wartime relationship, 1939–1942, *The Pacific Historical Review*, May: 251–271
9 Battellino, R. (2010) *Mining Booms and the Australian Economy*, Address to the Sydney Institute, Sydney: Reserve Bank of Australia, 23rd February www.rba.gov.au/speeches/2010/sp-dg-230210.html
10 As predicted by Horne (1964), op cit
11 Warhaft, S. (2021) Linear equation: Barry Jones charts a different path for urban growth, *Cosmos Magazine*, 25th June https://cosmosmagazine.com/people/linear-equation-barry-jones-charts-a-different-path-for-urban-growth/
12 Wyeth, G. (2022) Australia's lack of economic complexity is a problem, *The Diplomat*, 31st March https://thediplomat.com/2022/03/australias-lack-of-economic-complexity-is-a-problem/
13 Wiseman, J. and Edwards, T. (2011) Sleepers wake! With courage we can build a post-carbon Australia, *The Conversation*, 30th May https://theconversation.com/sleepers-wake-with-courage-we-can-build-a-post-carbon-australia-1531
14 Lester, M., dela Rama, M. and Crews, J. (2021) COVID-19 governance, legitimacy, and sustainability: Lessons from the Australian experience, *Corporate Governance and Sustainability Review*, 5 (1): 143–153 https://doi.org/10.22495/cgsrv5i1sip5
15 Australian National Audit Office (ANAO) (2022) *Australia's COVID-19 Vaccine Rollout*, Auditor General Report No 3 of 2022–23, Performance Audit Report, 17th August www.anao.gov.au/work/performance-audit/australia-covid-19-vaccine-rollout
16 Jones, B. (2021) The democratic crisis: Whatever happened to courage, principle, commitment, accountability? *Pearls and Irritations: Public Policy Journal*, 29th September https://johnmenadue.com/the-democratic-crisis-whatever-happened-to-courage-principle-commitment-accountability/
17 Megalogenis, G. (2023) The two-party system is cooked, and the Liberals are leftovers, *Sydney Morning Herald*, 8th August www.smh.com.au/politics/federal/the-two-party-system-is-cooked-and-the-liberals-are-leftovers-20230406-p5cyp6.html

18 Wolpe, B. (2023) If Trump dismantles American democracy, Australia faces an existential question, *The Guardian*, 14th June www.theguardian.com/us-news/2023/jun/14/if-trump-dismantles-american-democracy-australia-faces-an-existential-question
19 Bernhard, M. (2021) Democratic backsliding in Poland and Hungary, *Slavic Review*, 80 (3): 585–607
20 Müller, J.W. (2011) The Hungarian tragedy, *Dissent*, 58 (2): 5–10
21 Bogaards, M. (2018) De-democratization in Hungary: Diffusely defective democracy, *Democratization*, 25 (8): 1481–1499
22 Madlovics, B. and Magyar, B. (2023) Hungary's Dubious loyalty: Orbán's regime strategy in the Russia-Ukraine war, in Madlovics, B. and Magyar, B. (eds) *Russia's Imperial Endeavor and Its Geopolitical Consequences: The Russia-Ukraine War*, Volume 2, pp. 255–286, Budapest: Central European University Press https://doi.org/10.7829/jj.3985460.15
23 Shevtsova, L. (2020) Russia's Ukraine obsession, *Journal of Democracy*, 31 (1): 138–147
24 Pisano, J. (2022) How Zelensky has changed Ukraine, *Journal of Democracy,* 33 (3): 5–13
25 Black, J.L. (2023) *Eternal Putin? Confronting Navalny, the Pandemic, Sanctions, and War with Ukraine*, London: Rowman & Littlefield
26 So, A.Y. (2019) The rise of authoritarianism in China in the early 21st century, *International Review of Modern Sociology*, 45 (1): 49–70
27 Saad-Filho, A. and Boffo, M. (2021) The corruption of democracy: Corruption scandals, class alliances, and political authoritarianism in Brazil, *Geoforum*, 124, August: 300–309
28 Murphy, K. (2021) Veteran liberal MP Kevin Andrews loses pre-selection battle for Menzies, *The Guardian*, 31st January www.theguardian.com/australia-news/2021/jan/31/veteran-liberal-mp-kevin-andrews-loses-preselection-battle-for-menzies
29 University of Melbourne Newsroom (2020) *Despite Strong Gains in 2020 Australians Remain Disengaged with Politics, Poll Finds*, 13th October www.unimelb.edu.au/newsroom/news/2020/october/despite-strong-gains-in-2020-australians-remain-disengaged-with-politics,-poll-finds
30 Vromen, A. (2018) Political engagement in the Australian digital context, *Papers on Parliament*, 69, October: 93–115
31 Christiano, T. (2022) Algorithms, manipulation, and democracy, *Canadian Journal of Philosophy*, 52 (1): 109–124
32 Lumb, M. (2013) *The 43rd Parliament: Traits and Trends*, Parliamentary Library, Research Papers 2013–14 www.aph.gov.au/About_Parliament/Parliamentary_departments/Parliamentary_Library/pubs/rp/rp1314/43rdParl
33 Royal Australian Navy, *The AUKUS Nuclear-Powered Submarine Pathway: A Partnership for the Future* www.navy.gov.au/aukus-nuclear-powered-submarine-pathway-partnership-future
34 Briggs, P. (2023) How many nuclear-powered submarines for Australia? *ASPI: The Strategist*, 12th October www.aspistrategist.org.au/how-many-nuclear-powered-submarines-for-australia/
35 Twomey, A. (2021) Who decides when parliament sits and what happens if it doesn't? *The Conversation*, 29th November https://theconversation.com/who-decides-when-parliament-sits-and-what-happens-if-it-doesnt-172861
36 According to the Edelman Trust Barometer (2023), 'Australia is already on a path to polarisation, driven by a series of macro forces that are weakening the country's social fabric and creating increasing division in society. This year's report finds that almost half of Australians (45%) say the nation is more divided today, than in the past – with the rich and powerful identified as a major dividing force (72%), followed by hostile foreign governments (69%), journalists (51%), and government leaders (49%)'. See www.edelman.com.au/trust/2023/trust-barometer

37 Steketee, M. (2017) Why we need full public funding of election campaigns, *Inside Story*, 12th July https://insidestory.org.au/why-we-need-full-public-funding-of-election-campaigns/
38 McHugh, F. (2023) How much Clive Palmer spent to win one United Australia Party seat in parliament, *SBS News*, 1st February www.sbs.com.au/news/article/how-much-clive-palmer-spent-to-win-one-united-australia-party-seat-in-parliament/yfk694ie1
39 Johnson, M. and Livingstone, C. (2021) Measuring influence: An analysis of Australian gambling industry political donations and policy decisions, *Addiction Research & Theory*, 29 (3): 196–204
40 Orr, G. (2023) Proposed spending caps may at last bring genuine reform to national election rules, *The Conversation*, 19th June https://theconversation.com/proposed-spending-and-donations-caps-may-at-last-bring-genuine-reform-to-national-election-rules-208031
41 Puzo, M. (2000) *Omerta*, New York: Random House
42 Dunn, M. (2022) The truth about Omerta, the Mafia's scared code of silence that hid their crimes for generations, *All That's Interesting*, 9th March https://allthatsinteresting.com/omerta
43 Tham, J.-C. and Ng, Y.-F. (2022) How to deal with fossil fuel lobbying and its influence in Australian politics, *The Conversation*, 18th August https://theconversation.com/how-to-deal-with-fossil-fuel-lobbying-and-its-growing-influence-in-australian-politics-188515
44 Karp, P. (2023) Unions call for energy transition authority to help workers exiting fossil fuel sector, *The Guardian*, 27th March www.theguardian.com/business/2023/mar/27/unions-call-for-energy-transition-authority-to-help-workers-exiting-fossil-fuel-sector
45 Nethery, A. (2022) Networks and money: The inside story of how the teals won Australia's six richest electorates, *The Conversation*, 29th November https://theconversation.com/networks-and-money-the-inside-story-of-how-the-teals-won-australias-six-richest-electorates-192096
46 Kenny, M. (2023) Halfway through their term, the 'teal' MPs look here to stay – and may present a huge challenge in 2025, *The Conversation*, 13th November https://theconversation.com/halfway-through-their-term-the-teal-mps-look-here-to-stay-and-may-present-a-huge-challenge-in-2025-216528
47 dela Rama, M.J., Lester, M.E. and Staples, W. (2022) The challenges of political corruption in Australia, the proposed commonwealth integrity Commission Bill (2020) and the Application of the APUNCAC, *Laws*, 11 (1): 7 https://doi.org/10.3390/laws11010007
48 Wellauer, K., Williams, C. and Brennan, B. (2023) Why the voice failed, *ABC News*, 16th October www.abc.net.au/news/2023-10-16/why-the-voice-failed/102978962
49 Zhou, N. (2023) The failure of Australia's attempt to create an indigenous voice to Parliament, *New Yorker*, 19th October www.newyorker.com/news/daily-comment/the-failure-of-australias-attempt-to-create-an-indigenous-voice-to-parliament
50 Warhurst, J. (2009) *The Trajectory of the Australian Republic Debate*, Papers on Parliament, No 51, June www.aph.gov.au/About_Parliament/Senate/Powers_practice_n_procedures/pops/pop51/warhurst
51 Kelly, B. (2023) *The People's Constitution: The Path to Empowerment of Australians in a 21st Century Democracy*, Australian Community Futures Planning (ACFP) www.austcfp.com.au/publications
52 BBC News (2002) Royal assent, *BBC News*, 14th October http://news.bbc.co.uk/2/hi/programmes/bbc_parliament/2327561.stm
53 UK Parliament, 1689–1714, www.parliament.uk/about/living-heritage/evolutionofparliament/parliamentaryauthority/revolution/keydates/keydates1689-1714/
54 McDonald, M. (2005) Fair weather friend? Ethics and Australia's approach to global climate change, *Australian Journal of Politics & History*, 51 (2): 216–234

29 Conclusion

Towards Complex Systems of Governance

This chapter bookends this work, summarises the key takeaways of each interview and concludes themes of the book: national systems of innovation and sustainability, climate change adaptation and energy transitions, regenerative agriculture for biodiversity and appreciating the complex systems of governance for innovation and sustainability.

Section I: National Systems of Innovation and Sustainability

What matters most about innovation is its impact on the everyday lives of people by enabling a better quality of life and standard of living (Mark Dodgson). Communicating a positive public understanding and acceptance of innovation and technological change as its principal driver is a challenge. There are justified public fears about job losses, industry closures and community breakups, in the face of the processes of Joseph Schumpeter's 'creative destruction' that accompany improved productivity and economic growth.

Entrepreneurs play a central role in driving innovation, and they have become highly visible and attractive role models during the digital era in the form of the Silicon Valley 'start-up' culture and their subsequent rise to global billionaires. However, their image as lone 'geniuses' working with few resources out of their garages obscures the extent to which their successes and their ultimate public impact build upon the resources and activities of wider economic, government and community institutions known as the 'national innovation system'.

A clear scientific and quantitative understanding of innovation drivers and its impact are elusive (Kevin Fox). Economists with an interest in studying growth have moved beyond traditional models driven by labour and capital which treat technology and its impact as a factor outside their models rationalised as an unexplained 'black box' residual known as 'total factor productivity' (TFP). The importance of hard-to-measure human capital, business adaptability, and the role of government and institutions are increasingly acknowledged and researched.

Measurement problems have loomed even larger in the digital era with the emergence of a 'productivity paradox'; investment in information, technology

DOI: 10.4324/9781003280316-33

and computer equipment is visible everywhere, including in its impact on jobs, but does not show up in productivity improvements. Possible explanations of the paradox include a lag in diffusion or adaptation of practices to these technologies, particular difficulties in measuring service sector productivity, as well as in setting prices and imputing monetary values to the services often delivered at zero marginal cost.

From an economics perspective, looking more closely at the role of digital era entrepreneurs, the manner in which they operate and their impact sheds some light on the 'black box' nature of the innovation process (Nicholas Gruen). Typically characterised as 'geeks' rather than traditional corporate business leaders, they adopt a generally visionary image and even idealistic aspirations to 'make a difference'.

Equally significant though is the nature of digital technologies which make it easier for entrepreneurs to form start-up companies and to scale them up to enormous scale at an unprecedented rate. The traditional barriers to entry in starting businesses are reduced; less capital is required; market risk is reduced by adopting lean start-up structures utilising digital platforms, cloud infrastructure and data algorithms. They can cheaply and repeatedly experiment with their offerings in the market, adapting and learning as they proceed.

These same technologies when scaled to big tech companies take advantage of a 'winner takes all' network economies of increasing scale returns and discriminatory pricing that lead to market power and dominance. Visionary idealism is overtaken by 'commoditisation' and 'monetisation' of data in pursuit of market power. This limits competition and innovation, and social impact at the expense of privacy and democracy. Ultimately, the ability and the role of government to exercise control in the public interest in a timely manner is challenged and public trust is eroded.

The United States, despite its historic global leadership in innovation, its risk-taking culture of entrepreneurship and the many global leading' big tech' companies, has reached a 'tipping point' with global challenges to its digital tech-based national competitiveness (Robert Atkinson).

The successful lessons of the past important systematic role of government, particularly during the Cold War years, in actively supporting research, technology and innovation across many institutions has diminished and largely been forgotten. The more recent 'financialisation' of corporate business, the 'hollowing out of manufacturing' and the general adoption of 'liberalisation' and 'small government' have held sway.

Rebuilding national security, competitiveness and innovation leadership is a political challenge for the current President. The past shows it requires urgent 'long-term' focused, 'mission-oriented' intervention by the government working closely with the business sector.

For its part, Australia's 'national innovation system' and its many components and institutions are arguably incoherent, uncoordinated, inconsistent and lacking long-term visionary leadership (Roy Green). Its very existence as an institutional 'system' of governance is open to question. Its inability to capitalise on Australia's traditionally strong publicly funded research base through commercialisation, innovation and industry development speaks to an underdeveloped 'system'.

This is reflected in a long-term loss of standing in international rankings of innovation and competitiveness. Political ideologies of neoliberalism, and vested interests in the wealth-generating minerals and energy 'boom-and-bust' sectors, have bred a comfortable complacency that may yet be the undoing of the 'lucky country'.

There is no shortage of innovation options and pathways to a wealthy and sustainable future built on renewable energy technology transformation which are slow in opening up.

The politicisation of climate change policies leads to emissions targets and policies that from a technical perspective are less than economically efficient or effective (Ross Garnaut). Economists, including Nobel Laureate William Nordhaus, have long agreed that imposing a carbon emissions charge is the best policy approach in response to the market failure that leads to underpricing and hence overproduction of carbon emissions.

There are various technical options for designing and implementing such a charge as well as options on the rate of the charge that balance costs and benefits of abatement that create a *de facto* market for trading in carbon emissions; a national cap-and-trade approach known as an emissions trading scheme (ETS) was rejected in the US but picked up by some states.

Europe adopted a carbon market price albeit set at a very low price. Australia implemented an effective emissions trading scheme (ETS) in the form of a carbon pollution reduction scheme (CPRS) for a couple of years before it was scrapped on party political grounds. Despite the best of economic advice and options, the net effect of politicisation over at least two decades has been the slowing down of effective and integrated economy-wide and global climate action.

Attempts to counter the 'toxic political paralysis' holding back effective climate action in the face of a global 'tragedy of the commons' need to tackle head on the 'political economy' and opposition of vested fossil fuel and other business interests (Warwick McKibbin). Such approaches respond directly to the varying climate policy risks and uncertainties faced by businesses in all sectors.

Modelling the technical complexity of climate policies impacts across the economy that uses scenario-building methodologies enables development of feasible 'hybrid' approaches. These approaches move away from the notion of single economy-wide or global targets and prices to create 'constituencies' of commercial and financial self-interest in climate policy providing 'insurance' for polluters in the form of 'climate bonds'.

A broader approach to sustainability that goes beyond tackling climate change is the notion of a 'circular economy' that systemically minimises waste and materials use by transforming business models as well as consumer lifestyles (Sami Kara). Related ideas of such innovation have been around for decades by names such 'closed-loop', 'cradle-to-grave', 'whole-of-life' product life cycles and 'zero-waste economy'.

However, leaving the transformation to market mechanisms has had little traction in overcoming 'market failure' and requires systemic changes. Products need to be reconceived and redesigned to minimise the waste stream and environmental impacts at every stage of the life cycle: design, sourcing, manufacture, distribution, repair, recycling and re-use. Consumer behaviours will need to change accordingly.

Tentative systematic policies to support even basic recycling have had little impact in the absence of effective pricing and market demand. The technology and innovation challenge is to develop technologies that have a one-to-one displacement; otherwise, new business opportunities for recirculated products lead to even more material consumption and environmental impact.

Section II: Climate Change Adaptation and Energy Transitions

The global energy industry is on the verge of a historic disruptive technology transition from an essentially fossil fuel base to renewable energy in response to the climate change challenge (Giles Parkinson). The rapid fall in costs of the new renewable technologies and developments in associated battery storage and 'smart grid' systems are disrupting industry business models, leaving assets stranded, but facilitating new more sustainable distributed networks and creating new jobs.

In Australia, the transition has been politicised and resisted by incumbent vested interests resulting in policy uncertainty and lack of stability. This undermines investor confidence in making the large investments required for rebuilding the electricity infrastructure to deliver consistent dispatchable power. Despite a change to a more favourably disposed government, the policy domain and pathway to innovative sustainable renewables remains highly contested and slow moving.

The power of dirty party politics to frustrate electricity emissions reductions in Australia is exemplified by the case of the National Energy Guarantee (NEG) proposal (Chris Dunstan). This was a complex attempt involving trade-offs between significant policy objectives to integrate within the national electricity grid the objectives of emissions targets, renewable energy technologies and affordable electricity prices.

The compromises within the context of a toxic internal party political debate resulted in a rigid framework that was 'ineffectual' in all respects. It was also economically inefficient in minimising the low-cost abatement in electricity vis-à-vis higher cost abatement in other sectors. The proponents stymied long-term renewables investment while promoting government underwriting of new investments in coal-fired assets in the name of securing 'base load' network stability.

Australia's tortured path to renewables transition is well exemplified by its laggard adoption of electric vehicles (EV) technology with widespread diffusion among consumers thwarted by lack of a cohesive national strategy (Peter Khoury). Consumer adoption faces expensive vehicles, 'range anxiety' with few offsetting incentives, resistance to vehicle fuel efficiency standards, painfully slow investment in infrastructure, and only latterly a belated recognition of associated opportunities in development of lithium resources and battery technologies.

The electrification path to sustainability is also unexpectedly problematic from the point of view of much wider digitalisation of economies, involving computers and communications systems and its associated technologies as can be seen in the case of the emergence of digital cryptocurrency (Sean Foley). Their 'Dirty Little Secret' is their considerable use of electricity, for example, in the operation of enormous 'server farms', including for the use of 'cloud computing'.

Rapidly evolving cryptocurrency such as Bitcoin in particular, as potentially disruptive to the global finance industry, is not only exploitative of cheap labour but reliant on enormous amounts of cheap electricity on the scale of small countries. This is required for the authentication and validation of their highly encrypted 'mining', and 'proof-of-work' processes utilising their underlying 'blockchain' technology.

With their transformative potential across many mainstream sectors and applications, these technologies challenge regulatory systems as well as needing to transition to less energy-intensive processes and or transitioning to renewable sources.

Nuclear power and technology, particularly in the form of innovative, 'small modular reactors' (SMR), has regained momentum and profile in Australia as a 'clean' renewable energy source that can play a role in decarbonisation to net zero, albeit also backed by growing geopolitically driven national defence security concerns (Jim Green). The global nuclear power industry has hit a 30-year plateau in wake of the 2011 Japanese Fukushima nuclear disaster and primarily by its soaring costs and the need for enormous subsidies.

Despite SMRs' long-touted cost-effective innovation, only a handful of attempts have been made over a couple of decades to build them successfully except for niche military and remote area applications. They cannot compete on cost with renewable energy alternatives and have very long lead times that mean they cannot deliver on emissions targets timelines. In any event, they are not required in Australia given its vast renewable energy resources. They are also problematic given Australia's long non-nuclear history, and its obligations under various nuclear anti-proliferation treaties, notwithstanding the more recent AUKUS nuclear submarine commitments.

Not all new 'alternative' energy technologies guarantee a path to sustainability as in the case of the much-touted transformative potential of the renewable or clean 'hydrogen' economy (Tony Wood). The potential of its carbon-free, benign oxygen, emissions burning technology has underwritten a 'grand vision' for Australia as a low-carbon superpower shipping clean energy in the form of 'sunshine to the world'.

Clean hydrogen has the potential to transform Australia's vast mineral resources in the form of green, decarbonised, high-value-added products such as steel, aluminium, ammonia, fertiliser and explosives.

However, not all clean hydrogen is equally clean; varying from the rainbow colours of green, blue, brown, pink or black, depending upon the carbon content of the hydrogen production processes used and the materials supply chains involved. The optional innovative pathways for hydrogen fuel are manifold, complex, varied, risky and costly as well as highly 'path-dependent' on finance, skills and government interventions.

Section III: Regenerative Agriculture for Biodiversity

Australia's agriculture sector is a globally competitive exporter of food and a major user of land and water resources in a large but driest continent that faces challenges of sustainability in the face of climate change (Richard Heath). The trade-exposed sector has maintained its competitiveness on the back of effective, largely publicly funded research, extension services and accompanying significant structural adjustment to predominantly large-scale industrialised production.

Digital technologies are playing a substantial role in introducing agricultural practice innovation that sustains competitiveness and resilience to escalating climate disruptions, as well as reducing its carbon emissions. Continuing development and adoption of cutting-edge agricultural technologies, or AgTech, that can drive productivity requires systematic shifts in approaches to data-sharing, enhanced skills, changed behaviour and practices, and finance.

Innovation is changing the traditional agricultural ways and moving to a more 'integrated', 'biologically derived economic structure' based on 'natural accounting systems' and methods. It is building trust in the sector's integrity and positive environmental impact, in closer partnership between farmers, government and the public.

New synthetic biology and food technologies are opening up transformational opportunities for enhanced 'food security' and more sustainable agriculture on a global scale. These are referred to collectively as 'the second domestication' of dairy and beef: producing protein food without animals, colloquially known as Food 2.0 (Lesley Hughes).

Technologies of protein fermentation include plant alternatives to a range of dairy products with the decade of 2020s described speculatively as 'peak cow', as well as emerging plant-based meat alternatives. Cell-based products produced in labs are developing new meat alternatives but are still experimental and costly.

The potential environmental benefits of such synthetic 'designer' food production as a replacement for factory-based and extensive pastoral livestock production are enormous, given the scale of global land and water resources currently utilised. The reductions in pollution, land degradation and methane emissions will be central to meeting climate emissions targets and long-term sustainability.

Significant improvements in animal health and welfare will enhance social licence, while large-scale adjustments will need to be supported for producers and regions, as well as cultural adaptation by consumers recognising that 'eating is a political act'.

Agriculture is, by far, the major user of water. The sustainable management of water resources in the driest continent of Australia has proved historically an insurmountable challenge for innovative policies and programmes, and the latest failed attempts to restore and maintain the health of the country's single, largest river water resource – the Murray–Darling River Basin (MDRB) – constitutes an 'environmental catastrophe' of federalism politics (Richard Beasley).

With water resources as the constitutional responsibility of the states, the federal government enacted a visionary interstate basin-wide management plan legitimised by its international treaty-making powers to legislate for the restoration of overallocated water to the environment of entitlements held by farmers and irrigators. In setting the required diversions, the 'best available scientific advice' was not adopted and climate change implications were ignored.

Significant funding of A$13 billion was allocated to measures including grants to landholders and voluntary purchases of water from entitlement holders. In the face of unprecedented protests by farmers, irrigators and local communities, the plans were abandoned and water buybacks halted but not before most of the funds were expended with no marked improvement in river health and sustainability. Still hotly contested, politically and methodologically, attempts continue to modify and revive the plan.

Sixty thousand years of Australia's more than 300 First Nations' continuous habitation, experience and accumulated knowledge in adapting to, and living sustainably in, this harsh and dry continental landscape in the face of shifting climates from ice ages to their global thawing; has been effectively ignored since colonisation 250 years ago (Bruce Pascoe). Their holistic traditional knowledge systems and practices encompass cosmology, social organisation, agricultural technologies and trading networks draw on understanding of the self-regenerative characteristics of our unique continental environment.

This systemic and integrated knowledge was not only ignored but its very existence denied in what has been called 'the great Australian silence'. It is only recently being recognised as relevant to our pursuit of sustainability, but still not without contestation. It is being brought into the open and slowly integrated into our scientific knowledge base, as changing industry processes, and adopted in management practices for land, water, flora and fauna.

A variety of modern-day practices of more sustainable, regenerative agricultural and land management have long been under development in many countries under many names, such as organic farming and minimum tillage, and are well understood; but their widespread diffusion and adoption confronts the obstacles of long-held farming culture and practices as well as resistance from the formidable economic and political power of global and industrialised agriculture and agribusiness (Charles Massy).

Historically, successful government-funded research and extension services in agricultural methods and practices have given way by policy decisions to private-sector research and support by industrial equipment, seed, chemical and fertiliser industries delivered through commercial stock and station agents and salespeople. While a regenerative agriculture movement is gathering momentum, albeit slowly at the grassroots level, individual farming innovators pay a personal and financial price for attempting to adopt more sustainable, regenerative practices.

The farmer's role is essentially to stand back and empower the naturally complex, regenerative systems to develop their emergent complexity, resilience, adaptability and biodiversity in the new farming paradigm.

Section IV: Appreciating the Complex Systems of Governance for Innovation and Sustainability

The 'Silicon Valley Consensus' is a form of 'technological determinism' that has not only motivated national government innovation policy but also contributed to a populist and nationalist backlash in politics from those who feel 'left behind' by growing inequality and loss of jobs (Michael Piore). Public policy has hollowed out manufacturing by offshoring while the economy has become financialised.

It is, in effect, a 'self-fulfilling prophecy' that posits high-technology disruption driven by individual creative entrepreneurs, by reduced corporate R&D investment in favour of short-term profits, demanding ever higher levels of STEM education and skills without subsequent jobs, and in which 'tacit knowledge' and 'experiential learning' are undervalued.

If social and political harmony are to be revived and sustained, a public policy paradigm shift is required away from its roots in the 'Washington Consensus'. The ideas of 'market fundamentalism', monetised and commoditised 'knowledge economy', and Silicon Valley's over-emphasis on individual entrepreneurs need to be replaced by engaging 'intellectual communities' for innovation, competitiveness, job security and more equal distribution, and promoting the broad welfare of society.

As the public has lost trust in government and its institutions, it has seemingly placed relatively more trust in corporations to take up 'the business of climate change' where governments have failed (Bob Carr). This is ironic given that it has been the powerful and sustained climate policy lobbying and public relations campaigns of climate denial, scientific undermining, by well-funded fossil fuel corporations that have both reframed and stymied government climate action.

Experience in NSW, which successfully introduced the world's first mandatory carbon-trading scheme in 2003, suggests lessons can be learnt on how governments can work with business constructively by recognising business 'material interests' involving realities around investment risks, time horizons and market mechanisms. Such schemes face difficult problems of implementation around standards, metrics, monitoring.

There are signs that corporations are engaged in reimagining their role and long-standing profit-focused corporate governance practices towards broader norms more consistent with maintaining their 'social licence' and their sustainability. A wave of revelations around unethical and even criminal behaviour of large corporations in a number of sectors has put into question their accountability, transparency and directors' responsibilities and driven a crisis in corporate governance spurred by the challenges of new technologies, climate change and sustainability (Pru Bennett).

By 'harnessing capital' to new risks and sustainability, the principles of governance known as environmental, social and governance (ESG) are seen as potentially underpinning corporate sustainability in a profit sense, as well as their 'social licence'. They are driven by institutional investors, shareholder activism, broad stakeholder interests, and with regulatory and legal support albeit limited.

There is an absence of clear standards, metrics, accounting and regulatory frameworks at both the national and international levels that leaves the field open to corporate 'greenwashing' public relations. There is evidence that companies which have adopted ESG principles have enhanced profits alongside sustainability. A strong political and legislative backlash has emerged lately against such ethical approaches to investment as a manifestation of 'woke' ideological sensibilities suggesting sustainable approaches to corporate governance are very much a 'work in progress'.

Game-changing business opportunities are available in decarbonising and transforming the Australian economy by a transition to renewable energy 'superpower' (Ross Garnaut). Australia has long been a major commodities exporter of minerals such as iron ore and bauxite, and energy in the form of coal and gas.

The renewable energy transition has the potential to transform the industrial structure away from commodity exports to high-value-added 'green' products, including steel, aluminium, fertilisers and explosives. In addition, its vast agricultural, pastoral and forested landscapes offer significant potential for carbon capture and trading.

The country has world-class renewable solar and wind energy resources that could support development of a sustainable decarbonised 'hydrogen' economy that enables 'shipping sunshine to the world'. Falling costs of renewable energy alongside availability of attractive costs of capital will induce private-sector investment but will need to be supported by government actions, particularly investments in R&D to develop hydrogen and carbon capture technologies. This will require the long prevailing 'fog of politics' on climate change issues to lift from the path to zero emissions.

In a democracy, public trust and confidence in politics and institutions relies upon a free press able to objectively pursue public interest journalism, informing, exposing and holding to account the interests and actions on major issues such as COVID-19 and climate change (Allan Fels). This has been hindered by the lack of media competition and ownership concentration, as well as by the disruptive impact of digital technologies upon mainstream media.

There have been significant job losses in journalism, the closure of many print media outlets and a fall in journalism standards. The rise of largely unregulated social media and platforms has opened the way for misinformation, disinformation and fake news. Climate denial, scepticism about science and the culture wars have been given an accessible voice.

The issues of competition, transparency and accountability in the media are only slowly being addressed, in particular, with the introduction of payments from digital platforms to mainstream media for the use of their content, and the promotion of public interest journalism.

Tackling the climate crisis along with the more recent COVID-19 experience has highlighted the importance of building public trust and confidence in science and its methods and uncertainties (Aaron Mertz and Abhilash Mishra). The provision of scientific 'facts' and 'data' and their increasing accessibility on the internet is not sufficient to both fill any 'knowledge deficit' and bridge their 'cognitive dissonance'.

Talking the 'truth' at people risks their disengagement or even alienation and a new model of participative, community-based cooperative research, development and extension may be required. Scientists have a social responsibility to communicate and engage but lack training, incentives and support.

Politicians have a responsibility to seek out and heed expert scientific advice but scientists will need in times of crisis to stand up to power. Science journalists have a vital role in building engagement and trust. Building trust in science is even more challenging in the increasingly polarised and partisan political climate, now also fuelled by a 'diploma divide'.

Systems thinking offers an innovative approach to respond effectively to the evident dysfunctionality and failures of our current institutional systems of governance in the face of climate change in the Anthropocene era of the Sixth Extinction (Ray Ison). Existing governance based on 'command-and-control' hierarchies that seek out optimal solutions fall into 'end-state fallacy' and confront the 'death of stationarity' in a world of complex systems characterised by uncertainty and instability.

Effective responses to the global climate crisis require decentralised, distributed and empowered governance. Achieving transformational change means moving beyond first-order, systematic improvement changes to higher-order systemic change. Systemic governance is characterised by variety, subsidiarity and learning. The emergent qualities of self-organising adaptability and resilience are the key to sustainability in a 'complex adaptive system' such as human–global climate change interaction. Sustainable governance systems cannot be achieved without substantial redistribution of constitutional and institutional power and control.

The dysfunctionality of our democratic political system, evident in the lack of sufficiently robust and timely political responses to climate change, poses a moral challenge of existential proportions for the world (Barry Jones). Political parties are content if not complacent in their positions of power, aligned with powerful 'vested interests' and Australia has historically prospered as the 'lucky country' despite our 'second-rate' leadership.

With liberal democracies enmeshed in a form of 'political paralysis', the prospects of needed constitutional and governance reforms are not encouraging. Many countries are turning to authoritarian nationalistic leaders. A 'cone of silence' resembling the Mafia's *omerta* characterises the lack of transparency, accountability and lack of any real public debate on key issues such as climate change and sustainability.

Only with much greater public engagement and participation will the political transformation necessary for systemic sustainable governance can be realised.

Index